IP Networking Lab Manual
Second Edition

Wendell Odom, CCIE No. 1624
Jeffrey S. Beasley

Pearson Education, Inc.
800 East 96th Street
Indianapolis, Indiana 46240 USA

IP Networking Lab Manual, Second Edition

Wendell Odom, CCIE No. 1624
Jeffrey S. Beasley

Copyright© 2013 Pearson Education, Inc.

Published by:
Pearson IT Certification
800 East 96th Street
Indianapolis, IN 46240 USA

Printed in the United States of America

First Printing December 2012

Library of Congress Cataloging-in-Publication Data is on file.

ISBN-13: 978-0-7897-5093-8

ISBN-10: 0-7897-5093-7

Warning and Disclaimer

Every effort has been made to make this book as complete and as accurate as possible, but no warranty or fitness is implied.

The information is provided on an "as is" basis. The authors, Cisco Press, and Cisco Systems, Inc. shall have neither liability nor responsibility to any person or entity with respect to any loss or damages arising from the information contained in this book or from the use of the discs or programs that may accompany it.

The opinions expressed in this book belong to the author and are not necessarily those of Cisco Systems, Inc.

Trademark Acknowledgments

All terms mentioned in this book that are known to be trademarks or service marks have been appropriately capitalized. Cisco Press or Cisco Systems, Inc., cannot attest to the accuracy of this information. Use of a term in this book should not be regarded as affecting the validity of any trademark or service mark.

Publisher: Paul Boger

Associate Publisher: Dave Dusthimer

Executive Editor: Brett Bartow

Managing Editor: Sandra Schroeder

Development Editor: Andrew Cupp

Senior Project Editor: Tonya Simpson

Copy Editor: John Edwards

Technical Reviewers: Sean Wilkins, Elan Beer, Mark Dye, Andrew Whitaker, Juan Castro, Rich Bennett, Allan Johnson, Aubrey Adams

Editorial Assistant: Vanessa Evans

Book Designer: Gary Adair

Composition: Mary Sudul

About the Authors

Wendell Odom, CCIE No. 1624, has been in the networking industry since 1981. He has worked as a network engineer, consultant, systems engineer, instructor, and course developer; he currently writes and creates certification tools. He is the author of all the previous editions of the CCNA Exam Certification Guide series from Cisco Press, as well as the *CCNP ROUTE 642-902 Official Certification Guide* and the *CCIE Written Exam Certification Guide*. Find links to his Cisco certification blogs at http://www.certskills.com.

Jeffrey S. Beasley is with the Department of Engineering Technology and Surveying Engineering at New Mexico State University. He has been teaching with the department since 1988 and is the co-author of *Modern Electronic Communication* and *Electronic Devices and Circuits*, and the author of *Networking*.

About the Lab Contributing Authors

Rus Healy, No. CCIE #15025, is chief technology officer at the Cisco Commercial Partner of the Year for the Eastern U.S. and Canada, Annese & Associates. Rus has contributed to several Cisco Press projects with Wendell Odom, including the 2007 *CCIE Routing and Switching Exam Certification Guide, Third Edition*.

Andrew Whitaker (M.Sc., CISSP, CEI, LPT, ECSA, CHFI, CEH, CCSP, CCNP, CCVP, CCDP, CCNA, CCDA, CCENT, MCSE, MCTS, CNE, A+, Network+, Convergence+, Security+, CTP, EMCPA) is a recognized expert, trainer, and author in the field of penetration testing and security countermeasures. He works as the director of Enterprise InfoSec and Networking and is a senior ethical hacking instructor for Training Camp. Over the past several years, his courses have trained thousands of security professionals throughout the world. His security courses have also caught the attention of *The Wall Street Journal, BusinessWeek, San Francisco Gate*, and others.

Mark Dye was the technology manager and training manager for the Bevill Center at Gadsden State Community College, where he also managed and taught in the Cisco Academy program. He now works full time as an assessment and curriculum developer with Cisco. Mark also has maintained a private information technology consulting business since 1985. Mark's more than 30-year career has included roles as biomedical instrumentation technician, field service engineer, customer service supervisor, network engineer, and instructor.

Sean Wilkins is an accomplished networking consultant and has been in the field of IT since the mid-1990s working with companies like Cisco, Lucent, Verizon, and AT&T as well as several other private companies. Sean currently holds certifications with Cisco (CCNP/CCDP), Microsoft (MCSE), and CompTIA (A+ and Network+). He also has a Master of Science degree in information technology with a focus in network architecture and design, a Bachelor of Science degree in computer networking, and an Associate of Applied Science degree in computer information systems. In addition to working as a consultant, Sean spends a lot of his time as a technical writer and editor for various companies.

Juan Castro has been working in the IT field for more than 12 years. He currently teaches CCNA, CCDA, CTP, and MCDST boot camps for the Training Camp. In his off-time, Juan works as an independent consultant, offering technical services for customers with Cisco VoIP implementations. His certifications include CCNA, CCDA, CCNP, MCP, MCDST, MCT, CTP, and A+. Prior to working with the Training Camp, Juan provided network administration and engineer services for private corporations, specializing in VoIP and routing and switching.

Joe Harris, CCIE No. 6200, has more than 15 years of experience focusing on advanced technologies within the IT arena. Joe has been primarily focused on supporting various enterprise networks revolving around all aspects of Cisco technology. Joe has provided high-end consulting for both large and small corporations as well as government and federal agencies. Currently, Mr. Harris is a systems engineer at Cisco specializing in security and MPLS technologies. He has been published, most recently authoring *Cisco Network Security Little Black Book*, by Paraglyph Publishing (ISBN-13: 9781932111651). He is also a technical editor for several Cisco Press publications and is actively involved in writing various technical articles, white papers, and presentations on a wide variety of security-related technologies and topics. Throughout a long journey in which he achieved three CCIE certifications (R/S, Security, and SP), he has also been recognized by Cisco as a two-time SE Wall of Fame award winner. Joe resides in Frisco, Texas, with his beautiful wife Krystal and two children, Cameron and Lexi. Please be sure to drop by Joe's highly publicized, and very informative, website (and technical blog) located at http://www.6200networks.com.

Antoon (Tony) W. Rufi is the director of education, ECPI College of Technology, Newport News, Virginia. Before becoming an instructor for ECPI, he spent almost 30 years in the United States Air Force, working on numerous electronic projects and computer systems. Since his retirement, Tony has worked for ECPI College of Technology teaching Cisco Academy courses. The courses he has led include CCNA, CCNP, Fundamentals of Network Security, and IP Telephony. Tony received his associate's degree from the Community College of the Air Force, his bachelor's degree from Southern Illinois University, and his master's degree from the University of Maryland, and he is working on a Ph.D. from Walden University. Tony has been married to his wife Linda for 36 years and lives in Poquoson, VA.

Karl Solie, CCIE No. 4599, CCSI, is the founder of Solie Research, LLC, and has been an active CCIE for more than ten years. Karl has more than 20 years of experience in the field, working on some of the most complex and large IP-based networks in the United States, including working for many state and local government agencies, law enforcement, the DoD, as well as commercial clients. Karl is also the author and coauthor for two Cisco Press books, *CCIE Practical Studies, Volume I* and *CCIE Practical Studies, Volume II*. Karl can currently be found in the field doing strategic network design and consulting for Solie Research, LLC, or in the classroom for Ascolta, where he focuses on teaching MPLS, BGP, and advanced routing topics to the next generation of CCIEs.

Bob Vachon is the coordinator of the Computer Systems Technology program at Cambrian College in Sudbury, Ontario, Canada. He is CCNP certified since 2002 and has collaborated on many Networking Academy courses including CCNA, CCNP, and Network Security. Most recently, he coauthored the Networking Academy CCNA-Security course and was the team lead on the CCNA-4 Accessing the WAN course.

About the Technical Reviewers

Sean Wilkins is an accomplished networking consultant for SR-W Consulting (http://www.sr-wconsulting.com) and has been in the field of IT since the mid-1990s working with companies like Cisco, Lucent, Verizon, and AT&T as well as several other private companies. Sean currently holds certifications with Cisco (CCNP/CCDP), Microsoft (MCSE), and CompTIA (A+ and Network+). He also has a Master of Science degree in information technology with a focus in network architecture and design, a Master of Science degree in organizational management, a Master's Certificate in network security, a Bachelor of Science degree in computer networking, and an Associate of Applied Science degree in computer information systems. In addition to working as a consultant, Sean spends a lot of his time as a technical writer and editor for various companies.

Elan Beer, CCIE No. 1837, CCSI No. 94008, is a senior consultant and Certified Cisco Instructor. His internetworking expertise is recognized internationally through his global consulting and training engagements. As one of the industry's top internetworking consultants and Cisco instructors, Elan has used his expertise for the past 15 years to design, implement, and deploy multiprotocol networks for a wide international clientele. As a senior instructor and course developer, Elan has designed and presented public and implementation-specific technical courses spanning many of today's top technologies. Elan specializes in MPLS, BGP, QoS, and other internetworking technologies.

Mark Dye was the technology manager and training manager for the Bevill Center at Gadsden State Community College, where he also managed and taught in the Cisco Academy program. He now works full time as an assessment and curriculum developer with Cisco. Mark also has maintained a private information technology consulting business since 1985. Mark's more than 30-year career has included roles as biomedical instrumentation technician, field service engineer, customer service supervisor, network engineer, and instructor.

Andrew Whitaker (M.Sc., CISSP, CEI, LPT, ECSA, CHFI, CEH, CCSP, CCNP, CCVP, CCDP, CCNA, CCDA, CCENT, MCSE, MCTS, CNE, A+, Network+, Convergence+, Security+, CTP, EMCPA) is a recognized expert, trainer, and author in the field of penetration testing and security countermeasures. He works as the director of Enterprise InfoSec and Networking and is a senior ethical hacking instructor for Training Camp. Over the past several years, his courses have trained thousands of security professionals throughout the world. His security courses have also caught the attention of *The Wall Street Journal*, *BusinessWeek*, *San Francisco Gate*, and others.

Juan Castro has been working in the IT field for more than 12 years. He currently teaches CCNA, CCDA, CTP, and MCDST boot camps for the Training Camp. In his off-time, Juan works as an independent consultant, offering technical services for customers with Cisco VoIP implementations. His certifications include CCNA, CCDA, CCNP, MCP, MCDST, MCT, CTP, and A+. Prior to working with the Training Camp, Juan provided network administration and engineer services for private corporations, specializing in VoIP and routing and switching.

Rich Bennett (CCENT, B.S., M.Ed.) has considerable experience in the world of education, teaching classes in mathematics, logic, and the sciences. He works part-time for a small networking company. Rich used his combination of skills and experience to perform parts of several of the testing rounds for the labs, using his perspectives as an educator to help improve the use of the product for learning.

Allan Johnson entered the academic world in 1999 after ten years as a business owner/operator to dedicate his efforts to his passion for teaching. He holds both an MBA and an M.Ed. in occupational training and development. He taught CCNA courses at the high school level for seven years and has taught both CCNA and CCNP courses at Del Mar College in Corpus Christi, Texas. In 2003, Allan began to commit much of his time and energy to the CCNA Instructional Support Team, providing services to Networking Academy instructors worldwide and creating training materials. He now works full time for the Academy in Learning Systems Development.

Aubrey Adams is an electronic and computer system engineering lecturer and Cisco Networking Academy CCNA/IP Telephony instructor at Central College of Technical and Further Education (TAFE) in Perth, Western Australia. Coming from a background in telecommunications design, with qualifications in electronic engineering and management, and graduate diplomas in computing and education, he teaches across a broad range of related vocational education and training areas. In 2007, Aubrey took leave from Central TAFE to work as a member of the Networking Academy CCNA Exploration and Discovery course development teams. Since returning to teaching, he continues to contribute to Academy curriculum maintenance and development.

Contents at a Glance

Introduction   viii

Unit 1:   The TCP/IP Model, LANs, WANs, and IP Networks   1

Unit 2:   TCP/IP Network, Transport, and Application Layers   5

Unit 3:   IP Subnetting and Basic Router Configuration   29

Unit 4:   IP Routing with Connected, Static, and RIP-2 Routes   61

Unit 5:   IP Troubleshooting and EIGRP   193

Unit 6:   Subnet Design   237

Unit 7:   Advanced IP Routing Topics and OSPF   309

Unit 8:   Advanced IP Topics   441

Unit 9:   LANs   499

Unit 10:   WANs   569

Reader Services

Visit our website and register this book at http://www.pearsonitcertification.com/title/9780789750938 for convenient access to any updates, downloads, or errata that might be available for this book.

Introduction

Overview

College courses that use the *IP Networking* textbook need to use hands-on exercises to teach students the skills to work with routers and switches from Cisco Systems. Those skills can be learned using real Cisco equipment, but they can also be practiced with a simulator: software that acts like the user interface of the real gear. Simulators have an added advantage in that, as a product created for the sake of learning, most simulators include lab exercises.

The *IP Networking Lab Manual* serves as a book of lab exercises that can be used in courses that use the *IP Networking* textbook, specifically when that course uses the Pearson Network Simulator (referenced hereafter as "the Sim").

The *IP Networking* textbook organizes its material into ten units to match a particular college-level networking course. This lab book includes a set of lab exercises available in the Sim, organized into ten units to match the *IP Networking* text. For example, when using the materials in Unit 4 of the *IP Networking* textbook, you would use the labs in Unit 4 of this lab manual to learn more about the topic and develop your skills.

The Sim simulates the user interface of Cisco routers, commonly called the Cisco command-line interface (CLI). You install the Sim on your PC or Mac, start the software, and select a lab exercise. At that point, the Sim acts like the small network specified by that lab exercise. The lab topology includes devices that act like PCs, Cisco routers, and Cisco switches. The experience is mostly like what you would see if using real equipment, with some exceptions related to the fact that it simulates the interaction, rather than being real gear.

Check out the basics about the Sim at http://www.certskills.com/Sim, which includes links to a product demo.

Note that the Sim includes all the lab exercises already, but in PDF form. After you start the Sim, the next step is to select and start a lab. At that point, the Sim initializes the lab, setting the specific topology of routers, switches, and PCs, and loading some initial configuration into each device. The Sim also opens a window to display a PDF of the lab exercise.

This *IP Networking Lab Manual* includes labs from the Sim. Each lab includes some questions, a place to answer, and other information that needs to be collected into a table. This lab manual provides a convenient place to record the answers.

Navigation to the Correct Lab

The Sim user interface does not organize the labs the same way as the *IP Networking* textbook and this *IP Networking Lab Manual*. Instead, the Sim user interface organizes labs to match a two-book library related to a popular Cisco certification: Cisco Certified Network Associate, or CCNA. As a result, the organization of the labs in this lab manual differs somewhat from what you see in the Sim's user interface. This section describes how to find the labs as listed in this lab manual.

First, the Sim lists the labs on the right side of the user interface. In the commercial version of the Pearson CCNA Network Simulator, that side lists two divisions: ICND1 and ICND2. In the Academic version of the Sim, which includes additional labs for use in the classroom, three divisions exist, as shown in Figure I-1.

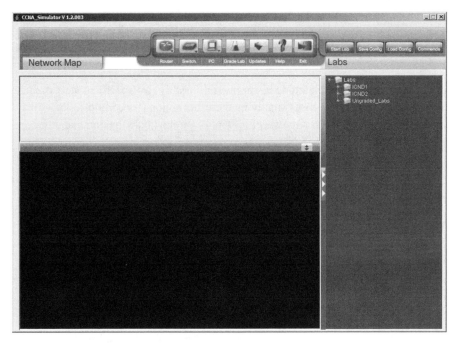

Figure I-1 Main User Interface Window, Academic Sim

The image in Figure I-1 shows the entire Sim window. The upper-left part of the window shows a network diagram, with the lower left being where you type commands in the CLI. The far right holds the menu of labs.

To focus on navigation, Figure I-2 shows the same window, zoomed on the menu on the far right.

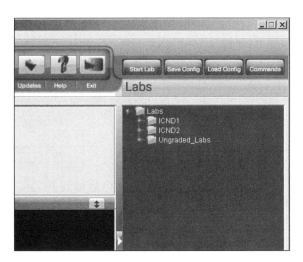

Figure I-2 Main User Interface Window, Focus on the Menu

The menu of the Academic version of the Sim, shown in Figure I-2, lists three main headings. This lab book includes labs from all three sections.

Types of Labs

The next division in the user interface lists the type of lab. Four types of labs exist in the ICND1 and ICND2 sections of the product, as follows:

- **Skill Builder (SB):** These labs focus on exercising and learning about one or possibly two specific concepts each. The instructions list the specific mental steps, in some cases supplying the exact action (for example, "type this command"), or in other cases, telling you the idea but not the specifics (for example, "type the command that does X").

- **Configuration Scenario (CS):** These labs help your view and understand a network based on both the major tasks and the specific steps required to do those tasks. These labs have more complex lab steps (for example, "configure RIP on interface F0/0"). These labs give the user some room to fail and make mistakes, with a safety net of hints and answers at the end of the lab.

- **Troubleshooting Scenario (TS):** These labs give you a chance to experience the network behavior when mis-configured slightly. Each lab begins with a mostly working network, except the configuration has been purpose-fully broken (usually two, three, or four commands). To solve the lab, students choose from two paths: 1) start with the big-picture problem and solve it any way they want, or 2) walk through specific lab steps that guide them through the troubleshooting process.

- **Subnetting Exercises (SE):** These labs focus exclusively on subnetting practice. A foundational skill for net-working professionals, subnetting is the process of dividing an organization's growing network into separate sub-networks to provide for better manageability, efficiency, and security. Subnetting is one of the most challenging things for inexperienced networkers to learn and is difficult even for experienced professionals to perform quick-ly or without the aid of subnetting calculators. These new labs help you perform subnetting calculations quickly and accurately, a critical skill for success on the CCNA exams. These new labs are divided into five different types of subnetting practice, helping you master subnet ID calculation, IP address rejection, IP route selection, VLSM overlap, and VLSM route selection.

Each unit of this lab manual begins with a table that lists labs. The table lists the category (ICND1, ICND2, or Ungraded Labs) and the lab type (Skill Builder, Configuration Scenario, Troubleshooting Scenario, or Subnetting Exercise), as shown in Figure I-3. (To move from the menu shown in Figure I-2 to the menu in Figure I-3, just click the text "ICND1" on the menu.)

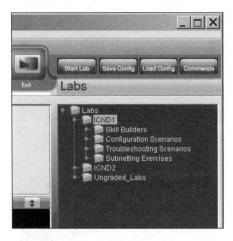

Figure I-3   Choosing from Four Types of Labs

General Lab Topics: Lab Parts

After you have selected the ICND1, ICND2, or Ungraded Labs category, and then the lab type, the Sim user interface lists general topics. For instance, in ICND1, Skill Builder labs include three parts. Figure I-4 shows an example, with the three parts for ICND1 Skill Builder labs.

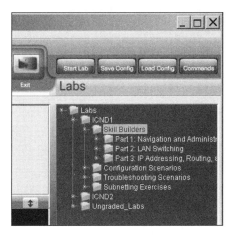

Figure I-4   General Topics: Sim Lab Parts

To select a part, just double-click the text of the part.

Lab Names, Numbers, and the Index Table for Each Unit

Inside a lab part, the Sim lists the labs in a particular sequence, but that sequence does not match the same sequence of topics in the *IP Networking* textbook. Unfortunately, the lab menu does not number the labs, and they are not in alphabetical order, so finding the right lab requires some extra effort. (The labs are ordered based on a sequence that is meaningful for the Cisco CCNA exam preparation.)

To help you find each lab, this lab manual lists an index table to begin each unit. This table lists the labs, including the category (ICND1, ICND2, or Ungraded Labs), the lab type (SB, CS, TS, or SE), and the part. The table also lists the relative number of the lab.

For example, Table I-1 lists labs for Unit 2 with a category of ICND1, type SB (short for Skill Builder), and part number 1. It lists individual labs, including one with a name "Switch CLI Exec Mode" and another called "Booting a New Router IOS."

I-1   Unit 2 Labs

Date	ICND1/ ICND2	Type	Part	Number	Name	Page
	ICND1	SB	1	1	Switch CLI Exec Mode	
	ICND1	SB	1	21	Booting a New Router IOS	

As you can see in Figure I-5, the list of labs happens to show lab "Switch CLI Exec Mode" as the very first lab in the list, so it is a little easier to find. The second lab in the table, "Booting a New Router IOS," is harder to find. However, the table's reference to number 21 lets you guess how far down the list to start scanning for the lab name.

Figure I-5   Lab Names: ICND1, Skill Builder, Part I

In summary, when you need to load a lab in the Sim, after you start the software, do the following steps in the menu on the right:

Step 1.   Choose the major category (ICND1, ICND2, or Ungraded Labs).

Step 2.   Choose the lab type.

Step 3.   Choose the lab part.

Step 4.   Choose the lab by name or number.

The TCP/IP Model, LANs, WANs, and IP Networks

Table 1-1 lists the labs for this unit. Check with your instructor or class syllabus to confirm what labs you should perform for class.

Table 1-1   Unit 1 Labs

Date	ICND1/ ICND2	Type	Part	Number	Name	Page
	ICND1	SB	1	1	Switch CLI Exec Mode	1

ICND1 Skill Builders

Part 1: Navigation and Administration

Lab 1: Switch CLI Exec Mode

Overview

This lab guides you through the process of navigating through a switch command-line interface, specifically the user and enable exec modes.

Topology

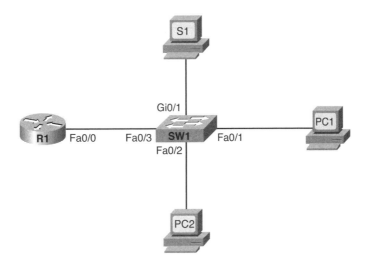

Figure 1   Network Topology for This Lab

This lab uses only the switch (SW1) with no activities on the other devices.

Detailed Lab Steps

Step 1.   Connect to SW1 from the simulator user interface.

Step 2.   Connect to SW1's console port using the simulator. The window will look like a terminal emulator with a cursor at the bottom of the screen and the center of the screen mostly blank.

Step 3.   From the simulator's terminal-emulator screen, press **Enter**.

Step 4.   If you do not see a command prompt, press **Enter** until you do.

Step 5.   Press the **?** key to look at the available commands. Write down the most interesting two or three commands that you see listed.

_____

_____

_____

_____

_____

Step 6.   Try to enter privileged mode using the **enable** command. Are you prompted for a password?

_____

Step 7.   When you are in privileged mode, use help by pressing the **?** key to see the current list of commands. Are there more commands than were shown in user mode?

_____

_____

_____

Step 8.   Use help (**?**) in both user mode and enable mode to confirm that help lists the **configure** and **reload** commands when in enable mode but not when in user mode. To do so, move back to user mode by entering the **disable** command, and then use the **enable** command to move back to enable mode.

Hints and Answers

Table 1 provides hints and tips for any lab steps that do not supply complete details and provides answers for any lab steps that ask questions.

Table 1   Hints and Answers

Step	Hint or Answer
3	The simulator should display a prompt with switch> after you press Enter. If it does not appear, click inside the window to make that window the focus of your computer desktop, and press **Enter** again.
6	This lab begins with the switch having all default configuration, which means that no passwords are configured.
7	You should see more commands listed when using **?** in enable mode than when using **?** in user mode. For example, the **configure** and **reload** commands will not be shown when getting help in user mode.

Configuration Steps

This lab does not require any configuration.

TCP/IP Network, Transport, and Application Layers

Table 2-1 lists the labs for this unit. Check with your instructor or class syllabus to confirm what labs you should perform for class.

Table 2-1   Unit 2 Labs

Date	ICND1/ ICND2	Type	Part	Number	Name	Page
	ICND1	SB	1	1	Switch CLI Exec Mode	5
	ICND1	SB	1	2	Switch CLI Configuration Process I	8
	ICND1	SB	1	3	Switch CLI Configuration Process II	10
	ICND1	SB	1	4	Router CLI Exec Mode I	13
	ICND1	SB	1	5	Router CLI Exec Mode II	15
	ICND1	SB	1	6	Router CLI Configuration Process	18
	ICND1	SB	1	7	Setting Switch Passwords	20
	ICND1	SB	1	9	Setting Router Passwords	23
	ICND1	SB	3	23	Configuring Hostnames	25

ICND1 Skill Builders

Part 1: Navigation and Administration

Lab 1: Switch CLI Exec Mode

Overview

This lab guides you through the process of navigating through a switch command-line interface, specifically the user and enable exec modes.

Topology

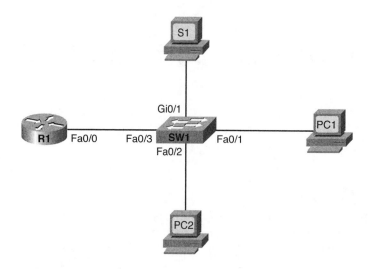

Figure 1   Network Topology for This Lab

This lab uses only the switch (SW1) with no activities on the other devices.

Detailed Lab Steps

Step 1.   Connect to SW1 from the simulator user interface.

Step 2.   Connect to SW1's console port using the simulator. The window will look like a terminal emulator with a cursor at the bottom of the screen and the center of the screen mostly blank.

Step 3.   From the simulator's terminal-emulator screen, press **Enter**.

Step 4.   If you do not see a command prompt, press **Enter** until you do.

Step 5.   Press the **?** key to look at the available commands. Write down the most interesting two or three commands that you see listed.

_____

_____

_____

_____

_____

_____

Step 6. Try to enter privileged mode using the **enable** command. Are you prompted for a password?

_____

Step 7. When you are in privileged mode, use help by pressing the **?** key to see the current list of commands. Are there more commands than were shown in user mode?

_____

_____

_____

Step 8. Use help (**?**) in both user mode and enable mode to confirm that help lists the **configure** and **reload** commands when in enable mode but not when in user mode. To do so, move back to user mode by entering the **disable** command, and then use the **enable** command to move back to enable mode.

Hints and Answers

Table 1 provides hints and tips for any lab steps that do not supply complete details and provides answers for any lab steps that ask questions.

Table 1   Hints and Answers

Step	Hint or Answer
3	The simulator should display a prompt with switch> after you press Enter. If it does not appear, click inside the window to make that window the focus of your computer desktop, and press **Enter** again.
6	This lab begins with the switch having all default configuration, which means that no passwords are configured.
7	You should see more commands listed when using **?** in enable mode than when using **?** in user mode. For example, the **configure** and **reload** commands will not be shown when getting help in user mode.

Configuration Steps

This lab does not require any configuration.

ICND1 Skill Builders

Part 1: Navigation and Administration

Lab 2: Switch CLI Configuration Process I

Overview

This lab is intended to force you to try several features of the CLI. You can, and should, branch out to try other commands. You should also repeat this lab until you have memorized all its commands and their syntax, and you no longer need to ask for help to remember the commands and their options.

Topology

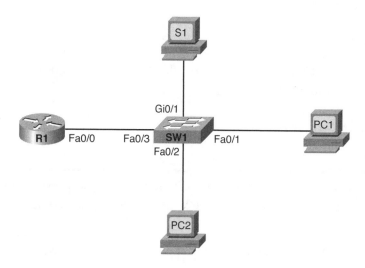

Figure 1   Network Topology for This Lab

This lab uses only the switch (SW1) with no activities on the other devices.

Detailed Lab Steps

Step 1.   Connect to SW1's console port using the simulator. The window will look like a terminal emulator with a cursor at the bottom of the screen and the center of the screen mostly blank.

Step 2.   From the simulator's terminal-emulator screen, press **Enter**.

Step 3.   Enter privileged mode using the **enable** command. Are you prompted for a password?

Step 4.   Enter configuration mode using the **configure terminal** command.

Step 5.   Using help (**?**) in configuration mode, find the command that changes the switch's hostname. List that command on the line below.

_____

Step 6.   Use the **hostname Fred** command to change your switch's hostname. What happened to the prompt after you entered the **hostname** command?

_____

Step 7.   Exit configuration mode (press **Ctrl-Z** or enter **end**).

Step 8.   Use the **show running-config** command to view the currently in-use switch configuration. Can you see the **hostname** command?

_____

_____

Step 9.   Use the **show startup-config** command to view the switch configuration that will be used the next time the switch is reloaded. Can you see the **hostname** command?

_____

_____

Step 10. Use the **copy running-config startup-config** command to replace the startup-config file with the contents of the running-config file.

Step 11. Use the **show startup-config** command to view the switch configuration that will be used the next time the switch is reloaded. Can you see the **hostname** command?

_____

_____

Hints and Answers

Table 1 provides hints and tips for any lab steps that do not supply complete details and provides answers for any lab steps that ask questions.

Table 1   Hints and Answers

Step	Hint or Answer
3	This lab begins with the switch having all default configuration, which means that no passwords are configured.
5	The command is the **hostname** global configuration command.
6	Switches (and routers) immediately accept and use the commands issued in configuration mode. Because the **hostname** command defines the text at the beginning of the command prompt, the next command prompt shows the new hostname.

continues

Table 1   **Hints and Answers**   *continued*

Step	Hint or Answer
8	The switch put a copy of the **hostname Fred** command into the running-config file. If you do not initially see the command, look for the phrase "—-more" at the bottom of the screen; if it is there, press **Spacebar** to display the group of messages.
9	The switch does not automatically copy the running-config file, or any commands configured in configuration mode, into the configuration file used the next time the switch reloads: the startup-config file. So, the **show startup-config** file will not currently display the **hostname Fred** command.
11	After the **copy running-config startup-config** command, the running-config and startup-config files should be identical.

Configuration Steps

Example 1 shows a sample of the lab exercise being completed from the router's CLI.

Example 1   Example of Performing This Lab

```
(Press enter)
Switch>enable
Switch#configure terminal
Switch(config)#hostname Fred
Fred(config)#end
Fred#
```

ICND1 Skill Builders

Part 1: Navigation and Administration

Lab 3: Switch CLI Configuration Process II

Overview

This lab guides you through the process of entering configuration mode and through the configuration of a couple of commonly used configuration commands: **description** and **enable secret**.

Topology

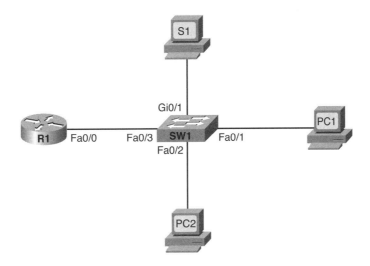

Figure 1   Network Topology for This Lab

This lab uses only the switch (SW1) with no activities on the other devices.

Detailed Lab Steps

Step 1.   Connect to SW1's console port using the simulator. The window will look like a terminal emulator with a cursor at the bottom of the screen and the center of the screen mostly blank.

Step 2.   From the simulator's terminal-emulator screen, press **Enter**.

Step 3.   Enter privileged mode using the **enable** command. Are you prompted for a password?

_____

Step 4.   Enter configuration mode using the **configure terminal** command. What does the command prompt look like after this command? What CLI mode does the prompt imply?

_____

_____

Step 5.   Enter interface configuration mode for interface FastEthernet 0/1 using the **interface fastethernet 0/1** command. What does the command prompt look like after this command? What CLI mode does the prompt imply?

_____

_____

Step 6.   Use the **description this is the connection to PC1** command to define an interface description for interface Fa0/1.

Step 7. Move back to global configuration mode using the **exit** command.

Step 8. Use the **enable secret ciscopress** command to set an enable password so that **ciscopress** must be entered when a user tries to enter privileged mode.

Step 9. Use the **end** command to move back to enable mode.

Step 10. Use the **disable** command to move back to user exec mode.

Step 11. Use the **enable** command to try to move back to enable exec mode. Are you prompted for a password?

_____

_____

_____

Step 12. Use the password **ciscopress** to enter enable mode.

Hints and Answers

Table 1 provides hints and tips for any lab steps that do not supply complete details and provides answers for any lab steps that ask questions.

Table 1   Hints and Answers

Step	Hint or Answer
3	This lab begins with the switch having all default configuration, which means that no passwords are configured.
4	The command prompt should be Switch(config)#, which implies that you are in global configuration mode.
5	The command prompt should be Switch(config-if)#, which implies that you are in interface configuration mode.
11	You should be prompted for a password now, as a result of having configured the **enable secret** command earlier in the lab.

Configuration Steps

Example 1 shows a sample of the lab exercise being completed from the router's CLI.

Example 1   Example of Performing This Lab

```
(Press enter)
Switch>enable
Switch#configure terminal
Switch(config)#interface fastethernet0/1
Switch(config-if)#description this is the connection to PC1
Switch(config-if)#exit
Switch(config)#enable secret ciscopress
Switch(config)#end
Switch#
```

ICND1 Skill Builders

Part 1: Navigation and Administration

Lab 4: Router CLI Exec Mode I

Overview

This lab guides you through the process of moving between user exec mode and enable exec mode, showing you some of the differences between the two modes.

Topology

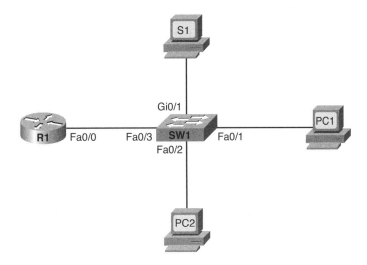

Figure 1   Network Topology for This Lab

This lab uses only the router (R1) with no activities on the other devices.

Detailed Lab Steps

Step 1. Connect to R1's console port using the simulator. The window will look like a terminal emulator with a cursor at the bottom of the screen and the center of the screen mostly blank.

Step 2. From the simulator's terminal-emulator screen, press **Enter**.

Step 3. Press the **?** key to look at the available commands. Look for the **reload** and **show** commands. Do you see either command listed?

_____

_____

_____

Step 4. Try to enter privileged mode using the **enable** command. Are you prompted for a password?

_____

Step 5. When you are in privileged mode, use help by pressing the **?** key to see the current list of commands. Look for the **reload** and **show** commands. Do you see either command listed?

_____

_____

_____

Step 6. Move back to user mode by entering the **disable** command.

Step 7. Issue the **reload** command, which, if successful, reboots or reloads the router. What kind of response do you get? Does the router reload?

_____

_____

_____

Step 8. Type in some letters that do not form a valid command, for example, **xyz123**, and press **Enter**. What kind of response do you get? Is it the same message you got when you tried the **reload** command from user mode?

_____

_____

_____

Step 9. Use the **enable** command to move back to enable mode.

Step 10. Try the **reload** command from enable mode. Does the command work now? (You should answer **yes** to any prompts.)

Hints and Answers

Table 1 provides hints and tips for any lab steps that do not supply complete details and provides answers for any lab steps that ask questions.

Table 1   Hints and Answers

Step	Hint or Answer
2	The simulator should display a prompt with the text Router> after you press **Enter**. If this text does not appear, click inside the window to make that window the focus of your computer desktop, and press **Enter** again.
3	You should see the **show** command, because it is supported in user mode. However, you should not see the **reload** command, because it is not supported in user mode.
4	This lab begins with the router having all default configuration, which means that no passwords are configured.
5	You should see both commands, **reload** and **show**, because both are available in enable mode.
7	The router rejects the **reload** command, stating "% Bad IP address or host name."
8	The router rejects the command with the same error message seen in the previous step.
10	The router will accept the **reload** command, and if you answer **yes**, that you want to reload the router, the router will reload.

Configuration Steps

This lab does not require any configuration.

ICND1 Skill Builders

Part 1: Navigation and Administration

Lab 5: Router CLI Exec Mode II

Overview

This lab guides you through the process of using several router commands: **show version**, **ping**, and **show ip arp**.

Topology

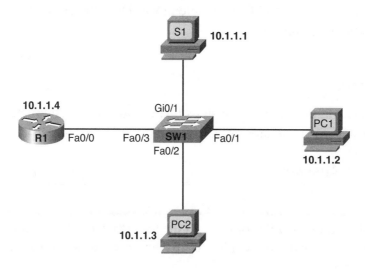

Figure 1   Network Topology for This Lab

This lab uses only the router (R1) with no activities on the other devices.

Detailed Lab Steps

Step 1.   Connect to R1's console port using the simulator. The window will look like a terminal emulator with a cursor at the bottom of the screen and the center of the screen mostly blank.

Step 2.   From the simulator's terminal-emulator screen, press **Enter**.

Step 3.   Enter privileged mode using the **enable** command. Are you prompted for a password?

_____

Step 4.   Use the **show version** command to list the version of the router IOS. Record the IOS version information on the lines below.

_____

_____

Step 5.   From that same command output, what is the name of the file in flash memory?

_____

_____

Step 6.   Again from that same command output, what was the time of the last reload?

_____

Step 7. Issue the **ping 10.1.1.1** command to test whether the router can send packets back and forth to server S1. Does the **ping** command work? Does it show five exclamation points?

_____

_____

_____

_____

Step 8. Use the **show ip arp** command, and list all the MAC addresses and their corresponding IP addresses.

_____

_____

_____

_____

Step 9. Use the **ping** command to test connectivity to server S1 (10.1.1.1), PC1 (10.1.1.2), and PC2 (10.1.1.3).

Hints and Answers

Table 1 provides hints and tips for any lab steps that do not supply complete details and provides answers for any lab steps that ask questions.

Table 1   Hints and Answers

Step	Hint or Answer
3	The router has not been configured with an enable password, so the router did not request a password.
4	The version is 12.4(7h).
5	The filename is c2800nm-advipservicesk9-mz.124-7h.bin.
6	The output lists the time in the 7th line of text output. The time will vary depending on how long ago you started this lab in the Simulator.
7	The command should work, partly as a result of the preconfiguration of the router's Fa0/0 interface and the preconfiguration of server S1. The command output should show five exclamation points.
8	The ARP table should show an entry for server S1 (10.1.1.1) and for the router (10.1.1.4). The other PCs on the LAN will also be listed.
9	The pings for each device should work.

Configuration Steps

This lab does not require any configuration.

ICND1 Skill Builders

Part 1: Navigation and Administration

Lab 6: Router CLI Configuration Process

Overview

This lab guides you through the process of changing the running-config file, seeing those results, and demonstrating that the commands added into configuration mode are not automatically added to the startup-config file.

Topology

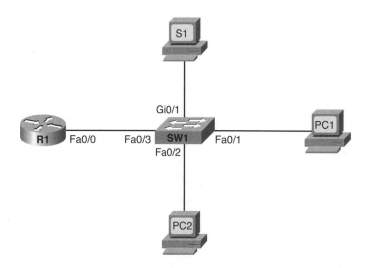

Figure 1   Network Topology for This Lab

This lab uses only the router (R1) with no activities on the other devices.

Detailed Lab Steps

Step 1.   Connect to R1's console port using the simulator and press **Enter**. (You should see a user mode command prompt of Router>.)

Step 2.   Enter privileged mode using the **enable** command.

Step 3.   Enter configuration mode using the **configure terminal** command.

Step 4.   Use the **hostname R1** command to change your router's hostname. Did the command prompt change as soon as you pressed **Enter** at the end of the command?

_____

Step 5.   Exit configuration mode (press **Ctrl-Z** or enter **end**).

Step 6. Use the **show running-config** command to view the currently in-use router configuration. Can you see the **hostname** command?

Step 7. Use the **reload** command to reboot your router. (Note: A physical router may require a minute or two to reboot, but the simulated switch should boot quickly.) When asked if you want to save the configuration, answer **no**. When asked to confirm that you want to reload, just press **Enter**, which selects the default answer, in brackets, of "confirm."

Step 8. When the router has finished the boot process, move into enable mode, and then use the **show running-config** command to look for the **hostname R1** command. Do you see the command in the output?

Step 9. According to the command prompt, what is the router hostname now?

Hints and Answers

Table 1 provides hints and tips for any lab steps that do not supply complete details and provides answers for any lab steps that ask questions.

Table 1   Hints and Answers

Step	Hint or Answer
1	The simulator should display a prompt with the text Router> after you press **Enter**. If it does not appear, click inside the window to make that window the focus of your computer desktop, and press **Enter** again.
4	Routers (and switches) immediately accept and use the commands issued in configuration mode. Because the **hostname** command defines the text at the beginning of the command prompt, the next command prompt shows the new hostname.
6	The router put a copy of the **hostname R1** command into the running-config file. If you do not initially see the command, look for the phrase "—-more" at the bottom of the screen; if it is there, press **Spacebar** to display the group of messages.
8	The configuration process changes the running-config file, but it does not change the startup-config file, which is used the next time the router boots. By answering **no** in Step 8 when asked if you want to save the configuration, you failed to save the **hostname R1** command that you had just configured.
9	The hostname is "Router," because the hostname sits at the beginning of the command prompt.

Configuration Steps

The only configuration added in this lab is the **hostname R1** command.

ICND1 Skill Builders

Part 1: Navigation and Administration

Lab 7: Setting Switch Passwords

Overview

This lab guides you through the process of configuring and testing a switch's telnet and enable secret passwords.

Topology

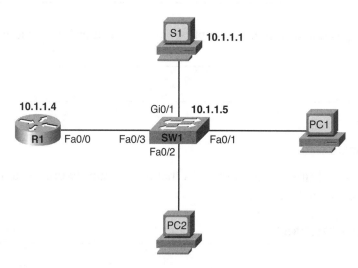

Figure 1   Network Topology for This Lab

Detailed Lab Steps

Step 1. Connect to SW1's console port using the simulator. The window will look like a terminal emulator with a cursor at the bottom of the screen and the center of the screen mostly blank.

Step 2. From the simulator's terminal-emulator screen, press **Enter**.

Step 3. Enter privileged mode using the **enable** command and use the **configure terminal** command to move into configuration mode.

Step 4. Configure the switch to require users that telnet into SW1 to use a password of **ciscopress**. To do so, start by issuing the **line vty 0 15** configuration command, which moves you to vty configuration mode. What does the command prompt look like after using this command?

_____

_____

_____

_____

Step 5. Use the **password ciscopress** vty mode configuration command to set the password value.

Step 6. Use the **login** vty mode configuration command to tell the switch to require a simple password from a user that telnets into the switch.

Step 7. Configure the switch to expect a password of its-a-secret for users to reach privileged mode, by using the **enable secret its-a-secret** global configuration command. What command prompt was displayed after you issued this command?

_____

_____

Step 8. Exit configuration mode (press **Ctrl-Z** or enter **end**).

Step 9. From the simulator user interface, connect to router R1, and press **Enter** to display the user mode prompt.

Step 10. From R1, use the **telnet 10.1.1.5** command to telnet to the switch, and use the vty password of **ciscopress** to access the switch. What does the command prompt look like now? What CLI mode are you in?

_____

_____

_____

_____

Step 11. Use the **enable** command to move to enable mode, and use the enable password of **its-a-secret** to access the switch. What does the command prompt look like now?

_____

_____

Hints and Answers

Table 1 provides hints and tips for any lab steps that do not supply complete details and provides answers for any lab steps that ask questions.

Table 1   Hints and Answers

Step	Hint or Answer
1	The simulator should display a prompt with the text Switch> after you press **Enter**. If it does not appear, click inside the window to make that window the focus of your computer desktop, and press **Enter** again.
4	The prompt should change to Switch(config-line)#.
7	When using a global configuration command from a nonglobal configuration mode, unless the command is designed to change the user to a different configuration mode, IOS puts the user back in global configuration mode. So, the command prompt will be Switch(config)#.
10	After the successful telnet, you should be in user mode on the switch with a command prompt of Switch>.
11	As usual, the **enable** command moves the CLI to enable mode. With a (default) hostname of Switch, the switch displays a prompt of Switch#.

Configuration Steps

Example 1 shows a sample of the lab exercise being completed from SW1's CLI.

Example 1   Example of Performing This Lab

```
(Press enter)
Switch>enable
Switch#configure terminal
Switch(config)#line vty 0 15
Switch(config-line)password ciscopress
Switch(config-line)#login
Switch(config-line)#enable secret its-a-secret
Switch(config)#end
Switch#
```

ICND1 Skill Builders

Part 1: Navigation and Administration

Lab 9: Setting Router Passwords

Overview

This lab guides you through the process of configuring and testing a router's console and enable passwords.

Topology

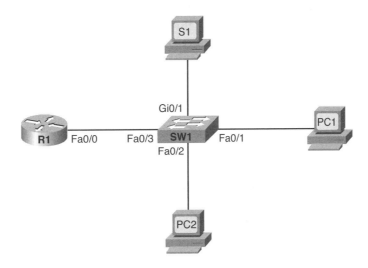

Figure 1   **Network Topology for This Lab**

Detailed Lab Steps

Step 1.   Connect to R1's console port using the simulator. The window will look like a terminal emulator with a cursor at the bottom of the screen and the center of the screen mostly blank.

Step 2.   From the simulator's terminal-emulator screen, press **Enter**.

Step 3.   Enter privileged mode using the **enable** command and then move into configuration mode using the **configure terminal** command.

Step 4. Configure the router to require a password of ciscopress when connecting through the console. To do so, start by issuing the **line con 0** configuration command, which moves you to console line configuration mode. What does the command prompt look like after using this command?

_____

_____

_____

_____

Step 5. Use the **password ciscopress** console mode configuration command to set the password value.

Step 6. Use the **login** console mode configuration command to tell the switch to require a simple password from a user that connects through the router console.

For this lab, you will configure two different enable passwords—one generally called the "enable password" and one called "enable secret"—and see which is used.

Step 7. Configure the **enable password fred** global configuration command.

Step 8. Configure the **enable secret barney** global configuration command.

Step 9. Exit configuration mode (press **Ctrl-Z** or enter **end**).

Step 10. Use the **exit** command to log out of the router.

Step 11. Press **Enter**. Does the router prompt you for a password? Does the password **ciscopress** work?

_____

_____

_____

Step 12. Use the **enable** command to move from user mode to enable mode. Which of the two passwords (**fred** or **barney**) works? Which configuration command did you use to configure that password?

_____

_____

_____

_____

Hints and Answers

Table 1 provides hints and tips for any lab steps that do not supply complete details and provides answers for any lab steps that ask questions.

Table 1   Hints and Answers

Step	Hint or Answer
1	The simulator should display a prompt with the text Router> after you press **Enter**. If it does not appear, click inside the window to make that window the focus of your computer desktop, and press **Enter** again.
4	The prompt should change to Router(config-line)#.
11	When connecting again through the console, the router will now require the console password ciscopress, which was configured at Step 5.
12	If both commands that configure an enable password are configured, routers (and switches) use the password as configured in the **enable secret** command. As a result, the router in this case requires you to use the password barney.

Configuration Steps

Example 1 shows a sample of the lab exercise being completed from R1's CLI.

Example 1   Example of Performing This Lab

```
(Press enter)
Router>enable
Router#configure terminal
Router(config)#line con 0
Router(config-line)password ciscopress
Router(config-line)#login
Router(config-line)#enable password fred
Router(config)#enable secret barney
Router(config)#end
Router#
```

ICND1 Skill Builders

Part 3: IP Addressing, Routing, and WANs

Lab 23: Configuring Hostnames

Overview

In this lab, you'll learn about using the **ip host** command so that you can ping another router using a hostname instead of an IP address. You'll begin with a working configuration of two routers that are already configured with IP addresses and RIP version 2.

Topology

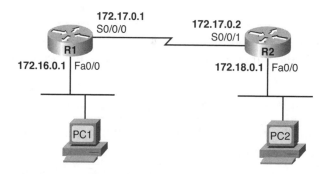

Figure 1   Network Topology for This Lab

The IP addresses used in this lab are shown in Table 1.

Table 1   IP Addresses

Router	Interface	IP Address
R1	FastEthernet 0/0	172.16.0.1
	Serial 0/0/0	172.17.0.1
R2	FastEthernet 0/0	172.18.0.1
	Serial 0/0/1	172.17.0.2

Detailed Lab Steps

Step 1. Connect to R1 from the simulator user interface and enter user mode by using the console password **ciscopress**.

Step 2. Enter privileged exec mode by entering **enable** and the password **ciscopress**.

Step 3. From R1, ping R2's FastEthernet 0/0 and Serial 0/0/1 interface IP addresses. Did the pings work?

_____

Step 4. Enter global configuration mode by entering the **configure terminal** command.

Step 5. Create one host table entry for R2's serial interface using the **ip host R2-serial 172.17.0.2** command.

Step 6. Create one host table entry for R2's LAN interface using the **ip host R2-LAN 172.18.0.1** command.

Step 7. Exit back to privileged exec mode by entering the **exit** command.

Step 8. Enter the **ping R2-serial** command to ping R2's serial IP address. Did the ping work? Do you see R2's serial IP address in the command output?

_____

_____

Step 9. Enter the **ping R2-LAN** command to ping R2's LAN IP address. Did the ping work? Do you see R2's LAN IP address in the command output?

_____

_____

Step 10. Enter the **show hosts** command. Do you see the information from both of the **ip host** configuration commands?

_____

_____

Hints and Answers

Table 2 provides hints and tips for any lab steps that do not supply complete details and provides answers for any lab steps that ask questions.

Table 2   Hints and Answers

Step	Hint or Answer
3	The IP addresses to use are found in Table 1. The pings should work.
8	The ping will again work. The IP address configured in the **ip host R2-serial 172.17.0.2** command is also listed in the **ping** command's output.
9	The ping will again work. The IP address configured in the **ip host R2-LAN 172.18.0.1** command is also listed in the **ping** command's output.
10	The **show hosts** command does indeed list all hostnames known to the local router.

Configuration Steps

Example 1 shows a sample of the lab exercise being completed from R1's CLI.

Example 1 Example of Performing This Lab

```
(Press enter)
Password: ciscopress
R1>enable
Password: ciscopress
R1#configure terminal
R1(config)#ip host R2-serial 172.17.0.2
R1(config)#ip host R2-LAN 172.18.0.1
R1(config)#exit
R1#
```

IP Subnetting and Basic Router Configuration

Table 3-1 lists the labs for this unit. Check with your instructor or class syllabus to confirm what labs you should perform for class.

Table 3-1 Unit 3 Labs

Date	ICND1/ ICND2	Type	Part	Number	Name	Page
	ICND1	SB	1	9	Setting Router passwords	29
	ICND1	SB	1	10	Configuring Router IP settings	32
	ICND1	SB	1	12	Configuring SSH	34
	ICND1	SB	1	22	Terminal History I	38
	ICND1	CS	1	3	Rebuild a Configuration	40
	ICND1	CS	1	4	SSH and Telnet	48
	Ungraded	CL	1	1	Basic Router Configuration and the CLI	55

ICND1 Skill Builders

Part 1: Navigation and Administration

Lab 9: Setting Router Passwords

Overview

This lab guides you through the process of configuring and testing a router's console and enable passwords.

Topology

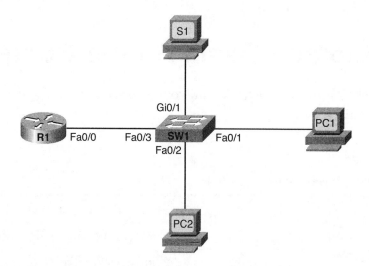

Figure 1   Network Topology for This Lab

Detailed Lab Steps

Step 1.   Connect to R1's console port using the simulator. The window will look like a terminal emulator with a cursor at the bottom of the screen and the center of the screen mostly blank.

Step 2.   From the simulator's terminal-emulator screen, press **Enter**.

Step 3.   Enter privileged mode using the **enable** command and then move into configuration mode using the **configure terminal** command.

Step 4.   Configure the router to require a password of ciscopress when connecting through the console. To do so, start by issuing the **line con 0** configuration command, which moves you to console line configuration mode. What does the command prompt look like after using this command?

_____

_____

_____

_____

Step 5.   Use the **password ciscopress** console mode configuration command to set the password value.

Step 6.   Use the **login** console mode configuration command to tell the switch to require a simple password from a user that connects through the router console.

For this lab, you will configure two different enable passwords—one generally called the "enable password" and one called "enable secret"—and see which is used.

Step 7. Configure the **enable password fred** global configuration command.

Step 8. Configure the **enable secret barney** global configuration command.

Step 9. Exit configuration mode (press **Ctrl-Z** or enter **end**).

Step 10. Use the **exit** command to log out of the router.

Step 11. Press **Enter**. Does the router prompt you for a password? Does the password **ciscopress** work?

_____

_____

Step 12. Use the **enable** command to move from user mode to enable mode. Which of the two passwords (**fred** or **barney**) works? Which configuration command did you use to configure that password?

_____

_____

_____

_____

Hints and Answers

Table 1 provides hints and tips for any lab steps that do not supply complete details and provides answers for any lab steps that ask questions.

Table 1   Hints and Answers

Step	Hint or Answer
1	The simulator should display a prompt with the text Router> after you press **Enter**. If it does not appear, click inside the window to make that window the focus of your computer desktop, and press **Enter** again.
4	The prompt should change to Router(config-line)#.
11	When connecting again through the console, the router will now require the console password ciscopress, which was configured at Step 5.
12	If both commands that configure an enable password are configured, routers (and switches) use the password as configured in the **enable secret** command. As a result, the router in this case requires you to use the password barney.

Configuration Steps

Example 1 shows a sample of the lab exercise being completed from R1's CLI.

Example 1   Example of Performing This Lab

```
(Press enter)
Router>enable
Router#configure terminal
Router(config)#line con 0
Router(config-line)password ciscopress
Router(config-line)#login
Router(config-line)#enable password fred
Router(config)#enable secret barney
Router(config)#end
Router#
```

ICND1 Skill Builders

Part 1: Navigation and Administration

Lab 10: Configuring Router IP Settings

Overview

This lab guides you through the process of configuring an IP address on a router interface.

Topology

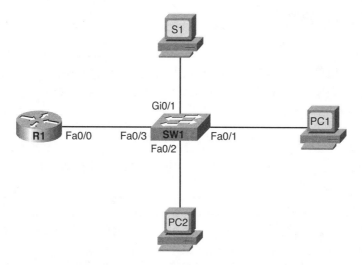

Figure 1   Network Topology for This Lab

Detailed Lab Steps

Step 1. Connect to R1's console port using the simulator. The window will look like a terminal emulator with a cursor at the bottom of the screen and the center of the screen mostly blank.

Step 2. From the simulator's terminal-emulator screen, press **Enter**.

Step 3. Enter privileged mode using the **enable** command.

Step 4. Use the **show ip interface brief** command to view all interfaces. Which interfaces have an IP address configured? What are the addresses and the corresponding masks?

_____

_____

_____

_____

Step 5. Enter configuration mode using the **configure terminal** command.

Step 6. Issue the **interface Fa0/0** command to enter configuration mode for the FastEthernet 0/0 interface.

Step 7. Configure the router to use IP address 10.1.1.4, mask 255.255.255.0, on that Fa0/0 interface using the **ip address 10.1.1.4 255.255.255.0** command.

Step 8. Still in interface Fa0/0 configuration mode, also administratively enable the interface using the **no shutdown** command.

Step 9. Exit back to enable mode (press **Ctrl-Z** or enter **end**).

Step 10. Use the **show ip interface brief** command to view all interfaces. Is the router's Fa0/0 IP address now listed? What is the IP address?

_____

_____

_____

_____

Step 11. Confirm that R1's Fa0/0 interface is working by pinging PC1 (10.1.1.1). Did the command output imply that R1 can send packets to and from PC1?

_____

_____

Hints and Answers

Table 1 provides hints and tips for any lab steps that do not supply complete details and provides answers for any lab steps that ask questions.

Table 1   Hints and Answers

Step	Hint or Answer
4	The output should list several interfaces, none of which has an IP address assigned at this point.
10	The router's Fa0/0 interface should now have IP address 10.1.1.4 assigned to it.
11	The **ping 10.1.1.1** command output should list several exclamation points, meaning that the ping worked.

Configuration Steps

Example 1 shows a sample of the lab exercise being completed from the router's CLI.

Example 1   Example of Performing This Lab

```
(Press enter)
R1>enable
R1#configure terminal
R1(config)#interface fa0/0
R1(config-if)#ip address 10.1.1.4 255.255.255.0
R1(config-if)#no shutdown
R1(config-if)#end
R1#
```

ICND1 Skill Builders

Part 1: Navigation and Administration

Lab 12: Using and Suspending Telnet Connections

Overview

This lab guides you through the process of using the **telnet** command to connect to multiple other devices, suspend those Telnet connections, and then resume using previously suspended Telnet connections.

Topology

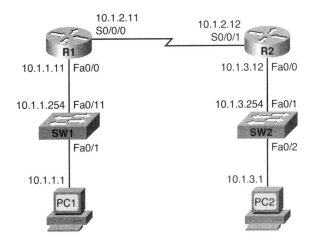

Figure 1   Network Topology for This Lab

Detailed Lab Steps

Step 1.   Connect to R1's console port using the simulator. The window will look like a terminal emulator with a cursor at the bottom of the screen and the center of the screen mostly blank.

Step 2.   From the simulator's terminal-emulator screen, press **Enter**. Respond with password **ciscopress**. What does the command prompt look like?

_____

_____

_____

_____

_____

_____

Step 3.   From R1's user mode command prompt, use the **telnet 10.1.2.12** command to telnet to R2's serial IP address. When prompted, use the password **ciscopress**. What does the command prompt look like? Which device will interpret the next command you enter from this prompt?

_____

_____

_____

_____

Step 4. Suspend R1's Telnet connection to R2 by pressing **Ctrl-Shift-6** (all three keys), then releasing those keys, and then pressing and releasing the **x** key. What is displayed as the current command prompt? Which device will interpret the next command you enter from this prompt?

_____

_____

_____

Step 5. Telnet to SW2 using the **telnet 10.1.3.254** command, using the **ciscopress** password when prompted. What is displayed as the current command prompt? Which device will interpret the next command you enter from this prompt?

_____

_____

_____

Step 6. Suspend R1's Telnet connection to SW2 by pressing **Ctrl-Shift-6**, then releasing those keys, and then pressing the **x** key. What is displayed as the current command prompt? Which device will interpret the next command you enter from this prompt?

_____

_____

_____

Step 7. On R1, use the **show sessions** command to list information about any suspended Telnet connections. For each line of output from this command, record the connection number, IP address or hostname, and which line lists an * in the front of the output.

_____

_____

_____

Step 8. Resume using the most recently suspended Telnet connection by using the **resume** command. Note that the **resume** command, with no parameters, resumes the most recently suspended Telnet connection. (Note that to make the destination device, SW2, respond, you must also press **Enter** after resuming the connection.) Based on the command prompt, to which device did you reconnect?

_____

_____

Step 9. Issue the **show interface vlan 1** command (a command that is not supported on routers) both to confirm that you are connected to a LAN switch and to confirm the IP address (10.1.3.254) of switch SW2. Does this command indeed list 10.1.3.254 as the switch's IP address?

Step 10. Suspend R1's Telnet connection to SW2 by pressing **Ctrl-Shift-6**, then releasing those keys, and then pressing the **x** key.

Step 11. On R1, repeat the **show sessions** command, noting that the Telnet session to R2 is listed as session number 1. Then use the **resume 1** command to resume the Telnet connect to router R2. (Note that to make the destination device, R2, respond, you must also press **Enter** after resuming the connection.)

Step 12. Use the **show ip interface brief** command to confirm that the command prompt is truly from router R2, verifying R2's LAN IP address of 10.1.3.12 and serial IP address of 10.1.2.12.

Hints and Answers

Table 1 provides hints and tips for any lab steps that do not supply complete details and provides answers for any lab steps that ask questions.

Table 1   Hints and Answers

Step	Hint or Answer
2	The command prompt should be R1>, because you are connected to R1's console, and you have just entered user mode, which is designated by a > at the end of the command prompt.
3	The command prompt should be R2>, meaning that you are logged into router R2, in user mode. If you were to enter a command now, you would get a response from R2.
4	The command prompt should be R1>, meaning that you are now communicating with R1 again, in the same mode you were using before the telnet in the previous step. If you were to enter a command now, you would get a response from R1.
5	The command prompt should be SW2>, meaning that you are now communicating with SW2. If you were to enter a command now, you would get a response from SW2.
6	The command prompt should be R1>, meaning that you are now communicating with R1 again, in the same mode you were using before the telnet in the previous step. If you were to enter a command now, you would get a response from R1.
7	The line with the * is the most recently suspended Telnet connection.
8	The command prompt will change to SW2> as a result of resuming the connection to SW2.
9	The command will list the correct IP address of 10.1.3.254.

Configuration Steps

This lab does not require any configuration.

ICND1 Skill Builders

Part 1: Navigation and Administration

Lab 22: Terminal History I

Overview

In this lab, you will gain experience with viewing your terminal history. You will begin with a topology already preconfigured with IP addresses and RIP version 2. Next, you will gain valuable experience viewing the history of commands you enter on a Cisco router and modifying the number of commands you can view in your terminal history.

Topology

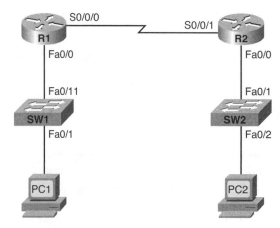

Figure 1   Network Topology for This Lab

Detailed Lab Steps

Step 1. Connect to R1 from the simulator user interface. Use the password **ciscopress** to log into the router.

Step 2. Enter privileged exec mode by entering the **enable** command and the password **ciscopress**.

Step 3. To begin viewing your routing table, enter **show ip route**.

Step 4. Press **Up Arrow** to view your previous command. Add the word **connected** to the end. This will show you only your directly connected routes in your routing table.

Step 5. Press **Up Arrow** again to bring up your **show ip route connected** command. Press **Backspace** to remove the **connected** keyword, and replace it with **rip**. What does this command show you?

_____

_____

Step 6. Enter the **show history** command to view your complete terminal history. How many commands do you see?

_____

_____

Step 7. You can control the number of lines you see in the output of **show history** by using the **terminal history size** command. Go ahead and change this size by entering **terminal history size 2**.

Step 8. To verify your configuration, enter **show history** again. How many commands do you see now?

_____

_____

Hints and Answers

Table 1 provides hints and tips for any lab steps that do not supply complete details and provides answers for any lab steps that ask questions.

Table 1   Hints and Answers

Step	Hint or Answer
5	The **show ip route rip** command shows you routes learned by the RIP routing protocol.
6	You should see 5 commands: **enable**, **show ip route**, **show ip route connected**, **show ip route rip**, and **show history**.
8	You should see only two commands now.

Configuration Steps

This lab does not require any configuration.

ICND1 Configuration Scenarios
Part 1: Navigation and Administration

Lab 3: Rebuild a Configuration

Overview

This lab begins with a mostly configured internetwork. The internetwork would be functional, allowing both hosts to ping each other, if R1's interfaces were enabled. Your job is to examine R1's configuration, make notes, and then erase the configuration and reload R1. Then, you must configure the same features, plus enable R1's interfaces, proving you completed the task by pinging from PC1 to PC2.

Note: Any password necessary for this lab, unless otherwise specified, is **ciscopress**.

Topology

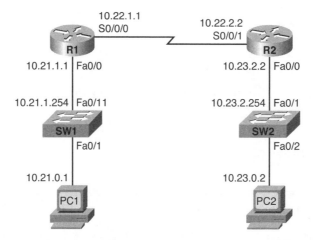

Figure 1   Network Topology for This Lab

Detailed Lab Steps

Part 1: Examine the Configuration and Initial State

Step 1. Connect to R1 from the simulator user interface, and move to enable mode.

Step 2. Use the **show running-config** command to examine the current configuration of the router. Make notes regarding any non-default configuration you see in the configuration file, including the following:

- IP addresses/masks

- Hostnames
- Passwords
- Routing protocol configuration
- **shutdown/no shutdown** on each interface

_____

_____

_____

_____

_____

_____

_____

_____

_____

_____

_____

Step 3. Connect to the PC1 user interface from the simulator, and use the **ping 10.21.0.1** command to confirm that PC1 can ping its own IP address. Did the ping work?

_____

Step 4. Again from PC1, find the default gateway setting that is currently configured on PC1. Is that the IP address configured on R1's Fa0/0 interface? From PC1, ping that IP address. Did the ping work?

_____

_____

Step 5. Connect to the PC2 user interface from the simulator, and use the **ping 10.23.0.2** command to confirm that PC2 can ping its own IP address. Did the ping work?

_____

Step 6. Again from PC2, find the default gateway setting that is currently configured on PC2. Is that the IP address configured on R2's Fa0/0 interface (according to the figure)? From PC2, ping that IP address. Did the ping work?

_____

_____

Step 7. Move back to R1 from the simulator user interface, and then use the **erase startup-config** command to erase the entire startup-config file on R1.

Step 8. Reload router R1 using the **reload** command. If the router asks if you want to save the config or not, answer **no**.

Step 9. The next question asks if you want to enter the Initial Configuration Dialogue. Answer **no** and press **Enter**.

Step 10. At this point, the router tells you to "press return to get started," so go ahead and press **Enter**.

Part 2: Replace the Configuration

Part 2 guides you through the process of reconfiguring R1 to match its original configuration. However, if you want to try to complete the configuration without any help, configure R1 based on the notes you took in Part 1, ignore the steps in this part of the lab exercise and move on to Part 3.

Step 11. Move into configuration mode on router R1.

Step 12. Configure the **hostname** command to set the hostname to match the setting you recorded in Step 1. What command did you enter?

_____

_____

Step 13. Configure the global command that tells the router to not attempt to ask a DNS for name resolution. What command did you enter?

_____

_____

Step 14. Configure the password used to reach privileged mode, choosing the configuration command that is most secure. What command did you enter?

_____

_____

Step 15. Move to the configuration mode from which you can configure the console password. What command did you enter? To what configuration mode have you moved?

_____

_____

Step 16. Configure the console so that R1 asks the user for a password and so that the required text password is "ciscopress." Which commands did you use?

_____

_____

Step 17. Move to the configuration mode from which you can configure the passwords used when R1 accepts Telnet connections. What command did you enter? To what configuration mode have you moved?

_____

_____

Step 18. Configure the vty ports so that R1 asks the user for a password and so that the required text password is "ciscopress." Which commands did you use?

_____

_____

Step 19. Move to the configuration mode from which you can configure the Fa0/0 interface. What command did you enter? To what configuration mode have you moved?

_____

_____

Step 20. Configure the interface's IP address/mask and any other settings that were previously configured. Which commands did you use?

_____

_____

_____

Step 21. Move to the configuration mode from which you can configure the S0/0/0 interface. What command did you enter? To what configuration mode have you moved? Did you have to move back to global configuration mode first?

_____

_____

Step 22. Configure the interface's IP address/mask and any other settings that were previously configured. Which commands did you use?

_____

_____

_____

Step 23. Move to the configuration mode from which you can configure RIP version 2. What command did you enter? To what configuration mode have you moved? Did you have to move back to global configuration mode first?

_____

_____

Step 24. Configure RIP using the identical RIP subcommands found during Part 1 of this lab. Which commands did you use?

_____

_____

_____

_____

Step 25. Exit configuration mode and save your configuration using the **copy running-config startup-config** exec command.

Part 3: Test the Internetwork and Bring Up the Interfaces

At this point, if you followed the instructions literally, R1 is back to its original state—including the fact that R1's Fa0/0 and S0/0/0 interfaces are shut down. This part guides you though the process of bringing up those interfaces and then testing connectivity between the PCs.

Step 26. Go back to configuration mode, and then move into the correct mode for configuring details about interface Fa0/0. What commands did you use?

_____

_____

Step 27. Issue the command to administratively enable the interface. What command did you use?

_____

_____

Step 28. Watch the screen for a few seconds—do you see an unsolicited message that Fa0/0 is now up?

_____

_____

Step 29. Bring up the S0/0/0 interface as well by moving into configuration mode for S0/0/0, and issue the **no shutdown** interface subcommand.

Step 30. Watch the screen for a few seconds—do you see an unsolicited message that S0/0/0 is now up?

_____

_____

Step 31. Move back to enable mode and use the **show ip route** command to display R1's routing table. Do you see the three subnets used in this internetwork? Which subnets are listed?

_____

_____

_____

_____

Step 32. Connect to the PC1 user interface from the simulator and use the **ping 10.21.0.1** command to confirm that PC1 can ping its own IP address. Did the ping work?

_____

Step 33. Again from PC1, find the default gateway setting that is currently configured on PC1. Is that the IP address configured on R1's Fa0/0 interface? From PC1, ping that IP address. Did the ping work?

_____

_____

Step 34. From PC1, ping PC2's IP address using the **ping 10.23.0.2** command. Did the ping work?

_____

_____

Step 35. If the ping did not work, then you may have made a mistake during the configuration process. Check the items in Part 2 of this lab, as well as the final configuration for R2 as listed in the "Configuration Steps" section.

Hints and Answers

Table 1 provides hints and tips for any lab steps that do not supply complete details and provides answers for any lab steps that ask questions.

Table 1   Hints and Answers

Step	Hint or Answer
3	PC1 should be able to successfully ping its own IP address.
4	The ping of R1's LAN IP address (**ping 10.21.1.1**) should fail, because R1's Fa0/0 interface is shut down.
5	PC2 should be able to successfully ping its own IP address.
6	The ping of R2's LAN IP address (**ping 10.23.2.2**) should work.
10	This step must be followed as listed so that you can configure R1 from the CLI.
11	Use the **configure terminal** command to move from enable mode to configuration mode.
12	Use the **hostname R1** command.
13	Use the **no ip domain-lookup** command.
14	Use the **enable secret ciscopress** command.
15	Use the **line console 0** command. This command moves a user to console configuration mode.
16	Use the **password ciscopress** and **login** commands.
17	Use the **line vty 0 4** command. This command moves a user to vty configuration mode.
18	Use the **password ciscopress** and **login** commands.
19	Use the **interface fastethernet 0/0** command. This command moves a user to interface configuration mode for the Fa0/0 interface.
20	Use the **ip address 10.21.1.1 255.255.0.0** and **description LAN connected to PC1** commands.
21	Use the **interface serial 0/0/0** command. This command moves a user to interface configuration mode for the Serial 0/0/0 interface. You did not have to move back to global configuration mode first—IOS accepts any command that moves you to another mode from any configuration mode.
22	Use the **ip address 10.22.1.1 255.255.0.0**, **description Serial link to R2**, and **clock rate 1536000** commands.
23	Use the **router rip** command. This command moves a user to RIP configuration mode. You do not have to first revert to global configuration mode using the **exit** command.
24	Use the **version 2** and **network 10.0.0.0** commands.
26	Use the **configure terminal** command to move to configuration mode and the **interface Fa0/0** command to move to interface configuration mode.
27	Use the **no shutdown** interface subcommand.
28 & 30	Because you have connected through the simulated router's console, log messages show up on the console screen by default.

continues

Table 1   **Hints and Answers** *continued*

Step	Hint or Answer
31	Three routes should be displayed. Note that you may have to wait about a minute for the one RIP-learned route to be displayed. The three routes are: 10.22.0.0/16 (connected) 10.21.0.0/16 (connected) 10.23.0.0/16 (RIP)
32	PC1's ping of its own IP address should have worked at any point in this lab exercise.
33	The ping should work now that R1's Fa0/0 interface is in an "up and up" state.
34	The ping will work.

Configuration Steps

Example 1 shows the configuration commands added to R1 during this lab, after the router's start-up-config file had been erased in Part 1 of the lab.

Example 1   Configuration on R1 Added During This Lab

```
hostname R1
no ip domain-lookup

enable secret ciscopress

line con 0
 login
 password ciscopress
line vty 0 4
 login
 password ciscopress

interface Fa0/0
 ip address 10.21.1.1 255.255.0.0
 description LAN connected to PC1
 no shutdown

interface Serial 0/0/0
 clock rate 1536000
 ip address 10.22.1.1 255.255.0.0
```

continues

Example 1   Configuration on R1 Added During This Lab *continued*

```
description Serial link to R2
no shutdown


router rip
 version 2
 network 10.0.0.0
```

ICND1 Configuration Scenarios
Part 1: Navigation and Administration

Lab 4: SSH and Telnet

Overview

During this lab, you will configure the two routers so that they can accept inbound Telnet and SSH connections.

The initial configurations at the beginning of this lab have enough configuration to allow each device to ping each other device, but the routers are missing configuration necessary to support Telnet and SSH. This lab guides you through the process of configuring the additional parameters to support Telnet as well as SSH.

Note: Any password necessary for this lab, unless otherwise specified, is **ciscopress**.

Topology

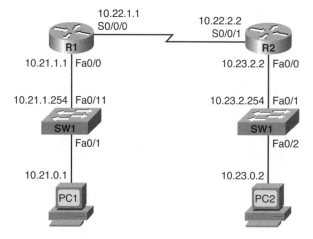

Figure 1   Network Topology for This Lab

Detailed Lab Steps

Part 1: Experiment with Telnet and SSH Before Configuring Anything Else

Step 1. Connect to PC1 from the simulator user interface, and test the internetwork by pinging all IP addresses shown in Figure 1. List the IP addresses from any of the **ping** commands that failed.

_____

_____

_____

Step 2. Connect to the R1 user interface from the simulator, and move into enable mode. Did R1 ask for a password for you to get into user mode? To get into enable mode?

_____

_____

Step 3. Examine the currently used configuration on R1. What commands told R1 to require a password when you first logged in? What commands are missing that would have made R1 ask for a password for you to reach enable mode?

_____

_____

Step 4. Use the **telnet** command to attempt to telnet to R1's Fa0/0 IP address. What command did you use? What happened?

_____

_____

_____

Step 5. Still on R1, ping R2's serial and LAN interface IP addresses, and note the result.

_____

Step 6. Repeat the **telnet** command, this time attempting to telnet to R2's Fa0/0 IP address. What command did you use? What happened?

_____

_____

_____

Step 7. Move to R2 from the simulator user interface and move to enable mode. Did R2 ask for a password for you to get into user mode? To get into enable mode?

_____

_____

Step 8. Examine the currently used configuration on R2. What commands told R2 to require a password when you first logged in? What commands are missing that would have made R2 ask for a password for you to reach enable mode?

_____

_____

Step 9. Further examine the currently used configuration on R2. What configuration commands are listed under the **line vty 0 4** configuration command? Do any of these commands set a password for incoming Telnet connections?

_____

_____

Part 2: Configure R2 to Accept Incoming Telnet Connections

Cisco routers require that a vty password be configured before they will accept incoming Telnet requests. Additionally, a router also requires that an enable password be configured to allow incoming Telnet users to reach enable mode. Both of these standards help protect a new router after it has been connected to a network but before the configuration has been completed.

Part 2 of this lab configures those passwords and tests Telnet.

Step 10. Move into configuration mode on router R2 and then move into vty line configuration mode.

Step 11. Configure the two vty subcommands that make a router ask for a password of ciscopress and ask for a password. Record the two commands on the lines below.

_____

_____

Step 12. Connect to the R1 user interface from the simulator and move into enable mode.

Step 13. Repeat the **telnet** command, again attempting to telnet to R2's Fa0/0 IP address. What command did you use? What happened? How does this differ from what happened in Step 6?

_____

_____

Step 14. Use the **enable** command to try to move to enable mode on R2. What happens? Record the text of any messages.

_____

_____

Step 15. Terminate the Telnet connection from R1 to R2 by using the **exit** command.

Step 16. Move to R2 from the simulator user interface and move to configuration mode.

Step 17. From global configuration mode, configure an enable password of ciscopress, using the more secure of the two command options. Record the command you used on the lines below.

_____

_____

Step 18. Move back to R1 from the simulator user interface and move to user mode on R1.

Step 19. Repeat the **telnet** command again to attempt to telnet to R2's Fa0/0 IP address. Do you still reach user mode on R2, as in Step 13?

_____

_____

_____

Step 20. Repeat Step 14 by using the **enable** command to try to move to enable mode on R2. What happens? Does it differ from what happened in Step 14?

_____

_____

Part 3: Configure R2 to Accept Incoming SSH Connections

Compared with Telnet, SSH provides the equivalent ability to access remote routers and switches, but it does so much more securely. Telnet does not attempt to hide the password text as it crosses the network, whereas SSH uses a secure authentication method. When available, SSH is the option of choice today.

SSH requires many configuration steps. The router vty lines must be configured to use username/password pairs instead of just a simple password. The router must be configured to accept SSH, instead of using the default of just accepting incoming Telnet connections. The router needs a domain name configured and, finally, needs a security key that is used during the authentication process. Part 3 of this lab guides you through the configuration and testing process.

Note: You should still be connected from R1 to R2, and in enable mode on R2, at the end of the previous step.

Step 21. Display the contents of the currently used configuration on R2. Record all subcommands you see under the **line vty 0 4** global command. (There should be two such commands.)

_____

_____

Step 22. Terminate the Telnet connection from R1 to R2 by using the **exit** command.

Step 23. Test the ability to use SSH to connect from R1 to R2 by using the **ssh –l fred 10.23.2.2** command from R1. What are the results? Record any messages you see.

_____

_____

Step 24. Move to R2 from the simulator user interface and move to configuration mode.

Step 25. From global configuration mode, move to vty configuration mode.

Step 26. Tell R2 to require Telnet and SSH connections to use a locally configured username/password pair by configuring the **login local** vty subcommand.

Step 27. Tell R2 to accept both incoming Telnet and SSH connections, rather than the default of just Telnet, by configuring the **transport input telnet ssh** vty subcommand.

The previous two steps configured the only vty subcommands required for SSH support. The rest of the configuration steps add three global configuration commands required for SSH.

Step 28. Move back to global configuration mode using the **exit** command.

Step 29. Configure a domain name on R2 using the **ip domain-name example.com** global command.

Step 30. Add a username/password pair using the **username fred password barney** global command.

Step 31. Generate a cryptography key, which will then be used to securely exchange authentication information with SSH clients, by using the **crypto key generate rsa** global command. If prompted, take the default number of bits for the length of the key.

Step 32. Move back to privileged mode on R2 using the **exit** command.

Part 4: Test SSH from R1 to R2

This final short part of the lab tests the SSH connection from R1 to R2.

Step 33. From the simulator user interface, connect to R1 and move into user mode.

Step 34. Use the **ssh –l fred 10.23.2.2** command, which tells R1 to attempt an SSH connection to 10.23.2.2 using username fred. Note that the –1 is a dash and then the letter "l," not the numeral "1." What is the next message you see? How does this differ from the results at Step 23?

_____

_____

Step 35. Supply the password you configured for user fred in Step 30.

Step 36. What does the command prompt look like now? To what device, and in what mode, are you connected?

_____

_____

Step 37. Move to enable mode on R2, and display the running configuration. As an additional confirmation that you are in R2, look for the configuration commands you added for SSH support on R2 in Steps 26 through 31.

Hints and Answers

Table 1 provides hints and tips for any lab steps that do not supply complete details and provides answers for any lab steps that ask questions.

Table 1   Hints and Answers

Step	Hint or Answer
1	The pings to all IP addresses should work at the beginning of this lab.
2	R1 required a password (ciscopress) to move into user mode, but it did not request a password to move into enable mode.
3	Use the **show running-config** command to list the running-config file. The output lists the **login** and **password ciscopress** commands under line con 0, which made R1 require a console password. (When you click an icon from the simulator user interface, the simulator acts as if you have connected via that device's console.) The **enable secret** or **enable password** global configuration commands would have configured an enable password.
4	Use the **telnet 10.21.1.1** command to telnet to R1's own Fa0/0 IP address. The output says that a password was required, but none is set.
5	Both pings succeed.
6	Use the **telnet 10.23.2.2** command to telnet to R2's Fa0/0 IP address. Just like in Step 4, the output says that a password was required, but none is set.
7	Like R1 at Step 2, R2 required a password (ciscopress) to move into user mode, but it did not request a password to move into enable mode.

continues

Table 1   **Hints and Answers**   *continued*

Step	Hint or Answer
8	The results are the same as in Step 3 on R1—R2 has a console password configured, but no enable password.
9	Neither R1 nor R2 has a vty password configured.
10	First use the **configure terminal** command and then use the **line vty 0 4** global command.
11	First use the **password ciscopress** subcommand and then use the **login** subcommand (even though the **login** command is already configured).
13	The **telnet** command works, with R2 asking for a password. You should end this step in user mode with R2's command prompt of R2>.
14	The **enable** command is rejected with a message of "% No password set." The reason is that R2 does not have an enable password configured.
17	Use the **enable secret ciscopress** global command, which is more secure than the **enable password ciscopress** command.
19	You should still be able to reach user mode on R2, ending with a command prompt of R2>.
20	Because R2 now has an enable password, R2 supplies a password prompt. You should now be in enable mode on R2 with a prompt of R2#.
21	You should see the **password ciscopress** subcommand and the **login** subcommand as configured in Step 11.
23	The command is rejected with a message that reads "% Connection refused by remote host."
25	Use the **line vty 0 4** global command.
34	The next message should be a password prompt.
35	The password is barney.
36	You are now in user mode on R2 with a prompt of R2>.

Configuration Steps

Example 1 shows the configuration commands added to R2 during this lab.

Example 1   Configuration on R2 Added During This Lab

```
enable secret ciscopress
line vty 0 4
 login
 password ciscopress


! Commands added to support ssh
```

```
line vty 0 4
 login local
 transport input telnet ssh

ip domain-name example.com
crypto key generate rsa
username fred password barney
```

Configuration Labs

Part 1: Router Configuration

Lab 1: Basic Router Configuration and the Command-Line Interface

Overview

The overall objective of this laboratory exercise is to gain experience with basic Cisco router configuration commands using the CCNA 640-802 Network Simulator and gain an introductory understanding of the following:

- Operating in the Cisco privileged mode
- Configuring the router's FastEthernet interface
- Configuring the computer's network interface
- Troubleshooting the router interface

Topology

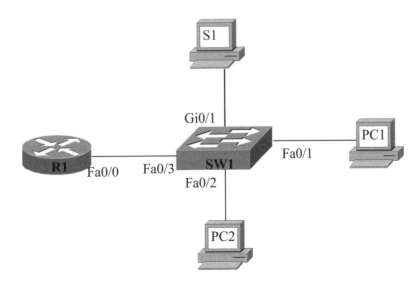

Figure 1   Network Topology for This Lab

Reference

The following simulator exercises provided with the CCNA 640-802 Network Simulator should be reviewed prior to starting this virtual laboratory exercise:

- Router CLI EXEC Mode I
- Router CLI EXEC Mode II
- Router CLI Configuration Process
- Setting Router Passwords
- Configuring Router IP Settings

Key Concepts

The following concepts, terms, commands, and steps should have been mastered in this exercise:

- Steps to enter the router's privileged EXEC mode (Router#).
- Use of the following commands to verify their operation in Cisco IOS:

  ?, show flash, show version [sh ver], show history [sh hist], show interfaces [sh int], configure terminal [conf t], interface FastEthernet [interface number], [int fa 0/0]

- What happens when you press the up-arrow key.
- How to change the host name of the router.
- How to configure the router's enable secret.
- How to set the vty password.
- The steps for configuring the IP address for FastEthernet interface 0/0 [Fa0/0] on your router.
- The use of the **no shut** command to enable the router interface.
- The use of the **sh ip int brief** command to verify that the interface has been configured.
- The use of the **ping** command to verify network connectivity.
- The use of **ipconfig /all**.

Reference Tables

Table 1 provides the IP address and mask of all necessary interfaces used to complete the lab.

Table 1   Computer IP Addresses, Subnet Masks, and Gateway Addresses for Lab 1

Computer	IP Address	Subnet Mask	Gateway Address
PC1	10.10.20.1	255.255.255.0	10.10.20.250
PC2	10.10.20.2	255.255.255.0	10.10.20.250
S1	10.10.20.3	255.255.255.0	10.10.20.250
FA 0/0	10.10.20.250	255.255.255.0	—

Detailed Lab Steps

Task 1

Step 1.   Use the following commands to verify their operation in Cisco IOS.

   a. What happens when you enter a ? at the Router# prompt?

   _____

   _____

   _____

   b. What information is displayed when you enter **show flash** at the Router# prompt?

   _____

   _____

   _____

   c. What command can you use to view the router's uptime?

   _____

   _____

   _____

   d. How long has the router been up?

   _____

   _____

   _____

   e. What version of the Cisco IOS software is running on this simulator?

   _____

   _____

   _____

   f. What command can you use to view the past entries on this router?

   _____

   _____

   _____

g. What happens when you press the up/down-arrow keys on your keyboard?

_____

_____

_____

Step 2. Change the host name of the router to RouterA. List the command sequence required to accomplish this task.

_____

_____

_____

Step 3. Configure the enable secret on the router to be **ciscopress**. List the command sequence required to accomplish this task.

_____

_____

_____

Step 4. Set the console password on the router to **ciscopress** and enable login. List the command sequence required to accomplish this task.

_____

_____

_____

Step 5. Set the vty password on the router to **ciscopress** and enable login. List the command sequence required to accomplish this task.

_____

_____

_____

Step 6. Configure the gateway address for FastEthernet 0/0 interface on RouterA. Use the IP address 10.10.20.250 and a subnet mask of 255.255.255.0. What does 0/0 mean relative to the FastEthernet interface?

_____

_____

_____

Step 7. Use the **no shut** command to enable the FastEthernet 0/0 interface. What does the **shut** command do?

_____

_____

_____

Step 8. Use the **sh ip int brief** command to verify that the FastEthernet interface has been configured and the router's status and protocol are both up and up. After you have completed the configuration, verify that each computer in the LAN can ping the other computers. Also verify that each computer can ping the router's gateway IP address [10.10.20.250]. If any of the assigned IP addresses fail to generate a reply, troubleshoot and correct the problem(s) until all interfaces can ping each other.

_____

_____

_____

Task 2: Configuration List

In this task, you are to issue the **show running-config** command from the RouterA# prompt.

The following is a partial list of the items displayed when you issue the **show running-config** [**sh run**] command. Your task is to define each item and its purpose. You might need to go to the Cisco website (http://www.cisco.com) and look up what each of these commands means.

1. Building configuration

_____

_____

_____

2. Current configuration

_____

_____

_____

3. !

_____

_____

_____

4. Version 12.4

_____

_____

_____

5. service timestamps debug datetime msec

_____

_____

_____

6. service timestamps log datetime msec

_____

_____

_____

IP Routing with Connected, Static, and RIP-2 Routes

Table 4-1 lists the labs for this unit. Check with your instructor or class syllabus to confirm what labs you should perform for class.

Table 4-1   Unit 4 Labs

Date	ICND1/ ICND2	Type	Part	Number	Name	Page
	ICND1	SB	3	5	Connected Routes	61
	ICND1	SB	3	1	Configuring IP Addresses I	64
	ICND1	SB	3	2	Configuring IP Addresses II	66
	ICND1	SB	3	6	Static Routes I	68
	ICND1	SB	3	15	RIP Configuration I	70
	ICND1	SB	3	16	RIP Configuration II	72
	ICND1	SB	3	21	RIP Verification I	76
	ICND1	CS	3	6	RIP-2 Configuration I	78
	ICND1	CS	3	8	RIP Auto-summary	91
	ICND1	SE	1	1–11	Subnet ID Calculation I–XI	101
	ICND1	SE	2	1–11	IP Address Rejection I–XI	134
	Ungraded	CL	1	2	Configuring Static Routes	178
	Ungraded	CL	1	3	Configuring RIPv2 Routing	185

ICND1 Skill Builders

Part 3: IP Addressing, Routing, and WANs

Lab 5: Connected Routes

Overview

In this lab, you'll learn how to use and interpret the **show ip route connected** command. You'll begin with R1's interfaces fully configured. R2's interfaces are partially configured and both are shut down. You'll bring them up and see the effects.

Topology

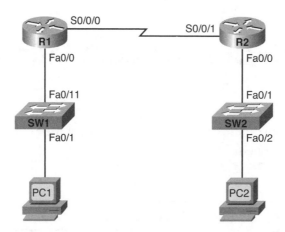

Figure 1   **Network Topology for This Lab**

Detailed Lab Steps

Step 1.   Connect to R1 from the simulator user interface; use password **ciscopress**.

Step 2.   Enter privileged exec mode by issuing the **enable** command; use password **ciscopress**.

Step 3.   Issue the **show ip route connected** command and view the output. How many connected routes do you see? Which ones are they?

_____

_____

Step 4.   Connect to R2 from the simulator user interface and enter privileged exec mode using the **enable** command. All passwords are **ciscopress**.

Step 5.   Repeat Step 3 on R2. How many connected routes do you see? Which ones are they?

_____

_____

Step 6.   Use the **show ip interface brief** command. Is there an IP address listed for interface S0/0/1? Interface Fa0/0?

_____

_____

Routers cannot add a connected route to the routing table unless the interface is in an "up and up" state. The following steps enable R2's two interfaces:

Step 7.   Move into interface configuration mode for interface S0/0/1 by using the **configure terminal** command followed by the **interface s0/0/1** command.

Step 8.   Enable the interface using the **no shutdown** command.

Step 9. Repeat Steps 7 and 8 for interface FastEthernet 0/0. Record the configuration commands you use.

_____

_____

Step 10. Exit configuration mode either by entering **end** or by pressing **Ctrl-Z**.

Step 11. Use the **show ip route connected** command, and view the output. How many connected routes do you see? Which ones are they? How is this different from what you saw in Step 7? Why is it different? Why is there no route associated with Fa0/0?

_____

_____

_____

_____

_____

Hints and Answers

Table 1 provides hints and tips for any lab steps that do not supply complete details and provides answers for any lab steps that ask questions.

Table 1   Hints and Answers

Step	Hint or Answer
3	The only route is 192.168.10.0/24 on Fa0/0.
5	After using the **show ip route connected** command again, you should see no connected routes on R2.
6	S0/0/1 has an IP address of 172.30.10.2. The command also lists both interfaces as "administratively down." Fa0/0 has no IP address, and it is administratively down.
9	Use the **interface fa0/0** command and then the **no shutdown** command.
11	The one route is 172.30.10.0/24 on Serial 0/0/1. Routers do not add a connected route for the subnet off an interface unless the interface is in an "up and up" state and the router has an IP address/mask configured. Fa0/0 does not have an IP address/mask configured.

Configuration Steps

Example 1 shows a sample of the lab exercise being completed from R2's CLI.

Example 1   Example of Performing This Lab

```
(Press enter)
Password: ciscopress
R2>enable
Password: ciscopress
R2#
R2#configure terminal
R2(config)#interface Serial0/0/1
R2(config-if)#no shutdown
R2(config-if)#interface Fastethernet0/0
R2(config-if)#no shutdown
R2(config-if)#end
R2#
```

ICND1 Skill Builders

Part 3: IP Addressing, Routing, and WANs

Lab 1: Configuring IP Addresses I

Overview

In this lab, you'll begin configuring IP addresses on Cisco switches. In this topology, IP addressing has been configured on everything except SW1. You'll configure SW1's IP address and the other parameters required to make SW1 communicate outside its own subnet, and then you'll test that connectivity.

Topology

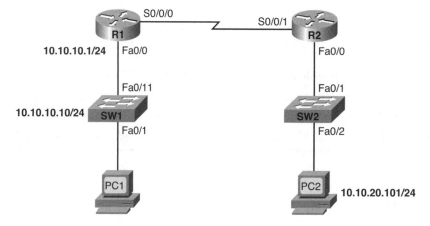

Figure 1   Network Topology for This Lab

Detailed Lab Steps

Step 1. Connect to SW1 from the simulator user interface; use password **ciscopress**.

Step 2. Enter privileged exec mode by entering the **enable** command and the password **ciscopress**.

Step 3. Enter global configuration mode using the **configure terminal** command.

Step 4. The switch's IP address is configured on the VLAN 1 interface. So, to begin configuring that address, enter VLAN 1 configuration mode using the command **interface vlan 1**.

Step 5. Assign VLAN 1 an IP address and subnet mask using the command **ip address 10.10.10.10 255.255.255.0**.

Step 6. The VLAN 1 interface on a switch sometimes defaults to a setting of **shutdown**, so to enable this interface, issue the **no shutdown** command.

The previous steps complete the configuration of a working IP address on switch SW1. However, to be able to communicate with hosts in subnets other than the subnet in which SW1 resides, SW1 also needs a default gateway setting, just like a host. The rest of the list provides the steps to add that setting.

Step 7. Enter **exit** to return to global configuration mode. What does the prompt look like now?

Step 8. Configure the default gateway, which is R1's Fa0/0 interface IP address, using the command **ip default-gateway 10.10.10.1**.

Step 9. Exit back to enable mode using the **end** command or by pressing **Ctrl-Z**.

Step 10. To verify your configuration, first test reachability to R1 by issuing the **ping 10.10.10.1** command. R1 should respond.

Step 11. Next, to test reachability to hosts on other subnets, ping PC2 using the command **ping 10.10.20.101**. PC2 should respond.

Hints and Answers

Table 1 provides hints and tips for any lab steps that do not supply complete details and provides answers for any lab steps that ask questions.

Table 1 **Hints and Answers**

Step	Hint or Answer
7	The prompt before the **exit** command will be SW1(config-if)# and will be SW1(config)# after the **exit** command.

Configuration Steps

Example 1 shows a sample of the lab exercise being completed from SW1's CLI.

Example 1 Example of Performing This Lab

```
SW1#configure terminal
SW1(config)#interface vlan 1
SW1(config-if)#ip address 10.10.10.10 255.255.255.0
SW1(config-if)#no shutdown
SW1(config-if)#exit
SW1(config)#ip default-gateway 10.10.10.1
SW1(config)#end
SW1#
```

ICND1 Skill Builders

Part 3: IP Addressing, Routing, and WANs

Lab 2: Configuring IP Addresses II

Overview

In this lab, you'll configure IP addressing and other required settings on a PC to make it communicate with other hosts in the network.

Topology

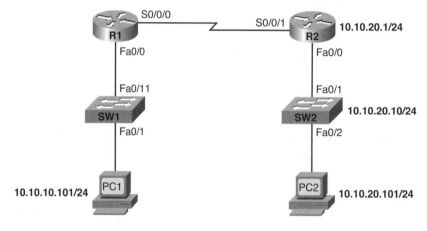

Figure 1   Network Topology for This Lab

Detailed Lab Steps

Step 1.   Connect to R2 from the simulator user interface; use password **ciscopress**.

Step 2. View R2's IP address configuration using the **show interfaces fa0/0** command. Record this IP address and mask on the lines below.

_____

_____

Step 3. Calculate the IP subnet number, broadcast address, and range of assignable IP addresses for the subnet, and record your answers on the lines below.

_____

_____

Note that the IP address assigned to R2's Fa0/0 interface will be configured as PC2's default gateway. PC2 will also use the same mask as R2.

Step 4. Connect to PC2 from the simulator user interface.

Step 5. Configure PC2's IP address as 10.10.20.101 using the **ip address 10.10.20.101 255.255.255.0** command. Note that this command is not a valid host OS command; it is a command created for use with the simulator.

Step 6. Configure PC2's default gateway as 10.10.20.1 using the **gateway 10.10.20.1** command. Note that this command is not a valid host OS command; it is a command created for use with the simulator.

Step 7. To verify your configuration, test reachability inside the local subnet by pinging SW2's IP address and R2's Fa0/0 IP address. To do so, from PC2's command prompt, use the **ping 10.10.20.1** and **ping 10.10.20.10** commands. Both pings should succeed.

Step 8. To verify that the default gateway setting worked, ping PC1's IP address using the **ping 10.10.10.101** command. The ping should succeed.

Hints and Answers

Table 1 provides hints and tips for any lab steps that do not supply complete details and provides answers for any lab steps that ask questions.

Table 1   **Hints and Answers**

Step	Hint or Answer
2	R2's Fa0/0 IP address is 10.10.20.1 with mask 255.255.255.0 (/24).
3	The subnet number is 10.10.20.0; the subnet broadcast address is 10.10.20.255; and the range of usable addresses of 10.10.20.1 through 10.10.20.254.

Configuration Steps

Example 1 Example of Performing This Lab

```
PC2

c:\ip address 10.10.20.101 255.255.255.0

c:\gateway 10.10.20.1
```

ICND1 Skill Builders

Part 3: IP Addressing, Routing, and WANs

Lab 6: Static Routes I

Overview

In this lab, you'll learn how to configure and test static routes by configuring a static route on R1 for the Class C network 192.168.20.0 located off R2's LAN interface.

Topology

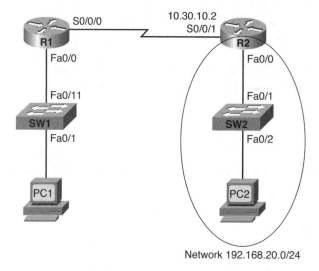

Network 192.168.20.0/24

Figure 1   Network Topology for This Lab

Detailed Lab Steps

Step 1.   Connect to R1 from the simulator user interface. All passwords are **ciscopress**.

Step 2.   Enter privileged exec mode by issuing the **enable** command.

Step 3.   Issue the command **configure terminal** to enter global configuration mode.

Step 4. Configure a static route on R1 that points to network 192.168.20.0/24, located off R2's LAN interface, using the **ip route 192.168.20.0 255.255.255.0 10.30.10.2** command. Whose IP address is listed as the next hop in this command?

_____

_____

Step 5. Return to the privileged exec prompt using the **end** command.

Step 6. Use the **show ip route** command and view the administrative distance of the static route that you created. What are the two numbers in brackets? Which is the administrative distance and which is the metric?

_____

_____

Step 7. Test your configuration by pinging PC2's IP address using the command **ping 192.168.20.101**. PC2 should answer.

Hints and Answers

Table 1 provides hints and tips for any lab steps that do not supply complete details and provides answers for any lab steps that ask questions.

Table 1   Hints and Answers

Step	Hint or Answer
4	10.30.10.2 is R2's S0/0/1 IP address.
6	The output lists [1/0], where 1 is the administrative distance and 0 is the metric.

Configuration Steps

Example 1 shows a sample of the lab exercise being completed from R1's CLI.

Example 1   Example of Performing This Lab

```
(Press enter)
Password: ciscopress
R1>enable
Password: ciscopress
R1#
R1#configure terminal
R1(config)#ip route 192.168.20.0 255.255.255.0 10.30.10.2
R1(config)#end
R1#
```

ICND1 Skill Builders

Part 3: IP Addressing, Routing, and WANs

Lab 15: RIP Configuration I

Overview

This lab begins with two routers and PCs that have correctly configured IP addresses. R2 has already been configured to support RIP version 2 on all interfaces. The objective of the lab is to configure RIP 2 on router R1.

Topology

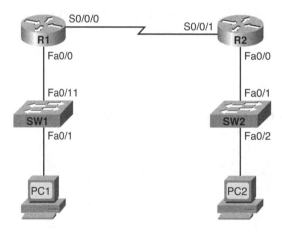

Figure 1   Network Topology for This Lab

Detailed Lab Steps

Step 1.   Connect to R1's console port using the simulator. The window will look like a terminal emulator with a cursor at the bottom of the screen and the center of the screen mostly blank.

Step 2.   From the simulator's terminal-emulator screen, press **Enter**, and use password **ciscopress** to reach user mode.

Step 3.   Enter privileged mode using the **enable** command; use password **ciscopress**.

Step 4. Issue the **show ip interface brief** command and record the IP addresses on R1's S0/0/0 and Fa0/0 interfaces. What classful network contains both of these addresses?

_____

_____

_____

_____

Step 5. Enter configuration mode using the **configure terminal** command.

Step 6. Enter RIP configuration mode using the **router rip** command. What did the command prompt look like before you pressed Enter? What did it look like after you pressed Enter?

_____

_____

_____

_____

Step 7. Issue the **version 2** RIP subcommand to tell R1 to only use RIP 2 on all enabled interfaces.

Step 8. Issue the **network 10.0.0.0** RIP subcommand, which enables RIP on all interfaces in classful network 10.0.0.0.

Step 9. Exit configuration mode (press **Ctrl-Z** or enter **end**).

Step 10. Issue the **show ip route** command and record the three IP routes shown there. Which of the three routes was learned using RIP?

_____

_____

_____

_____

Hints and Answers

Table 1 provides hints and tips for any lab steps that do not supply complete details and provides answers for any lab steps that ask questions.

Table 1   Hints and Answers

Step	Hint or Answer
4	R1's S0/0/0 interface's IP address is 10.1.2.1, and its Fa0/0 interface is 10.1.1.126. Both addresses are in Class A network 10.0.0.0.
6	The prompt begins with the global configuration prompt of R1(config)#. After the **router rip** command, the prompt changes to R1(config-router)#.
10	R1 will know three routes:
	10.1.1.0/25, a connected route off Fa0/0
	10.1.2.0/30, a connected route off S0/0/0
	10.1.1.128/25, a RIP-learned route learned from R2

Configuration Steps

Example 1 shows a sample of the lab exercise being completed from R1's CLI.

Example 1   Example of Performing This Lab

```
R1#configure terminal
R1(config)#route rip
R1(config-router)version 2
R1(config-router)#network 10.0.0.0
R1(config-router)#Ctrl-Z
R1#
```

ICND1 Skill Builders

Part 3: IP Addressing, Routing, and WANs

Lab 16: RIP Configuration II

Overview

In this lab, you'll configure a routing protocol, RIP 2, and advertise interfaces into it. You'll then verify that routers are learning routes from each other using the newly configured routing protocol.

Topology

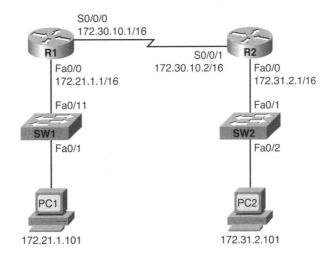

Figure 1 **Network Topology for This Lab**

Detailed Lab Steps

Step 1. Connect to R1 from the simulator user interface, using password **ciscopress** to reach user mode.

Step 2. Issue the **enable** command and log in with the password **ciscopress**.

Step 3. Enter global configuration mode using the **configure terminal** command.

Step 4. Enter router configuration mode using the **router rip** command.

Step 5. Configure RIP to use version 2 (RIP 2) by issuing the **version 2** command.

Step 6. Configure R1 using the **network 172.30.0.0** command. Using Figure 1 as a reference, what three things does R1 now do as a result of this command? And on which interfaces does R1 do these three things?

_____

_____

_____

Step 7. Configure R1 to advertise its LAN interface into RIP using the **network 172.21.0.0** command. On which interface(s) does this command enable RIP?

_____

Next, you will move to router R2 and enable RIP 2 on both of its working interfaces.

Step 8. Connect to R2 from the simulator user interface, and use the **enable** and **configure terminal** commands to reach global configuration mode. (All passwords are **ciscopress**.)

Step 9. Plan your RIP-2 configuration on R2 based on the configuration you added on R1, plus the information in Figure 1. Record the commands you expect to use on the lines below.

_____

_____

_____

_____

Step 10. Enter router configuration mode using the **router rip** command.

Step 11. Configure RIP to use RIP 2 by issuing the **version 2** command.

Step 12. Enable R2 on its S0/0/1 interface using the **network 172.30.0.0** command and on interface Fa0/0 using the **network 172.31.0.0** command.

Step 13. Exit from configuration mode and move back to R1 from the simulator user interface.

Step 14. On R1, use the **show ip route** command to view the routing table. What subnets/ networks are listed in connected routes? What subnets/networks are listed as RIP-learned routes?

_____

Step 15. Use the **show ip protocols** command to display information about RIP. What IP addresses are listed as a "source of routing information"? According to Figure 1, what router uses that IP address?

_____

Hints and Answers

Table 1 provides hints and tips for any lab steps that do not supply complete details and provides answers for any lab steps that ask questions.

Table 1   Hints and Answers

Step	Hint or Answer
6	R1 enables RIP on the matched interface(s), which in this case is only S0/0/0, because S0/0/0 is the only R1 interface shown in Figure 1 that has an IP address in Class B network 172.30.0.0. This command makes R1 do three things: 1. Send RIP updates out S0/0/0. 2. Listen/process RIP updates that arrive on S0/0/0. 3. Advertise about the subnet connected to S0/0/0.
7	R1 has only one interface in Class B network 172.21.0.0: Fa0/0.

Step	Hint or Answer
9	You will configure **router rip** **version 2** **network 172.30.0.0** **network 172.31.0.0**
14	The output shows two connected routes and one RIP-learned route, as follows: 172.21.0.0/16: Connected 172.30.0.0/16: Connected 172.31.0.0/16: RIP
15	The output lists 172.30.10.2 as a routing information source. This is the IP address configured for R2's S0/0/1 interface. This command output means that R1 has successfully received routing updates from router R2.

Configuration Steps

Example 1 shows a sample of the lab exercise being completed from the CLI of both R1 and R2.

Example 1   Example of Performing This Lab

```
! Configuration on router R1:
R1#configure terminal
R1(config)#router rip
R1(config-router)#version 2
R1(config-router)#network 172.30.0.0
R1(config-router)#network 172.21.0.0
R1(config-router)#end
R1#
! Configuration on router R2:
R2#configure terminal
R2(config)#router rip
R2(config-router)#version 2
R2(config-router)#network 172.30.0.0
R2(config-router)#network 172.31.0.0
R2(config-router)#end
R2#
```

ICND1 Skill Builders

Part 3: IP Addressing, Routing, and WANs

Lab 21: RIP Verification I

Overview

In this lab, you'll learn about verifying RIP by using the **debug ip rip** command. Working with routers preconfigured with IP addresses and RIP version 2 configuration, you will watch RIP updates in real time using this **debug** command.

Topology

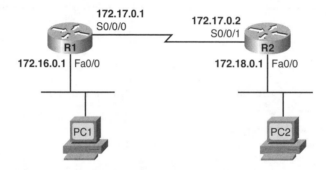

Figure 1   Network Topology for This Lab

Detailed Lab Steps

Step 1. Connect to R1 from the simulator user interface and enter user mode by using the console password **ciscopress**.

Step 2. Enter privileged exec mode by entering **enable** and the password **ciscopress**.

Step 3. Enter the **debug ip rip** command to enable debugging of RIP.

Step 4. Wait 30 seconds, then turn off debugging by entering **no debug ip rip**. Why did you have to wait at least 30 seconds?

_____

_____

Step 5. Examine the output. Where is R1 receiving updates from? What interface is the update being received on?

_____

_____

Step 6. What destination address does R1 use when sending an update? Why is this not the IP address of R2?

_____

_____

Step 7. What subnets/routes are being advertised out S0/0/0 on R1? What subnets/route are advertised out Fa0/0?

_____

_____

Hints and Answers

Table 1 provides hints and tips for any lab steps that do not supply complete details and provides answers for any lab steps that ask questions.

Table 1   Hints and Answers

Step	Hint or Answer
4	RIP sends updates every 30 seconds, so by waiting 30 seconds, you should see messages about RIP updates sent by R1 and messages about updates received from R2.
5	R1's RIP messages state that R1 is receiving RIP updates on R1's S0/0/0 interface, from IP address 172.17.0.2. Figure 1 shows that this is the serial link connected to R2, and that R2's serial IP address is 172.17.0.2.
6	RIP 2 sends update messages to a multicast IP address (224.0.0.9), instead of sending them to unicast (individual) IP addresses. All RIP 2 routers that receive these messages can then process the updates.
7	R1's debug messages that mention the update was sent out an interface list 172.18.0.0/16 and 172.17.0.0/16 in the update sent out Fa0/0. The messages for the update sent out S0/0/0 list a route for 172.16.0.0/16.

Configuration Steps

This lab does not require any configuration.

Lab 6: RIP-2 Configuration I

Overview

This lab uses an internetwork of three routers, three serial links, and three LANs. In this lab, you will take a preplanned IP addressing scheme, configure IP addresses on the routers, and then configure RIP on the routers as well. You will then confirm that all three routers have learned all the routes in the internetwork.

Note: All passwords are **ciscopress** unless otherwise noted.

Reference Tables

For convenience, Table 1 provides the IP address and mask of all necessary interfaces used to complete the lab.

Table 1   IP Address Table

Device	Interface	IP Address	Mask
R1	Fa0/0	172.21.44.201	255.255.255.192
	S0/0/0	192.168.1.5	255.255.255.252
	S0/0/1	192.168.1.13	255.255.255.252
R2	Fa0/0	172.22.88.102	255.255.255.224
	S0/0/0	192.168.1.9	255.255.255.252
	S0/0/1	192.168.1.6	255.255.255.252
R3	Fa0/0	172.23.132.3	255.255.255.240
	S0/0/0	192.168.1.14	255.255.255.252
	S0/0/1	192.168.1.10	255.255.255.252
PC1	—	172.21.44.200	255.255.255.192
PC2	—	172.22.88.100	255.255.255.224
PC3	—	172.23.132.1	255.255.255.240

Table 2 provides space to list the subnet numbers and mask for each subnet.

Table 2   IP Subnet Table

Location	Subnet Number	Mask
R1 Fa0/0		
R2 Fa0/0		
R3 Fa0/0		
R1-R2 link		
R1-R3 link		
R2-R3 link		

Topology

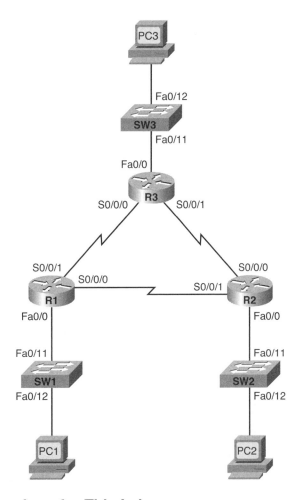

Figure 1   Network Topology for This Lab

Detailed Lab Steps

Part 1: Configure Router IP Addresses

Step 1. Connect to R1 from the simulator user interface and move into enable mode.

Step 2. Configure IP addresses and masks on all three of R1's interfaces using the details in Table 1. Also enable the interfaces. Record the commands you used on the lines below.

_____

_____

_____

_____

_____

_____

Note: The serial interfaces with DCE cables installed were preconfigured with a **clock rate** command.

Step 3. Issue the **show ip interface brief** command to confirm the right IP addresses were configured in the previous step. On the lines below, note which router interfaces are in an "up/up" state.

_____

_____

Step 4. Based on the commands configured in Step 2, calculate the subnet number in which each router IP address resides. List those subnet numbers on the lines below.

_____

_____

Step 5. Display the contents of the routing table. How many routes are listed? What types of routes? Do the subnet numbers confirm the answers you wrote down for the previous step? Once you are convinced of the subnet numbers, record them in Table 2.

_____

_____

_____

_____

Step 6. Connect to R2 from the simulator user interface and move into enable mode.

Step 7. Configure IP addresses and masks on all three of R2's interfaces using the details in Table 1. Also enable the interfaces. Record the commands you used on the lines below.

_____

_____

_____

_____

_____

Step 8. Issue the **show ip interface brief** command to confirm the right IP addresses were configured in the previous step. On the lines below, note which router interfaces are in an "up/up" state.

_____

_____

Step 9. Based on the commands configured in Step 7, calculate the subnet number in which each router IP address resides. List those subnet numbers on the lines below.

_____

_____

Step 10. Display the contents of the routing table. How many routes are listed? What types of routes? Do the subnet numbers confirm the answers you wrote down for the previous step? Once you are convinced of the subnet numbers, record them in Table 2.

_____

_____

_____

_____

Step 11. Connect to R3 from the simulator user interface and move into enable mode.

Step 12. Configure IP addresses and masks on all three of R3's interfaces using the details in Table 1. Also enable the interfaces. Record the commands you used on the lines below.

_____

_____

_____

_____

_____

_____

Step 13. Issue the **show ip interface brief** command to confirm the right IP addresses were configured in the previous step. On the lines below, note which router interfaces are in an "up/up" state.

_____

_____

Step 14. Based on the commands configured in Step 12, calculate the subnet number in which each router IP address resides. List those subnet numbers on the lines below.

_____

_____

Step 15. Display the contents of the routing table. How many routes are listed? What types of routes? Do the subnet numbers confirm the answers you wrote down for the previous step? Once you are convinced of the subnet numbers, record them in Table 2.

_____

_____

_____

_____

Part 2: Configure RIP 2 on R3

In this part, you will configure RIP 2 on router R3. In particular, this part focuses on the operation of the **network** command. The **network** command lists a classful network number—in other words, a Class A, B, or C network number. The router then enables RIP on all of its interfaces that reside in that classful network.

Step 16. Plan the network commands you will need to use to configure RIP on R3. To do so, on the lines below, list the three interface IP addresses on R3. Then write down the Class A, B, or C network number associated with each.

_____

_____

_____

_____

Step 17. Move back into configuration mode on R3.

Step 18. Use the **router rip** command to move into RIP configuration mode.

Step 19. Configure the **network 192.168.1.0** command. On what interface(s) should RIP now be enabled?

_____

_____

Step 20. Use the **end** command to move back to enable mode, and display RIP status information using the **show ip protocols** command. What interfaces are listed under the interface heading, roughly halfway through this command's output?

_____

_____

Step 21. Move back into configuration mode on R3 and move back into RIP configuration mode.

Step 22. Configure a **network** command that will enable RIP on the remaining interface on R3. What command did you use?

_____

_____

Step 23. Enable R3 to use only RIP 2 by configuring the **version 2** command.

Step 24. Use the **end** command or press **Ctrl-Z** to exit back to enable mode.

Step 25. Display information about RIP status using the **show ip protocol** command. Looking at the output, answer the following questions: What versions of RIP are running on each interface? On what interface is RIP enabled?

_____

_____

_____

_____

Step 26. Display the contents of R3's routing table. How many routes are listed? Are any RIP routes listed?

_____

_____

Part 3: Configure RIP 2 on R1 and R2

Now that you have a better understanding of RIP configuration, the next steps ask you to configure similar commands on routers R1 and R2.

Step 27. From the simulator user interface, move back to R1 and move into enable mode.

Step 28. Plan the **network** commands you will need to use to configure RIP on R1. To do so, on the lines below, list the three interface IP addresses on R1. Then write down the Class A, B, or C network number associated with each.

_____

_____

_____

_____

Step 29. Move into configuration mode on R1 and move into RIP configuration mode.

Step 30. Add configuration commands to enable RIP 2, to enable RIP on interface Fa0/0, and then to enable RIP on all other interfaces. List the commands you added on the lines below.

_____

_____

_____

_____

_____

Step 31. Use the **end** command to move back to enable mode and display RIP status information using the **show ip protocols** command. What interfaces are listed under the interface heading, roughly halfway through this command's output?

_____

_____

Step 32. From the simulator user interface, move to R2 and move into enable mode.

Step 33. Plan the **network** commands you will need to use to configure RIP on R2. To do so, on the lines below, list the three interface IP addresses on R1. Then write down the Class A, B, or C network number associated with each.

_____

_____

_____

_____

Step 34. Move into configuration mode on R2 and move into RIP configuration mode.

Step 35. Add configuration commands to enable RIP 2, to enable RIP on interface Fa0/0, and then to enable RIP on all other interfaces. List the commands you added on the lines below.

_____

_____

_____

_____

Step 36. Use the **end** command to move back to enable mode and display RIP status information using the **show ip protocols** command. What interfaces are listed under the interface heading, roughly halfway through this command's output?

_____

_____

Part 4: RIP Verification

Step 37.   Still on R2, display the contents of the IP routing table. How many routes do you see? How many are learned using RIP?

_____

_____

_____

Step 38.   Use the **show ip protocols** command to list information about RIP. What are the IP addresses listed as "Routing Information Sources"? According to Table 1, what devices/interfaces use these IP addresses?

_____

_____

_____

Hints and Answers

Table 3 is a completed version of the subnet planning chart, Table 2. Table 4 provides hints and tips for any lab steps that do not supply complete details and provides answers for any lab steps that ask questions.

Table 3   Completed IP Subnet Table

Location	Subnet Number	Mask
R1 Fa0/0	172.21.44.192	255.255.255.192
R2 Fa0/0	172.22.88.96	255.255.255.224
R3 Fa0/0	172.23.132.0	255.255.255.240
R1-R2 link	192.168.1.4	255.255.255.252
R1-R3 link	192.168.1.12	255.255.255.252
R2-R3 link	192.168.1.8	255.255.255.252

Table 4   Hints and Answers

Step	Hint or Answer
1	Use the **enable** command to move to enable mode.
2	Use the **configure terminal** command to move into global configuration mode. Then, use the following configuration commands: **interface fa0/0** **ip address 172.21.44.201 255.255.255.192** **no shutdown** **!** **interface Serial0/0/0** **ip address 192.168.1.5 255.255.255.252** **no shutdown** **!** **interface Serial0/0/1** **ip address 192.168.1.13 255.255.255.252** **no shutdown**
3	R1's Fa0/0, S0/0/0, and S0/0/1 interfaces are in an "up/up" state.
4	The subnet numbers are 172.21.44.192/26, 192.168.1.4/30, and 192.168.1.12/30.
5	R1's routing table will have three routes: the connected route for each working interface.
6	Use the **enable** command to move into enable mode.
7	Use the **configure terminal** command to move into global configuration mode. Then, use the following configuration commands: **interface fa0/0** **ip address 172.22.88.102 255.255.255.224** **no shutdown** **!** **interface Serial0/0/0** **ip address 192.168.1.9 255.255.255.252** **no shutdown** **!** **interface Serial0/0/1** **ip address 192.168.1.6 255.255.255.252** **no shutdown**
8	R2's Fa0/0, S0/0/0, and S0/0/1 interfaces are in an "up/up" state.
9	The subnet numbers are 172.22.88.96/27, 192.168.1.4/30, and 192.168.1.8/30.

continues

Table 4   **Hints and Answers**   *continued*

Step	Hint or Answer
10	R2's routing table will have three routes: the connected route for each working interface.
11	Use the **enable** command to move to enable mode.
12	Use the **configure terminal** command to move into global configuration mode. Then, use the following configuration commands: **interface fa0/0** **ip address 172.23.132.3 255.255.255.240** **no shutdown** **!** **interface Serial0/0/0** **ip address 192.168.1.14 255.255.255.252** **no shutdown** **!** **interface Serial0/0/1** **ip address 192.168.1.10 255.255.255.252** **no shutdown**
13	R3's Fa0/0, S0/0/0, and S0/0/1 interfaces are in an "up/up" state.
14	The subnets are 172.23.132.0/28, 192.168.1.8/30, and 192.168.1.12/30.
15	R3's routing table will have three routes: the connected route for each working interface.
16	The addresses and networks are 172.23.132.3 (Class B network 172.23.0.0) 192.168.1.10 (Class C network 192.168.1.0) 192.168.1.14 (Class C network 192.168.1.0)
19	The **network 192.168.1.0** command tells R3 to enable RIP on the two R3 interfaces in that network: S0/0/0 and S0/0/1.
20	The output lists the two serial interfaces, but it does not list interface Fa0/0.
21	Use the **configure terminal** command and then the **router rip** command.
22	Use the **network 172.23.0.0** command to enable RIP on R3's Fa0/0 interface.
25	The output states that only version 2 is used by virtue of listing only a "2" under the headings "Send" and "Recv." The output lists all three interfaces, namely Fa0/0, S0/0/0, and S0/0/1.
26	According to the **show ip route** command, R3 has only three routes, 172.23.132.0/28, 192.168.1.8/30, and 192.168.1.12/30.

Step	Hint or Answer
28	The addresses and networks are
	172.21.44.201 (Class B network 172.21.0.0)
	192.168.1.5 (Class C network 192.168.1.0)
	192.168.1.13 (Class C network 192.168.1.0)
29	Use the **configure terminal** command and then the **router rip** command.
30	The commands are **router rip** **version 2** **network 172.21.0.0** **network 192.168.1.0**
31	The output lists Fa0/0, S0/0/0, and S0/0/1.
33	The addresses and networks are
	172.22.88.102 (Class B network 172.22.0.0)
	192.168.1.6 (Class C network 192.168.1.0)
	192.168.1.9 (Class C network 192.168.1.0)
34	Use the **configure terminal** command and then the **router rip** command.
35	The commands are **router rip** **version 2** **network 172.22.0.0** **network 192.168.1.0**
36	The output lists Fa0/0, S0/0/0, and S0/0/1.
37	The output of the **show ip route** command on R2 should list six routes—three connected and three RIP routes.
38	The output lists 192.168.1.5, which is R1's S0/0/0 interface IP address, and 192.168.1.10, which is R3's S0/0/1 interface IP address.

Configuration

Example 1 shows the configuration commands added to R1, R2, and R3 during this lab.

Example 1   Configuration on R1, R2, and R3 During This Lab

```
R1's config:


interface fa0/0
 ip address 172.21.44.201 255.255.255.192
 no shutdown
!
interface Serial0/0/0
 ip address 192.168.1.5 255.255.255.252
 no shutdown
!
interface Serial0/0/1
 ip address 192.168.1.13 255.255.255.252
 no shutdown
!
router rip
 version 2
 network 172.21.0.0
 network 192.168.1.0



R2's config:


interface fa0/0
 ip address 172.22.88.102 255.255.255.224
 no shutdown
!
interface Serial0/0/0
 ip address 192.168.1.9 255.255.255.252
 no shutdown
!
interface Serial0/0/1
 ip address 192.168.1.6 255.255.255.252
 no shutdown
!
router rip
 version 2
```

continues

```
network 172.22.0.0
network 192.168.1.0
```

R3's config:

```
interface fa0/0
 ip address 172.23.132.3 255.255.255.240
 no shutdown
!
interface Serial0/0/0
 ip address 192.168.1.14 255.255.255.252
 no shutdown
!
interface Serial0/0/1
 ip address 192.168.1.10 255.255.255.252
 no shutdown
!
router rip
 version 2
 network 172.23.0.0
 network 192.168.1.0
```

ICND1 Configuration Scenarios

Part 3: IP Addressing, Routing, and WANs

Lab 8: RIP Auto-summary

Overview

This lab begins with a network design with two routers, two switches, and two PCs with a serial link between the routers. The design engineer has already specified the IP addresses and masks to use for each device and interface. Your job is to configure the IP addresses, configure RIP 2, and confirm that the two PCs can ping each other.

Note: All passwords are **ciscopress** unless otherwise noted.

Reference Tables

For convenience, Table 1 provides the IP address and mask of all necessary interfaces used to complete the lab.

Table 1   IP Address Table

Device	Interface	IP Address	Mask
R1	Fa0/0	10.0.1.1	255.255.255.0
	S0/0/0	172.16.12.1	255.255.255.0
R2	Fa0/0	10.0.2.2	255.255.255.0
	S0/0/1	172.16.12.2	255.255.255.0
PC1	—	10.1.1.11	255.255.255.0
PC2	—	10.1.2.22	255.255.255.0

Table 2 provides space to list the subnet numbers and range of addresses in each subnet.

Table 2   IP Subnet Table

Location	Subnet Number	Mask	Interface
R1			
R2			

Topology

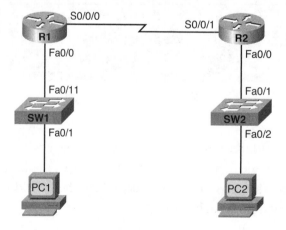

Figure 1   Network Topology for This Lab

Detailed Lab Steps

Part 1: Configure Router IP Addresses

Step 1.   Connect to R1 from the simulator user interface and move into enable mode.

Step 2.   Configure IP addresses and masks on both of R1's interfaces using the details in Table 1. Also enable the interfaces. Record the commands you used on the lines below.

_____

_____

_____

_____

_____

_____

Note: The serial interface was preconfigured with a **clock rate** command.

Step 3.   Issue the **show ip interface brief** command to confirm the right IP addresses were configured in the previous step. On the lines below, note which router interfaces are in an "up/up" state.

_____

_____

Step 4.   Based on the commands configured in Step 2, calculate the subnet number in which each router IP address resides. List those subnet numbers on the lines below.

_____

_____

Step 5.   Display the contents of the routing table. How many routes are listed? What types of routes? Do the subnet numbers confirm the answers you wrote down for the previous step? Once you are convinced of the subnet numbers, record them in Table 2.

_____

_____

_____

_____

Step 6. Connect to R2 from the simulator user interface and move into enable mode.

Step 7. Configure IP addresses and masks on both of R2's interfaces using the details in Table 1. Also enable the interfaces. Record the commands you used on the lines below.

_____

_____

_____

_____

_____

Step 8. Issue the **show ip interface brief** command to confirm the right IP addresses were configured in the previous step. On the lines below, note which router interfaces are in an "up/up" state.

_____

_____

Step 9. Based on the commands configured in Step 7, calculate the subnet number in which each router IP address resides. List those subnet numbers on the lines below.

_____

_____

Step 10. Display the contents of the routing table. How many routes are listed? What types of routes? Do the subnet numbers confirm the answers you wrote down for the previous step? Once you are convinced of the subnet numbers, record them in Table 2.

_____

_____

_____

_____

Part 2: Configure RIP 2 on R2

In this part, you will configure RIP 2 on router R2.

Step 11. Plan your RIP 2 configuration on the lines below. You should list all the commands required to enable RIP, use only version 2, and have RIP work on all interfaces that are currently in an "up/up" state.

_____

_____

_____

_____

_____

_____

Step 12. Configure RIP on R2 using the commands you planned in the previous step. When finished, press **Ctrl-Z** or use the **end** command to move back to enable mode.

Step 13. Display information about RIP status using the **show ip protocol** command. Looking at the output, answer the following questions: What versions of RIP are running on the interfaces? What is the state of auto-summarization? What IP addresses are listed in the "Routing Information Sources" section?

_____

_____

_____

Step 14. Display the contents of R2's routing table. How many routes are listed? Are any RIP routes listed?

_____

_____

Step 15. Enable RIP debugs using the **debug ip rip** command. Wait 45 seconds and then issue a **no debug all** command.

Step 16. Examine the RIP debug messages and look for any messages about updates sent out interface S0/0/1. What route was listed? Is that route one of the routes in R2's routing table as noted in Step 14?

_____

_____

Part 3: Configure RIP 2 on R1

In this part you will configure RIP 2 on router R1.

Step 17. From the simulator user interface, move back to R1 and move into enable mode.

Step 18. Plan your RIP 2 configuration on the lines below. You should list all the commands required to enable RIP, use only version 2, and have RIP work on all interfaces that are currently in an "up/up" state.

_____

_____

_____

_____

_____

Step 19. Configure RIP on R1 using the commands you planned in the previous step. When finished, press **Ctrl-Z** or use the **end** command to move back to enable mode.

Step 20. Display information about RIP status using the **show ip protocol** command. What in this output is different from the output of the same command on router R2 in Step 13?

_____

_____

_____

_____

Step 21. Display the contents of R1's routing table. How many routes are listed? Are any RIP routes listed? Record the subnet/mask for any RIP-learned routes on the lines below.

_____

_____

Step 22. Enable RIP debugs using the **debug ip rip** command. Wait 45 seconds and then issue a **no debug all** command.

Step 23. Examine the RIP debug messages and look for any messages about updates received on interface S0/0/0. What route was listed? Is that the same route noted in Step 16, when viewing R2's **debug ip rip** output?

_____

_____

Part 4: Disable Auto-Summary

RIP automatically summarizes routes into a route for the entire classful network when advertising that route into another classful network. In this internetwork, when R2 advertises a RIP update out S0/0/1, R2 notices the link is in Class B network 172.16.0.0. Instead of advertising a route for R2's connected subnet 10.0.2.0/24, R2 automatically changes that route advertisement to be the whole Class A network of 10.0.0.0/8. The final part of this lab disables the auto-summarization feature.

Step 24. Still on R1, move into RIP configuration mode.

Step 25. Disable auto-summary using the **no auto-summary** command, and then use the **end** command or press **Ctrl-Z** to return to enable mode.

Step 26. From the simulator user interface, move back to R2 and move into enable mode.

Step 27. Configure R2 to disable auto-summary as well, and then return to enable mode.

Step 28. From the simulator user interface, move back to R1 and move into enable mode.

Step 29. View the routing table on R1. Record the RIP routes on the lines below. Is there still a route for entire Class A network 10.0.0.0 (10.0.0.0/8)? Does R2's 10.0.2.0/24 route now show up in R1's routing table?

_____

_____

_____

Step 30. Enable RIP debugs using the **debug ip rip** command. Wait 45 seconds and then issue a **no debug all** command.

Step 31. Examine the RIP debug messages and look for any messages about updates received on interface S0/0/0. What route was listed? Is that the same route noted in Step 16, when viewing R2's **debug ip rip** output?

_____

_____

Hints and Answers

Table 3 is a completed version of the subnet planning table in Table 2. Table 4 provides hints and tips for any lab steps that do not supply complete details and provides answers for any lab steps that ask questions.

Table 3   Completed IP Subnet Table

Location	Subnet Number	Mask	Interface
R1	10.0.1.0	255.255.255.0	FastEthernet 0/0
	172.16.12.0	255.255.255.0	Serial 0/0/0
R2	10.0.2.0	255.255.255.0	FastEthernet 0/0
	172.16.12.0	255.255.255.0	Serial 0/0/1

Table 4   Hints and Answers

Step	Hint or Answer
1	Use the **enable** command to move to enable mode.
2	Use the **configure terminal** command to move into global configuration mode. Then, use the following configuration commands: **interface fa0/0** **ip address 10.0.1.1 255.255.255.0** **no shutdown** **interface Serial0/0/0** **ip address 172.16.12.1 255.255.255.0** **no shutdown**
3	R1's Fa0/0 and S0/0/0 interfaces are both in an "up/up" state.
4	The subnet numbers are 10.0.1.0/24 and 172.16.12.0/24.
5	R1's routing table will have two routes: the connected routes for the Fa0/0 and S0/0/0 interfaces, respectively.
6	Use the **enable** command to move to enable mode.
7	Use the **configure terminal** command to move into global configuration mode. Then, use the following configuration commands: **interface fa0/0** **ip address 10.0.2.2 255.255.255.0** **no shutdown** **interface Serial0/0/1** **ip address 172.16.12.2 255.255.255.0** **no shutdown**
8	R2's Fa0/0 and S0/0/1 interfaces are both in an "up/up" state.
9	The subnet numbers are 10.0.2.0/24 and 172.16.12.0/24.
10	R2's routing table will have two routes: the connected routes for the Fa0/0 and S0/0/1 interfaces, respectively.

Step	Hint or Answer

11	The configuration should include
	
	router rip
	  version 2
	  network 10.0.0.0
	  network 172.16.0.0

13	The output lists that Fa0/0 and S0/0/1 both use only version 2. It also says that auto-summarization is enabled, and it does not list anything in the "Routing Information Sources" section.
14	R2 still has only two routes—10.0.2.0/24, a connected route off Fa0/0, and 172.16.12.0/24, a connected route off R2's S0/0/1 interface.
16	The messages for the update sent out R2's S0/0/1 interface list a route for 10.0.0.0, mask 255.0.0.0. This route is for the entire classful Class A network 10.0.0.0, not subnet 10.0.2.0/24 as seen in Step 14.

18	The configuration should include
	
	router rip
	  version 2
	  network 10.0.0.0
	  network 172.16.0.0

20	The output on R1 lists one routing information source, 172.16.12.2, which is R2's Serial 0/0/1 IP address. This notation means that R1 is now hearing R2's routing updates.
21	R1 should learn one RIP route, namely the route for entire Class A network 10.0.0.0/8.
23	The output lists the received update from R2 (172.16.12.2), listing the route for 10.0.0.0/8 as the only route.
24	First use the **configure terminal** command and then the **router rip** command.

27	Use the following commands:
	
	configure terminal
	  router rip
	  no auto-summary
	  end

29	R1 no longer shows 10.0.0.0/8, but it does show 10.0.2.0/24.
31	The messages for R1's received update from R2 now list 10.0.2.0/24 instead of 10.0.0.0/8.

Configuration

Example 1 shows the configuration commands added to R1 and R2 during this lab.

Example 1   Configuration on R1 and R2 During This Lab

```
R1's config:


interface fa0/0
 ip address 10.0.1.1 255.255.255.0
 no shutdown
!
interface Serial0/0/0
 ip address 172.16.12.1 255.255.255.0
 no shutdown
!
router rip
 version 2
 network 10.0.0.0
 network 172.16.0.0
 no auto-summary
```

```
R2's config:


interface fa0/0
 ip address 10.0.2.2 255.255.255.0
 no shutdown
!
interface Serial0/0/1
 ip address 172.16.12.2 255.255.255.0
 no shutdown
!
router rip
 version 2
 network 10.0.0.0
 network 172.16.0.0
 no auto-summary
```

ICND1 Subnetting Exercises

Part 1: Subnet ID Calculation

Lab 1: Subnet ID Calculation I

Overview

In this exercise, you calculate the subnet IDs of the subnets in which two different IP addresses reside. Then, you configure the IP addresses on a router as a way to verify your calculation of the subnet IDs.

At the beginning of the lab, the interfaces on Router R1 are up but with no IP addresses configured. When you configure the IP addresses, the router calculates the subnet ID and places a route for that subnet into the routing table. You can then compare your calculated subnet ID to the subnet IDs calculated by the router.

The IP address assignments for R1, which you will configure in this lab, are as follows in Table 1.

Table 1   IP Address and Mask Reference

R1 Interface	IP Address	Subnet Mask
Serial0/0/0	10.20.30.40	255.255.255.0
FastEthernet0/0	10.30.20.10	255.255.255.0

Topology

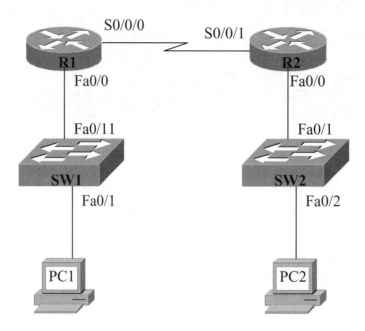

Figure 1   Topology for IP Address Configuration

Detailed Lab Steps

Step 1.   Calculate the subnet ID in which the IP addresses listed in the table at the beginning of this lab reside. List your answers on the following lines:

_____

_____

Step 2.   Connect to R1 from the simulator user interface. All passwords are **cs**.

Step 3.   Enter privileged exec ("enable") mode by issuing the **enable** command.

Step 4.   Enter global configuration mode using the **configure terminal** command.

Step 5.   First configure the Serial0/0/0 interface. To get into interface configuration mode, use the **interface s0/0/0** command.

Step 6.   Set the IP address and subnet mask using the **ip address 10.20.30.40 255.255.255.0** command.

Step 7.   Configure the FastEthernet0/0 interface by issuing the **interface fa0/0** command.

Step 8.   Set the IP address using the **ip address 10.30.20.10 255.255.255.0** command, and then exit configuration mode.

Because the two interfaces were already up, Router R1 adds a connected route to its routing table for each of the two connected subnets. At the next step, you will display these connected routes, which list the subnet ID. By comparing those values to the subnet ID values you calculated, you can confirm whether you calculated the correct subnet IDs.

Step 9.   To determine the subnet IDs as calculated by Router R1, issue the **show ip route** command. Look at the connected routes for interfaces F0/0 and S0/0/0. Do the subnet IDs match the values you predicted at Step 3?

Hints and Answers

Table 2 lists hints and tips for any lab steps that do not supply all the details in the lab step, and for lab steps that ask questions about the lab.

Table 2   Hints

Step	Hint
1	If you have not yet learned how to calculate the subnet ID based on an IP address/mask, check the book you are using for CCNA study. If you have not yet purchased such a book, check the ccentskills.com blog.
8	Use the **end** command or press Ctrl-z to exit configuration mode.
9	The output lists the mask in prefix format (/24) on a heading line and each route on a separate line just below the heading line. Because they are connected routes, you will see each route noted with a *C* in the far-left column. The subnet IDs will be 10.20.30.0 10.30.20.0

Configuration Steps

Example 1 shows a sample of the lab exercise being completed from R1's CLI.

Example 1   Example of Performing This Lab

```
(Press enter)
Password: cs
R1> enable
Password: cs
R1#
R1# configure terminal
R1(config)# interface Serial0/0/0
R1(config-if)# ip address 10.20.30.40 255.255.255.0
R1(config-if)# interface Fastethernet0/0
R1(config-if)# ip address 10.30.20.10 255.255.255.0
R1(config-if)# end
R1#
```

ICND1 Subnetting Exercises

Part 1: Subnet ID Calculation

Lab 2: Subnet ID Calculation II

Overview

In this exercise, you calculate the subnet IDs of the subnets in which two different IP addresses reside. Then, you configure the IP addresses on a router as a way to verify your calculation of the subnet IDs.

At the beginning of the lab, the interfaces on Router R1 are up but with no IP addresses configured. When you configure the IP addresses, the router calculates the subnet ID and places a route for that subnet into the routing table. You can then compare your calculated subnet ID to the subnet IDs calculated by the router.

The IP address assignments for R1, which you will configure in this lab, are as follows in Table 1.

Table 1   IP Address and Mask Reference

R1 Interface	IP Address	Subnet Mask
Serial0/0/0	10.20.99.1	255.255.240.0
FastEthernet0/0	10.20.199.1	255.255.240.0

Topology

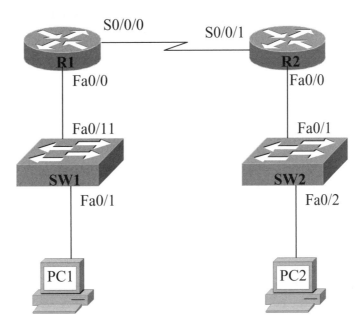

Figure 1 **Topology for IP Address Configuration**

Detailed Lab Steps

Step 1. Calculate the subnet ID in which the IP addresses listed in the table at the beginning of this lab reside. List your answers on the following lines:

_____

_____

Step 2. Connect to R1 from the simulator user interface. All passwords are **cs**.

Step 3. Enter privileged exec ("enable") mode by issuing the **enable** command.

Step 4. Enter global configuration mode using the **configure terminal** command.

Step 5. First configure the Serial0/0/0 interface. To get into interface configuration mode, use the **interface s0/0/0** command.

Step 6. Set the IP address and subnet mask using the **ip address 10.20.99.1 255.255.240.0** command.

Step 7. Configure the FastEthernet0/0 interface by issuing the **interface fa0/0** command.

Step 8. Set the IP address using the **ip address 10.20.199.1 255.255.240.0** command, and then exit configuration mode.

Because the two interfaces were already up, Router R1 adds a connected route to its routing table for each of the two connected subnets. At the next step, you will display these connected routes, which list the subnet ID. By comparing those values to the subnet ID values you calculated, you can confirm whether you calculated the correct subnet IDs.

Step 9. To determine the subnet IDs as calculated by Router R1, issue the **show ip route** command. Look at the connected routes for interfaces F0/0 and S0/0/0. Do the subnet IDs match the values you predicted at Step 3?

_____

_____

Hints and Answers

Table 2 lists hints and tips for any lab steps that do not supply all the details in the lab step, and for lab steps that ask questions about the lab.

Table 2   Hints

Step	Hint
1	If you have not yet learned how to calculate the subnet ID based on an IP address/mask, check the book you are using for CCNA study. If you have not yet purchased such a book, check the ccentskills.com blog.
8	Use the **end** command or press Ctrl-z to exit configuration mode.
9	The output lists the mask in prefix format (/20) on a heading line and each route on a separate line just below the heading line. Because they are connected routes, you will see each route noted with a *C* in the far-left column. The subnet IDs will be 10.20.96.0 10.20.192.0

Configuration Steps

Example 1 shows a sample of the lab exercise being completed from R1's CLI.

Example 1   Example of Performing This Lab

```
(Press enter)
Password: cs
R1> enable
Password: cs
R1#
R1# configure terminal
R1(config)# interface Serial0/0/0
R1(config-if)# ip address 10.20.99.1 255.255.240.0
R1(config-if)# interface Fastethernet0/0
R1(config-if)# ip address 10.20.199.1 255.255.240.0
R1(config-if)# end
R1#
```

ICND1 Subnetting Exercises

Part 1: Subnet ID Calculation

Lab 3: Subnet ID Calculation III

Overview

In this exercise, you calculate the subnet IDs of the subnets in which two different IP addresses reside. Then, you configure the IP addresses on a router as a way to verify your calculation of the subnet IDs.

At the beginning of the lab, the interfaces on Router R1 are up but with no IP addresses configured. When you configure the IP addresses, the router calculates the subnet ID and places a route for that subnet into the routing table. You can then compare your calculated subnet ID to the subnet IDs calculated by the router.

The IP address assignments for R1, which you will configure in this lab, are as follows in Table 1.

Table 1 IP Address and Mask Reference

R1 Interface	IP Address	Subnet Mask
Serial0/0/0	172.16.48.112	255.255.254.0
FastEthernet0/0	172.16.33.112	255.255.254.0

Topology

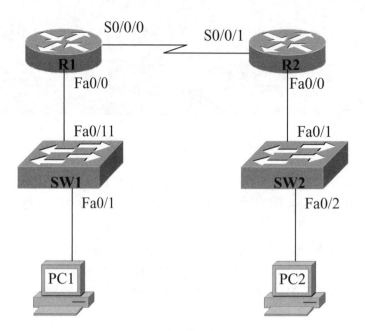

Figure 1   Topology for IP Address Configuration

Detailed Lab Steps

Step 1.   Calculate the subnet ID in which the IP addresses listed in the table at the beginning of this lab reside. List your answers on the following lines:

_____

_____

Step 2.   Connect to R1 from the simulator user interface. All passwords are **cs**.

Step 3.   Enter privileged exec ("enable") mode by issuing the **enable** command.

Step 4.   Enter global configuration mode using the **configure terminal** command.

Step 5.   First configure the Serial0/0/0 interface. To get into interface configuration mode, use the **interface s0/0/0** command.

Step 6.   Set the IP address and subnet mask using the **ip address 172.16.48.112 255.255.254.0** command.

Step 7.   Configure the FastEthernet0/0 interface by issuing the **interface fa0/0** command.

Step 8.   Set the IP address using the **ip address 172.16.33.112 255.255.254.0** command, and then exit configuration mode.

Because the two interfaces were already up, Router R1 adds a connected route to its routing table for each of the two connected subnets. At the next step, you will display these connected routes, which list the subnet ID. By comparing those values to the subnet ID values you calculated, you can confirm whether you calculated the correct subnet IDs.

Step 9. To determine the subnet IDs as calculated by Router R1, issue the **show ip route** command. Look at the connected routes for interfaces F0/0 and S0/0/0. Do the subnet IDs match the values you predicted at Step 3?

Hints and Answers

Table 2 lists hints and tips for any lab steps that do not supply all the details in the lab step, and for lab steps that ask questions about the lab.

Table 2   Hints

Step	Hint
1	If you have not yet learned how to calculate the subnet ID based on an IP address/mask, check the book you are using for CCNA study. If you have not yet purchased such a book, check the ccentskills.com blog.
8	Use the **end** command or press Ctrl-z to exit configuration mode.
9	The output lists the mask in prefix format (/23) on a heading line and each route on a separate line just below the heading line. Because they are connected routes, you will see each route noted with a *C* in the far-left column. The subnet IDs will be 172.16.48.0 172.16.32.0

Configuration Steps

Example 1 shows a sample of the lab exercise being completed from R1's CLI.

Example 1   Example of Performing This Lab

```
(Press enter)
Password: cs
R1> enable
Password: cs
R1#
R1# configure terminal
R1(config)# interface Serial0/0/0
R1(config-if)# ip address 172.16.48.112 255.255.254.0
R1(config-if)# interface Fastethernet0/0
R1(config-if)# ip address 172.16.33.112 255.255.254.0
R1(config-if)# end
R1#
```

ICND1 Subnetting Exercises

Part 1: Subnet ID Calculation

Lab 4: Subnet ID Calculation IV

Overview

In this exercise, you calculate the subnet IDs of the subnets in which two different IP addresses reside. Then, you configure the IP addresses on a router as a way to verify your calculation of the subnet IDs.

At the beginning of the lab, the interfaces on Router R1 are up but with no IP addresses configured. When you configure the IP addresses, the router calculates the subnet ID and places a route for that subnet into the routing table. You can then compare your calculated subnet ID to the subnet IDs calculated by the router.

The IP address assignments for R1, which you will configure in this lab, are as follows in Table 1.

Table 1   IP Address and Mask Reference

R1 Interface	IP Address	Subnet Mask
Serial0/0/0	172.16.133.233	255.255.255.128
FastEthernet0/0	172.16.133.1	255.255.255.128

Topology

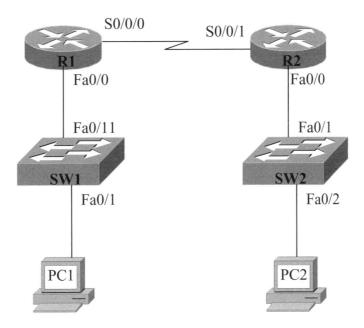

Figure 1   Topology for IP Address Configuration

Detailed Lab Steps

Step 1.   Calculate the subnet ID in which the IP addresses listed in the table at the beginning of this lab reside. List your answers on the following lines:

_____

_____

Step 2.   Connect to R1 from the simulator user interface. All passwords are **cs**.

Step 3.   Enter privileged exec ("enable") mode by issuing the **enable** command.

Step 4.   Enter global configuration mode using the **configure terminal** command.

Step 5.   First configure the Serial0/0/0 interface. To get into interface configuration mode, use the **interface s0/0/0** command.

Step 6.   Set the IP address and subnet mask using the **ip address 172.16.133.233 255.255.255.128** command.

Step 7.   Configure the FastEthernet0/0 interface by issuing the **interface fa0/0** command.

Step 8.   Set the IP address using the **ip address 172.16.133.1 255.255.255.128** command, and then exit configuration mode.

Because the two interfaces were already up, Router R1 adds a connected route to its routing table for each of the two connected subnets. At the next step, you display these connected routes, which list the subnet ID. By comparing those values to the subnet ID values you calculated, you can confirm whether you calculated the correct subnet IDs.

Step 9. To determine the subnet IDs as calculated by Router R1, issue the **show ip route** command. Look at the connected routes for interfaces F0/0 and S0/0/0. Do the subnet IDs match the values you predicted at Step 3?

Hints and Answers

Table 2 lists hints and tips for any lab steps that do not supply all the details in the lab step, and for lab steps that ask questions about the lab.

Table 2   Hints

Step	Hint
1	If you have not yet learned how to calculate the subnet ID based on an IP address/mask, check the book you are using for CCNA study. If you have not yet purchased such a book, check the ccentskills.com blog.
8	Use the **end** command or press Ctrl-z to exit configuration mode.
9	The output lists the mask in prefix format (/25) on a heading line and each route on a separate line just below the heading line. Because they are connected routes, you will see each route noted with a *C* in the far-left column. The subnet IDs will be 172.16.133.128 172.16.133.0

Configuration Steps

Example 1 shows a sample of the lab exercise being completed from R1's CLI.

Example 1   Example of Performing This Lab

```
(Press enter)
Password: cs
R1> enable
Password: cs
R1#
R1# configure terminal
R1(config)# interface Serial0/0/0
R1(config-if)# ip address 172.16.133.233 255.255.255.128
R1(config-if)# interface Fastethernet0/0
R1(config-if)# ip address 172.16.133.1 255.255.255.128
R1(config-if)# end
R1#
```

ICND1 Subnetting Exercises

Part 1: Subnet ID Calculation

Lab 5: Subnet ID Calculation V

Overview

In this exercise, you calculate the subnet IDs of the subnets in which two different IP addresses reside. Then, you configure the IP addresses on a router as a way to verify your calculation of the subnet IDs.

At the beginning of the lab, the interfaces on Router R1 are up but with no IP addresses configured. When you configure the IP addresses, the router calculates the subnet ID and places a route for that subnet into the routing table. You can then compare your calculated subnet ID to the subnet IDs calculated by the router.

The IP address assignments for R1, which you will configure in this lab, are as follows in Table 1.

Table 1   IP Address and Mask Reference

R1 Interface	IP Address	Subnet Mask
Serial0/0/0	192.168.9.151	255.255.255.224
FastEthernet0/0	192.168.9.121	255.255.255.224

Topology

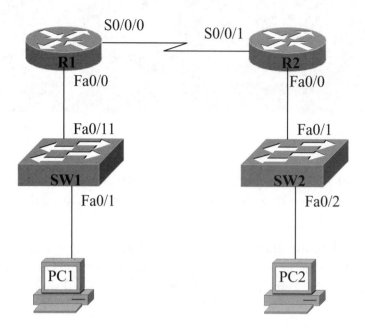

Figure 1   Topology for IP Address Configuration

Detailed Lab Steps

Step 1.   Calculate the subnet ID in which the IP addresses listed in the table at the beginning of this lab reside. List your answers on the following lines:

_____

_____

Step 2.   Connect to R1 from the simulator user interface. All passwords are **cs**.

Step 3.   Enter privileged exec ("enable") mode by issuing the **enable** command.

Step 4.   Enter global configuration mode using the **configure terminal** command.

Step 5.   First configure the Serial0/0/0 interface. To get into interface configuration mode, use the **interface s0/0/0** command.

Step 6.   Set the IP address and subnet mask using the **ip address 192.168.9.151 255.255.255.224** command.

Step 7.   Configure the FastEthernet0/0 interface by issuing the **interface fa0/0** command.

Step 8.   Set the IP address using the **ip address 192.168.9.121 255.255.255.224** command, and then exit configuration mode.

Because the two interfaces were already up, Router R1 adds a connected route to its routing table for each of the two connected subnets. At the next step, you will display these connected routes, which list the subnet ID. By comparing those values to the subnet ID values you calculated, you can confirm whether you calculated the correct subnet IDs.

Step 9. To determine the subnet IDs as calculated by Router R1, issue the **show ip route** command. Look at the connected routes for interfaces F0/0 and S0/0/0. Do the subnet IDs match the values you predicted at Step 3?

Hints and Answers

Table 2 lists hints and tips for any lab steps that do not supply all the details in the lab step, and for lab steps that ask questions about the lab.

Table 2   Hints

Step	Hint
1	If you have not yet learned how to calculate the subnet ID based on an IP address/mask, check the book you are using for CCNA study. If you have not yet purchased such a book, check the ccentskills.com blog.
8	Use the **end** command or press Ctrl-z to exit configuration mode.
9	The output lists the mask in prefix format (/27) on a heading line and each route on a separate line just below the heading line. Because they are connected routes, you will see each route noted with a *C* in the far-left column. The subnet IDs will be 192.168.9.128 192.168.9.96

Configuration Steps

Example 1 shows a sample of the lab exercise being completed from R1's CLI.

Example 1   Example of Performing This Lab

```
(Press enter)
Password: cs
R1> enable
Password: cs
R1#
R1# configure terminal
R1(config)# interface Serial0/0/0
R1(config-if)# ip address 192.168.9.151 255.255.255.224
R1(config-if)# interface Fastethernet0/0
R1(config-if)# ip address 192.168.9.121 255.255.255.224
R1(config-if)# end
R1#
```

ICND1 Subnetting Exercises

Part 1: Subnet ID Calculation

Lab 6: Subnet ID Calculation VI

Overview

In this exercise, you calculate the subnet IDs of the subnets in which two different IP addresses reside. Then, you configure the IP addresses on a router as a way to verify your calculation of the subnet IDs.

At the beginning of the lab, the interfaces on Router R1 are up but with no IP addresses configured. When you configure the IP addresses, the router calculates the subnet ID and places a route for that subnet into the routing table. You can then compare your calculated subnet ID to the subnet IDs calculated by the router.

The IP address assignments for R1, which you will configure in this lab, are as follows in Table 1.

Table 1   IP Address and Mask Reference

R1 Interface	IP Address	Subnet Mask
Serial0/0/0	192.168.9.211	255.255.255.248
FastEthernet0/0	192.168.9.11	255.255.255.248

Topology

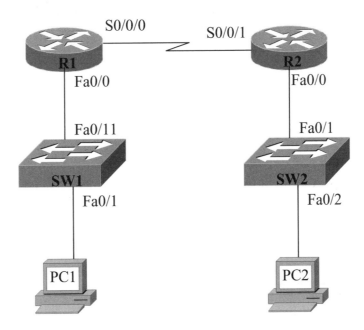

Figure 1   **Topology for IP Address Configuration**

Detailed Lab Steps

Step 1.   Calculate the subnet ID in which the IP addresses listed in the table at the beginning of this lab reside. List your answers on the following lines:

_____

_____

Step 2.   Connect to R1 from the simulator user interface. All passwords are **cs**.

Step 3.   Enter privileged exec ("enable") mode by issuing the **enable** command.

Step 4.   Enter global configuration mode using the **configure terminal** command.

Step 5.   First configure the Serial0/0/0 interface. To get into interface configuration mode, use the **interface s0/0/0** command.

Step 6.   Set the IP address and subnet mask using the **ip address 192.168.9.211 255.255.255.248** command.

Step 7.   Configure the FastEthernet0/0 interface by issuing the **interface fa0/0** command.

Step 8.   Set the IP address using the **ip address 192.168.9.11 255.255.255.248** command, and then exit configuration mode.

Because the two interfaces were already up, Router R1 adds a connected route to its routing table for each of the two connected subnets. At the next step, you display these connected routes, which list the subnet ID. By comparing those values to the subnet ID values you calculated, you can confirm whether you calculated the correct subnet IDs.

Step 9.   To determine the subnet IDs as calculated by Router R1, issue the **show ip route** command. Look at the connected routes for interfaces F0/0 and S0/0/0. Do the subnet IDs match the values you predicted at Step 3?

_____

_____

Hints and Answers

Table 2 lists hints and tips for any lab steps that do not supply all the details in the lab step, and for lab steps that ask questions about the lab.

Table 2   Hints

Step	Hint
1	If you have not yet learned how to calculate the subnet ID based on an IP address/mask, check the book you are using for CCNA study. If you have not yet purchased such a book, check the ccentskills.com blog.
8	Use the **end** command or press Ctrl-z to exit configuration mode.
9	The output lists the mask in prefix format (/29) on a heading line and each route on a separate line just below the heading line. Because they are connected routes, you will see each route noted with a *C* in the far-left column. The subnet IDs will be 192.168.9.208 192.168.9.8

Configuration Steps

Example 1 shows a sample of the lab exercise being completed from R1's CLI.

Example 1   Example of Performing This Lab

```
(Press enter)
Password: cs
R1> enable
Password: cs
R1#
R1# configure terminal
R1(config)# interface Serial0/0/0
R1(config-if)# ip address 192.168.9.211 255.255.255.248
R1(config-if)# interface Fastethernet0/0
R1(config-if)# ip address 192.168.9.11 255.255.255.248
R1(config-if)# end
R1#
```

ICND1 Subnetting Exercises

Part 1: Subnet ID Calculation

Lab 7: Subnet ID Calculation VII

Overview

In this exercise, you calculate the subnet IDs of the subnets in which two different IP addresses reside. Then, you configure the IP addresses on a router as a way to verify your calculation of the subnet IDs.

At the beginning of the lab, the interfaces on Router R1 are up but with no IP addresses configured. When you configure the IP addresses, the router calculates the subnet ID and places a route for that subnet into the routing table. You can then compare your calculated subnet ID to the subnet IDs calculated by the router.

The IP address assignments for R1, which you will configure in this lab, are as follows in Table 1.

Table 1 IP Address and Mask Reference

R1 Interface	IP Address	Subnet Mask
Serial0/0/0	192.168.1.5	255.255.255.252
FastEthernet0/0	172.25.100.113	255.255.255.128

Topology

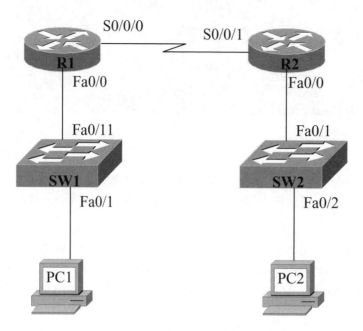

Figure 1   Topology for IP Address Configuration

Detailed Lab Steps

Step 1. Calculate the subnet ID in which the IP addresses listed in the table at the beginning of this lab reside. List your answers on the following lines:

_____

_____

Step 2. Connect to R1 from the simulator user interface. All passwords are **cs**.

Step 3. Enter privileged exec ("enable") mode by issuing the **enable** command.

Step 4. Enter global configuration mode using the **configure terminal** command.

Step 5. First configure the Serial0/0/0 interface. To get into interface configuration mode, use the **interface s0/0/0** command.

Step 6. Set the IP address and subnet mask using the **ip address 192.168.1.5 255.255.255.252** command.

Step 7. Configure the FastEthernet0/0 interface by issuing the **interface fa0/0** command.

Step 8. Set the IP address using the **ip address 172.25.100.113 255.255.255.128** command, and then exit configuration mode.

Because the two interfaces were already up, Router R1 adds a connected route to its routing table for each of the two connected subnets. At the next step, you display these connected routes, which list the subnet ID. By comparing those values to the subnet ID values you calculated, you can confirm whether you calculated the correct subnet IDs.

Step 9. To determine the subnet IDs as calculated by Router R1, issue the **show ip route** command. Look at the connected routes for interfaces F0/0 and S0/0/0. Do the subnet IDs match the values you predicted at Step 3?

_____

_____

Hints and Answers

Table 2 lists hints and tips for any lab steps that do not supply all the details in the lab step, and for lab steps that ask questions about the lab.

Table 2   Hints

Step	Hint
1	If you have not yet learned how to calculate the subnet ID based on an IP address/mask, check the book you are using for CCNA study. If you have not yet purchased such a book, check the ccentskills.com blog.
8	Use the **end** command or press Ctrl-z to exit configuration mode.
9	The IP addresses in this lab are in different classful networks. As a result, the output lists the mask in prefix format on a heading line for each network, and then each route on a separate line just below the respective heading line. Because they are connected routes, you will see each route noted with a *C* in the far-left column. The subnet IDs will be 172.25.100.0 192.168.1.4

Configuration Steps

Example 1 shows a sample of the lab exercise being completed from R1's CLI.

Example 1   Example of Performing This Lab

```
(Press enter)
Password: cs
R1> enable
Password: cs
R1#
R1# configure terminal
R1(config)# interface Serial0/0/0
R1(config-if)# ip address 192.168.1.5 255.255.255.252
R1(config-if)# interface Fastethernet0/0
R1(config-if)# ip address 172.25.100.113 255.255.255.128
R1(config-if)# end
R1#
```

ICND1 Subnetting Exercises

Part 1: Subnet ID Calculation

Lab 8: Subnet ID Calculation VIII

Overview

In this exercise, you calculate the subnet IDs of the subnets in which two different IP addresses reside. Then, you configure the IP addresses on a router as a way to verify your calculation of the subnet IDs.

At the beginning of the lab, the interfaces on Router R1 are up but with no IP addresses configured. When you configure the IP addresses, the router calculates the subnet ID and places a route for that subnet into the routing table. You can then compare your calculated subnet ID to the subnet IDs calculated by the router.

The IP address assignments for R1, which you will configure in this lab, are as follows in Table 1.

Table 1   IP Address and Mask Reference

R1 Interface	IP Address	Subnet Mask
Serial0/0/0	192.168.1.115	255.255.255.248
FastEthernet0/0	172.28.203.113	255.255.252.0

Topology

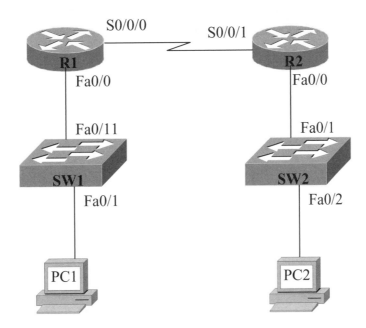

Figure 1   Topology for IP Address Configuration

Detailed Lab Steps

Step 1.   Calculate the subnet ID in which the IP addresses listed in the table at the beginning of this lab reside. List your answers on the following lines:

_____

_____

Step 2.   Connect to R1 from the simulator user interface. All passwords are **cs**.

Step 3.   Enter privileged exec ("enable") mode by issuing the **enable** command.

Step 4.   Enter global configuration mode using the **configure terminal** command.

Step 5.   First configure the Serial0/0/0 interface. To get into interface configuration mode, use the **interface s0/0/0** command.

Step 6.   Set the IP address and subnet mask using the **ip address 192.168.1.115 255.255.255.248** command.

Step 7.   Configure the FastEthernet0/0 interface by issuing the **interface fa0/0** command.

Step 8.   Set the IP address using the **ip address 172.28.203.113 255.255.252.0** command, and then exit configuration mode.

Because the two interfaces were already up, Router R1 adds a connected route to its routing table for each of the two connected subnets. At the next step, you display these connected routes, which list the subnet ID. By comparing those values to the subnet ID values you calculated, you can confirm whether you calculated the correct subnet IDs.

Step 9. To determine the subnet IDs as calculated by Router R1, issue the **show ip route** command. Look at the connected routes for interfaces F0/0 and S0/0/0. Do the subnet IDs match the values you predicted at Step 3?

_____

_____

Hints and Answers

Table 2 lists hints and tips for any lab steps that do not supply all the details in the lab step, and for lab steps that ask questions about the lab.

Table 2   Hints

Step	Hint
1	If you have not yet learned how to calculate the subnet ID based on an IP address/mask, check the book you are using for CCNA study. If you have not yet purchased such a book, check the ccentskills.com blog.
8	Use the **end** command or press Ctrl-z to exit configuration mode.
9	The IP addresses in this lab are in different classful networks. As a result, the output lists the mask in prefix format on a heading line for each network, and then each route on a separate line just below the respective heading line. Because they are connected routes, you will see each route noted with a *C* in the far-left column. The subnet IDs will be 172.28.200.0 192.168.1.112

Configuration Steps

Example 1 shows a sample of the lab exercise being completed from R1's CLI.

Example 1   Example of Performing This Lab

```
(Press enter)
Password: cs
R1> enable
Password: cs
R1#
R1# configure terminal
R1(config)# interface Serial0/0/0
R1(config-if)# ip address 192.168.1.115 255.255.255.248
R1(config-if)# interface Fastethernet0/0
R1(config-if)# ip address 172.28.203.113 255.255.252.0
R1(config-if)# end
R1#
```

ICND1 Subnetting Exercises

Part 1: Subnet ID Calculation

Lab 9: Subnet ID Calculation IX

Overview

In this exercise, you calculate the subnet IDs of the subnets in which two different IP addresses reside. Then, you configure the IP addresses on a router as a way to verify your calculation of the subnet IDs.

At the beginning of the lab, the interfaces on Router R1 are up but with no IP addresses configured. When you configure the IP addresses, the router calculates the subnet ID and places a route for that subnet into the routing table. You can then compare your calculated subnet ID to the subnet IDs calculated by the router.

The IP address assignments for R1, which you will configure in this lab, are as follows in Table 1.

Table 1   IP Address and Mask Reference

R1 Interface	IP Address	Subnet Mask
Serial0/0/0	192.168.1.215	255.255.255.240
FastEthernet0/0	172.18.93.113	255.255.255.192

Topology

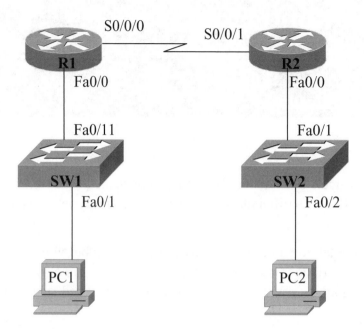

Figure 1   Topology for IP Address Configuration

Detailed Lab Steps

Step 1.   Calculate the subnet ID in which the IP addresses listed in the table at the beginning of this lab reside. List your answers on the following lines:

_____

_____

Step 2.   Connect to R1 from the simulator user interface. All passwords are **cs**.

Step 3.   Enter privileged exec ("enable") mode by issuing the **enable** command.

Step 4.   Enter global configuration mode using the **configure terminal** command.

Step 5.   First configure the Serial0/0/0 interface. To get into interface configuration mode, use the **interface s0/0/0** command.

Step 6.   Set the IP address and subnet mask using the **ip address 192.168.1.215 255.255.255.240** command.

Step 7.   Configure the FastEthernet0/0 interface by issuing the **interface fa0/0** command.

Step 8.   Set the IP address using the **ip address 172.18.93.113 255.255.255.192** command, and then exit configuration mode.

Because the two interfaces were already up, Router R1 adds a connected route to its routing table for each of the two connected subnets. At the next step, you display these connected routes, which list the subnet ID. By comparing those values to the subnet ID values you calculated, you can confirm whether you calculated the correct subnet IDs.

Step 9. To determine the subnet IDs as calculated by Router R1, issue the **show ip route** command. Look at the connected routes for interfaces F0/0 and S0/0/0. Do the subnet IDs match the values you predicted at Step 3?

_____

_____

Hints and Answers

Table 2 lists hints and tips for any lab steps that do not supply all the details in the lab step, and for lab steps that ask questions about the lab.

Table 2   Hints

Step	Hint
1	If you have not yet learned how to calculate the subnet ID based on an IP address/mask, check the book you are using for CCNA study. If you have not yet purchased such a book, check the ccentskills.com blog.
8	Use the **end** command or press Ctrl-z to exit configuration mode.
9	The IP addresses in this lab are in different classful networks. As a result, the output lists the mask in prefix format on a heading line for each network, and then each route on a separate line just below the respective heading line. Because they are connected routes, you will see each route noted with a *C* in the far-left column. The subnet IDs will be 172.18.93.64 192.168.1.208

Configuration Steps

Example 1 shows a sample of the lab exercise being completed from R1's CLI.

Example 1   Example of Performing This Lab

```
(Press enter)
Password: cs
R1> enable
Password: cs
R1#
R1# configure terminal
R1(config)# interface Serial0/0/0
R1(config-if)# ip address 192.168.1.215 255.255.255.240
R1(config-if)# interface Fastethernet0/0
R1(config-if)# ip address 172.18.93.113 255.255.255.192
R1(config-if)# end
R1#
```

ICND1 Subnetting Exercises

Part 1: Subnet ID Calculation

Lab 10: Subnet ID Calculation X

Overview

In this exercise, you calculate the subnet IDs of the subnets in which two different IP addresses reside. Then, you configure the IP addresses on a router as a way to verify your calculation of the subnet IDs.

At the beginning of the lab, the interfaces on Router R1 are up but with no IP addresses configured. When you configure the IP addresses, the router calculates the subnet ID and places a route for that subnet into the routing table. You can then compare your calculated subnet ID to the subnet IDs calculated by the router.

The IP address assignments for R1, which you will configure in this lab, are as follows in Table 1.

Table 1   IP Address and Mask Reference

R1 Interface	IP Address	Subnet Mask
Serial0/0/0	192.168.1.37	255.255.255.224
FastEthernet0/0	172.21.113.208	255.255.254.0

Topology

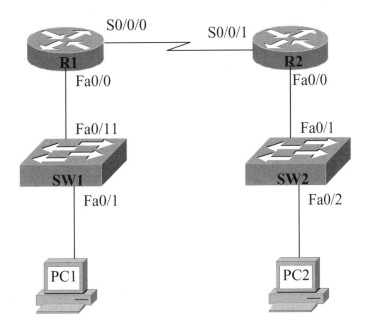

Figure 1   **Topology for IP Address Configuration**

Detailed Lab Steps

Step 1.   Calculate the subnet ID in which the IP addresses listed in the table at the beginning of this lab reside. List your answers on the following lines:

_____

_____

Step 2.   Connect to R1 from the simulator user interface. All passwords are **cs**.

Step 3.   Enter privileged exec ("enable") mode by issuing the **enable** command.

Step 4.   Enter global configuration mode using the **configure terminal** command.

Step 5.   First configure the Serial0/0/0 interface. To get into interface configuration mode, use the **interface s0/0/0** command.

Step 6.   Set the IP address and subnet mask using the **ip address 192.168.1.37 255.255.255.224** command.

Step 7.   Configure the FastEthernet0/0 interface by issuing the **interface fa0/0** command.

Step 8.   Set the IP address using the **ip address 172.21.113.208 255.255.254.0** command, and then exit configuration mode.

Because the two interfaces were already up, Router R1 adds a connected route to its routing table for each of the two connected subnets. At the next step, you display these connected routes, which list the subnet ID. By comparing those values to the subnet ID values you calculated, you can confirm whether you calculated the correct subnet IDs.

Step 9. To determine the subnet IDs as calculated by Router R1, issue the **show ip route** command. Look at the connected routes for interfaces F0/0 and S0/0/0. Do the subnet IDs match the values you predicted at Step 3?

_____

_____

Hints and Answers

Table 2 lists hints and tips for any lab steps that do not supply all the details in the lab step, and for lab steps that ask questions about the lab.

Table 2   Hints

Step	Hint
1	If you have not yet learned how to calculate the subnet ID based on an IP address/mask, check the book you are using for CCNA study. If you have not yet purchased such a book, check the ccentskills.com blog.
8	Use the **end** command or press Ctrl-z to exit configuration mode.
9	The IP addresses in this lab are in different classful networks. As a result, the output lists the mask in prefix format on a heading line for each network, and then each route on a separate line just below the respective heading line. Because they are connected routes, you will see each route noted with a _C_ in the far-left column. The subnet IDs will be 172.21.112.0 192.168.1.32

Configuration Steps

Example 1 shows a sample of the lab exercise being completed from R1's CLI.

Example 1   Example of Performing This Lab

```
(Press enter)
Password: cs
R1> enable
Password: cs
R1#
R1# configure terminal
R1(config)# interface Serial0/0/0
R1(config-if)# ip address 192.168.1.37 255.255.255.224
R1(config-if)# interface Fastethernet0/0
R1(config-if)# ip address 172.21.113.208 255.255.254.0
R1(config-if)# end
R1#
```

ICND1 Subnetting Exercises

Part 1: Subnet ID Calculation

Lab 11: Subnet ID Calculation XI

Overview

In this exercise, you calculate the subnet IDs of the subnets in which two different IP addresses reside. Then, you configure the IP addresses on a router as a way to verify your calculation of the subnet IDs.

At the beginning of the lab, the interfaces on Router R1 are up but with no IP addresses configured. When you configure the IP addresses, the router calculates the subnet ID and places a route for that subnet into the routing table. You can then compare your calculated subnet ID to the subnet IDs calculated by the router.

The IP address assignments for R1, which you will configure in this lab, are as follows in Table 1.

Table 1   IP Address and Mask Reference

R1 Interface	IP Address	Subnet Mask
Serial0/0/0	172.23.0.1	255.255.255.0
FastEthernet0/0	172.23.1.1	255.255.255.0

Topology

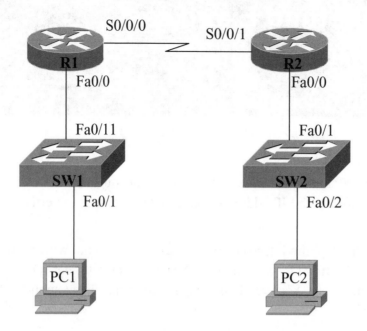

Figure 1   Topology for IP Address Configuration

Detailed Lab Steps

Step 1.   Calculate the subnet ID in which the IP addresses listed in the table at the beginning of this lab reside. List your answers on the following lines:

_____

_____

Step 2.   Connect to R1 from the simulator user interface. All passwords are **cs**.

Step 3.   Enter privileged exec ("enable") mode by issuing the **enable** command.

Step 4.   Enter global configuration mode using the **configure terminal** command.

Step 5.   First configure the Serial0/0/0 interface. To get into interface configuration mode, use the **interface s0/0/0** command.

Step 6.   Set the IP address and subnet mask using the **ip address 172.23.0.1 255.255.255.0** command.

Step 7.   Configure the FastEthernet0/0 interface by issuing the **interface fa0/0** command.

Step 8.   Set the IP address using the **ip address 172.23.1.1 255.255.255.0** command, and then exit configuration mode.

Because the two interfaces were already up, Router R1 adds a connected route to its routing table for each of the two connected subnets. At the next step, you display these connected routes, which list the subnet ID. By comparing those values to the subnet ID values you calculated, you can confirm whether you calculated the correct subnet IDs.

Step 9. To determine the subnet IDs as calculated by Router R1, issue the **show ip route** command. Look at the connected routes for interfaces F0/0 and S0/0/0. Do the subnet IDs match the values you predicted at Step 3?

Hints and Answers

Table 2 lists hints and tips for any lab steps that do not supply all the details in the lab step, and for lab steps that ask questions about the lab.

Table 2   Hints

Step	Hint
1	If you have not yet learned how to calculate the subnet ID based on an IP address/mask, check the book you are using for CCNA study. If you have not yet purchased such a book, check the ccentskills.com blog.
8	Use the **end** command or press Ctrl-z to exit configuration mode.
9	The output lists the mask in prefix format (/24) on a heading line and each route on a separate line just below the heading line. Because they are connected routes, you will see each route noted with a *C* in the far-left column. The subnet IDs will be 172.23.0.0 172.23.1.0 Note that the first of these subnets is a zero subnet.

Configuration Steps

Example 1 shows a sample of the lab exercise being completed from R1's CLI.

Example 1   Example of Performing This Lab

```
(Press enter)
Password: cs
R1> enable
Password: cs
R1#
R1# configure terminal
R1(config)# interface Serial0/0/0
R1(config-if)# ip address 172.23.0.1 255.255.255.0
R1(config-if)# interface Fastethernet0/0
R1(config-if)# ip address 172.23.1.1 255.255.255.0
R1(config-if)# end
R1#
```

ICND1 Subnetting Exercises

Part 2: IP Address Rejection

Lab 1: IP Address Rejection I

Overview

In this exercise, you begin by examining three IP addresses and masks. Each pair is a candidate to be configured on Router R1's FastEthernet0/0 interface. The question: Will R1 reject the IP address/mask combination as invalid for some reason? If rejected, what is the reason?

After you make your prediction in each case, you will configure the three IP addresses to see how the router reacts. The IP addresses to consider for this lab are as follows in Table 1.

Table 1   IP Address and Mask Reference

Address	Mask	Rejected? If so, why?
10.100.2.255	255.255.254.0	
10.100.2.255	255.255.255.0	
10.100.2.255	255.255.255.128	

Topology

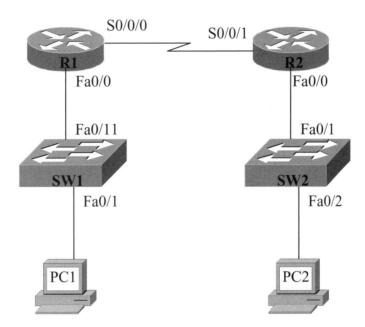

Figure 1   Topology for IP Address Configuration

Detailed Lab Steps

Step 1.   Connect to R1 from the simulator user interface. All passwords are **cs**.

Step 2.   Enter privileged exec ("enable") mode by issuing the **enable** command.

Step 3.   Examine the first of the three IP addresses and masks in the table at the beginning of this lab. Consider whether it is a valid unicast IP address and therefore will not be rejected when configured on a router interface. If you think of a reason for this address/mask pair to be rejected, note those reasons on the following lines. In particular, check to ensure that

- The address is in the range of class A, B, and C addresses

- The address is not the subnet ID or subnet broadcast address of its subnet

_____

_____

Step 4.   Repeat the previous step for both the second and third rows of the table, taking notes on the following lines.

_____

_____

Step 5.   Enter global configuration mode using the **configure terminal** command.

Step 6.   Configure the FastEthernet0/0 interface by issuing the **interface fa0/0** command.

Step 7. Set the IP address and mask for the first entry in the table at the beginning of this lab using the **ip address 10.100.2.255 255.255.254.0** command. Is the command rejected? If so, what does the error message tell you about the reason?

_____

_____

Step 8. Set the IP address and mask for the second entry in the table at the beginning of this lab. Record that IP address/mask on the following line. Is the command rejected? If so, what does the error message tell you about the reason?

_____

_____

Step 9. Set the IP address and mask for the last entry in the table at the beginning of this lab. Record that IP address/mask on the following line. Is the command rejected? If so, what does the error message tell you about the reason?

_____

_____

Hints and Answers

Table 2 lists hints and tips for any lab steps that do not supply all the details in the lab step, and for lab steps that ask questions about the lab.

Table 2   Hints

Step	Hint
3	Class A addresses begin with a first octet of 1 through 126, inclusive. Class B addresses begin with 128 through 191, and class C addresses begin with 192 through 223.
7	The number 10.100.2.255, with mask 255.255.254.0, is a valid IP address. It is in a subnet whose subnet ID is 10.100.2.0 with subnet broadcast address 10.100.3.255.
8	Use the **ip address 10.100.2.255 255.255.255.0** interface subcommand. In this case, the number 10.100.2.255, when using mask 255.255.255.0, is a subnet broadcast address in a subnet with subnet ID 10.100.2.0. Router R1 rejects this **ip address** command because the subnet broadcast address cannot be used as an interface IP address.
9	Use the **ip address 10.100.2.255 255.255.255.128** interface subcommand. In this case, number 10.100.2.255, when using mask 255.255.255.128, is a subnet broadcast address in a subnet with subnet ID 10.100.2.128. Router R1 rejects this **ip address** command because the subnet broadcast address cannot be used as an interface IP address.

Configuration Steps

Example 1 shows a sample of the lab exercise being completed from R1's CLI.

Example 1 Example of Performing This Lab

```
(Press enter)
Password: cs
R1> enable
Password: cs
R1#
R1# configure terminal
R1(config)# interface Fastethernet0/0
R1(config-if)# ip address 10.100.2.255 255.255.254.0
R1(config-if)# ip address 10.100.2.255 255.255.255.0
Bad mask /24 for address 10.100.2.255
R1(config-if)# ip address 10.100.2.255 255.255.255.128
Bad mask /25 for address 10.100.2.255
R1(config-if)# end
R1#
```

ICND1 Subnetting Exercises

Part 2: IP Address Rejection

Lab 2: IP Address Rejection II

Overview

In this exercise, you begin by examining three IP addresses and masks. Each pair is a candidate to be configured on Router R1's FastEthernet0/0 interface. The question: Will R1 reject the IP address/mask combination as invalid for some reason? If rejected, what is the reason?

After you make your prediction in each case, you will configure the three IP addresses to see how the router reacts. The IP addresses to consider for this lab are as follows in Table 1.

Table 1   IP Address and Mask Reference

Address	Mask	Rejected? If so, why?
10.9.1.1	255.254.0.0	
10.9.1.1	255.255.128.0	
10.9.127.127	255.255.128.0	

Topology

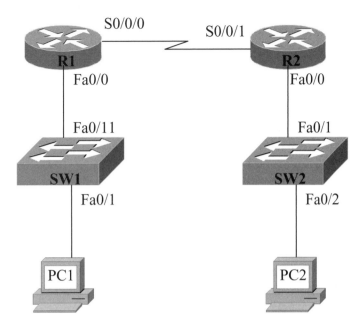

Figure 1   Topology for IP Address Configuration

Detailed Lab Steps

Step 1.   Connect to R1 from the simulator user interface. All passwords are **cs**.

Step 2.   Enter privileged exec ("enable") mode by issuing the **enable** command.

Step 3.   Examine the first of the three IP addresses and masks in the table at the beginning of this lab. Consider whether it is a valid unicast IP address and therefore will not be rejected when configured on a router interface. If you think of a reason for this address/mask pair to be rejected, note those reasons on the following lines. In particular, check to ensure that

- The address is in the range of class A, B, and C addresses

- The address is not the subnet ID or subnet broadcast address of its subnet

_____

_____

Step 4.   Repeat the previous step for both the second and third rows of the table, taking notes on the following lines.

_____

_____

Step 5.   Enter global configuration mode using the **configure terminal** command.

Step 6.   Configure the FastEthernet0/0 interface by issuing the **interface fa0/0** command.

Step 7. Set the IP address and mask for the first entry in the table at the beginning of this lab using the **ip address 10.9.1.1 255.254.0.0** command. Is the command rejected? If so, what does the error message tell you about the reason?

_____

_____

Step 8. Set the IP address and mask for the second entry in the table at the beginning of this lab. Record that IP address/mask on the following line. Is the command rejected? If so, what does the error message tell you about the reason?

_____

_____

Step 9. Set the IP address and mask for the last entry in the table at the beginning of this lab. Record that IP address/mask on the following line. Is the command rejected? If so, what does the error message tell you about the reason?

_____

_____

Hints and Answers

Table 2 lists hints and tips for any lab steps that do not supply all the details in the lab step, and for lab steps that ask questions about the lab.

Table 2   Hints

Step	Hint
3	Class A addresses begin with a first octet of 1 through 126, inclusive. Class B addresses begin with 128 through 191, and class C addresses begin with 192 through 223.
7	The number 10.9.1.1, with mask 255.254.0.0, is a valid IP address. It is in a subnet whose subnet ID is 10.8.0.0, with subnet broadcast address 10.9.255.255.
8	Use the **ip address 10.9.1.1 255.255.128.0** interface subcommand. In this case, the number 10.9.1.1, when using mask 255.255.128.0, is a valid IP address. It is in a subnet whose subnet ID is 10.9.0.0, with subnet broadcast address 10.9.127.255.
9	Use the **ip address 10.9.127.127 255.255.128.0** interface subcommand. In this case, the number 10.9.127.127, when using mask 255.255.128.0, is a valid IP address. It is in a subnet whose subnet ID is 10.9.0.0, with subnet broadcast address 10.9.127.255.

Configuration Steps

Example 1 shows a sample of the lab exercise being completed from R1's CLI.

Example 1   Example of Performing This Lab

```
(Press enter)
Password: cs
R1> enable
Password: cs
R1#
R1# configure terminal
R1(config)# interface Fastethernet0/0
R1(config-if)#ip address 10.9.1.1 255.254.0.0
R1(config-if)#ip address 10.9.1.1 255.255.128.0
R1(config-if)#ip address 10.9.127.127 255.255.128.0
R1(config-if)# end
R1#
```

ICND1 Subnetting Exercises

Part 2: IP Address Rejection

Lab 3: IP Address Rejection III

Overview

In this exercise, you begin by examining three IP addresses and masks. Each pair is a candidate to be configured on Router R1's FastEthernet0/0 interface. The question: Will R1 reject the IP address/mask combination as invalid for some reason? If rejected, what is the reason?

After you make your prediction in each case, you will configure the three IP addresses to see how the router reacts. The IP addresses to consider for this lab are as follows in Table 1.

Table 1   IP Address and Mask Reference

Address	Mask	Rejected? If so, why?
128.0.0.1	255.255.255.0	
127.1.1.1	255.255.255.0	
129.1.1.3	255.255.255.252	

Topology

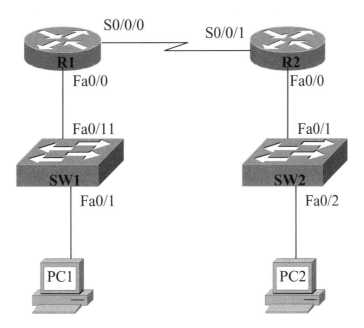

Figure 1   Topology for IP Address Configuration

Detailed Lab Steps

Step 1. Connect to R1 from the simulator user interface. All passwords are **cs**.

Step 2. Enter privileged exec ("enable") mode by issuing the **enable** command.

Step 3. Examine the first of the three IP addresses and masks in the table at the beginning of this lab. Consider whether it is a valid unicast IP address and therefore will not be rejected when configured on a router interface. If you think of a reason for this address/mask pair to be rejected, note those reasons on the following lines. In particular, check to ensure that

- The address is in the range of class A, B, and C addresses

- The address is not the subnet ID or subnet broadcast address of its subnet

_____

_____

Step 4. Repeat the previous step for both the second and third rows of the table, taking notes on the following lines.

_____

_____

Step 5. Enter global configuration mode using the **configure terminal** command.

Step 6. Configure the FastEthernet0/0 interface by issuing the **interface fa0/0** command.

Step 7. Set the IP address and mask for the first entry in the table at the beginning of this lab using the **ip address 128.0.0.1 255.255.255.0** command. Is the command rejected? If so, what does the error message tell you about the reason?

_____

_____

Step 8. Set the IP address and mask for the second entry in the table at the beginning of this lab. Record that IP address/mask on the following line. Is the command rejected? If so, what does the error message tell you about the reason?

_____

_____

Step 9. Set the IP address and mask for the last entry in the table at the beginning of this lab. Record that IP address/mask on the following line. Is the command rejected? If so, what does the error message tell you about the reason?

_____

_____

Hints and Answers

Table 2 lists hints and tips for any lab steps that do not supply all the details in the lab step, and for lab steps that ask questions about the lab.

Table 2   Hints

Step	Hint
3	Class A addresses begin with a first octet of 1 through 126, inclusive. Class B addresses begin with 128 through 191, and class C addresses begin with 192 through 223.
7	The number 128.0.0.1, with mask 255.255.255.0, is a valid IP address. It is in a subnet whose subnet ID is 128.0.0.0, with subnet broadcast address 128.0.0.255. Note that this subnet happens to be a zero subnet.
8	Use the **ip address 127.1.1.1 255.255.255.0** interface subcommand. In this case, the number 127.1.1.1 is illegal as an IP address to be assigned to an interface because the first octet is 127. IPv4 addressing rules reserves all addresses that begin with 127, and these addresses cannot be used as unicast IP addresses.
9	Use the **ip address 129.1.1.3 255.255.255.252** interface subcommand. In this case, number 129.1.1.3, when using mask 255.255.255.252, is a subnet broadcast address in a subnet with subnet ID 129.1.1.0. Router R1 rejects this **ip address** command because the subnet broadcast address cannot be used as an interface IP address.

Configuration Steps

Example 1 shows a sample of the lab exercise being completed from R1's CLI.

Example 1   Example of Performing This Lab

```
(Press enter)
Password: cs
R1> enable
Password: cs
R1#
R1# configure terminal
R1(config)# interface Fastethernet0/0
R1(config-if)#ip address 128.0.0.1 255.255.255.0
R1(config-if)#ip address 127.1.1.1 255.255.255.0
Not a valid host address - 127.1.1.1
R1(config-if)#ip address 129.1.1.3 255.255.255.252
Bad mask /30 for address 129.1.1.3
R1(config-if)# end
R1#
```

ICND1 Subnetting Exercises

Part 2: IP Address Rejection

Lab 4: IP Address Rejection IV

Overview

In this exercise, you begin by examining three IP addresses and masks. Each pair is a candidate to be configured on Router R1's FastEthernet0/0 interface. The question: Will R1 reject the IP address/mask combination as invalid for some reason? If rejected, what is the reason?

After you make your prediction in each case, you will configure the three IP addresses to see how the router reacts. The IP addresses to consider for this lab are as follows in Table 1.

Table 1   IP Address and Mask Reference

Address	Mask	Rejected? If so, why?
150.150.1.110	255.255.255.240	
150.150.1.111	255.255.255.240	
150.150.1.112	255.255.255.240	

Topology

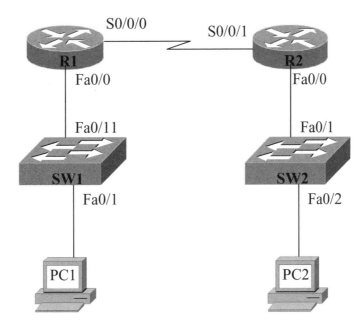

Figure 1 **Topology for IP Address Configuration**

Detailed Lab Steps

Step 1. Connect to R1 from the simulator user interface. All passwords are **cs**.

Step 2. Enter privileged exec ("enable") mode by issuing the **enable** command.

Step 3. Examine the first of the three IP addresses and masks in the table at the beginning of this lab. Consider whether it is a valid unicast IP address and therefore will not be rejected when configured on a router interface. If you think of a reason for this address/mask pair to be rejected, note those reasons on the following lines. In particular, check to ensure that

- The address is in the range of class A, B, and C addresses

- The address is not the subnet ID or subnet broadcast address of its subnet

_____

_____

Step 4. Repeat the previous step for both the second and third rows of the table, taking notes on the following lines.

_____

_____

Step 5. Enter global configuration mode using the **configure terminal** command.

Step 6. Configure the FastEthernet0/0 interface by issuing the **interface fa0/0** command.

Step 7. Set the IP address and mask for the first entry in the table at the beginning of this lab using the **ip address 150.150.1.110 255.255.255.240** command. Is the command rejected? If so, what does the error message tell you about the reason?

_____

_____

Step 8. Set the IP address and mask for the second entry in the table at the beginning of this lab. Record that IP address/mask on the following line. Is the command rejected? If so, what does the error message tell you about the reason?

_____

_____

Step 9. Set the IP address and mask for the last entry in the table at the beginning of this lab. Record that IP address/mask on the following line. Is the command rejected? If so, what does the error message tell you about the reason?

_____

_____

Hints and Answers

Table 2 lists hints and tips for any lab steps that do not supply all the details in the lab step, and for lab steps that ask questions about the lab.

Table 2 Hints

Step	Hint
3	Class A addresses begin with a first octet of 1 through 126, inclusive. Class B addresses begin with 128 through 191, and class C addresses begin with 192 through 223.
7	The number 150.150.1.110, with mask 255.255.255.240, is a valid IP address. It is in a subnet whose subnet ID is 150.150.1.96, with subnet broadcast address 150.150.1.111.
8	Use the **ip address 150.150.1.111 255.255.255.240** interface subcommand. In this case, number 150.150.1.111, when using mask 255.255.255.240, is a subnet broadcast address in a subnet with subnet ID 150.150.1.96. Router R1 rejects this **ip address** command because the subnet broadcast address cannot be used as an interface IP address.
9	Use the **ip address 150.150.1.112 255.255.255.240** interface subcommand. In this case, number 150.150.1.112, when using mask 255.255.255.240, is a subnet ID. Router R1 rejects this **ip address** command as a result.

Configuration Steps

Example 1 shows a sample of the lab exercise being completed from R1's CLI.

Example 1 Example of Performing This Lab

```
(Press enter)
Password: cs
R1> enable
Password: cs
R1#
R1# configure terminal
R1(config)# interface fastethernet0/0
R1(config-if)#ip address 150.150.1.110 255.255.255.240
R1(config-if)#ip address 150.150.1.111 255.255.255.240
Bad mask /28 for address 150.150.1.111
R1(config-if)#ip address 150.150.1.112 255.255.255.240
Bad mask /28 for address 150.150.1.112
R1(config-if)# end
R1#
```

ICND1 Subnetting Exercises

Part 2: IP Address Rejection

Lab 5: IP Address Rejection V

Overview

In this exercise, you begin by examining three IP addresses and masks. Each pair is a candidate to be configured on Router R1's FastEthernet0/0 interface. The question: Will R1 reject the IP address/mask combination as invalid for some reason? If rejected, what is the reason?

After you make your prediction in each case, you will configure the three IP addresses to see how the router reacts. The IP addresses to consider for this lab are as follows in Table 1.

Table 1   IP Address and Mask Reference

Address	Mask	Rejected? If so, why?
222.222.222.222	255.255.255.224	
223.223.223.223	255.255.255.224	
224.224.224.224	255.255.255.224	

Topology

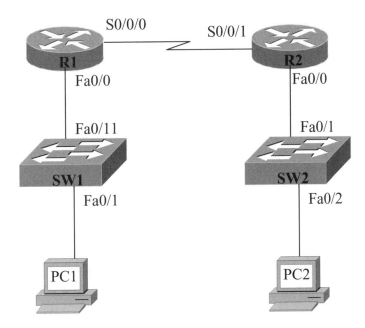

Figure 1   Topology for IP Address Configuration

Detailed Lab Steps

Step 1. Connect to R1 from the simulator user interface. All passwords are **cs**.

Step 2. Enter privileged exec ("enable") mode by issuing the **enable** command.

Step 3. Examine the first of the three IP addresses and masks in the table at the beginning of this lab. Consider whether it is a valid unicast IP address and therefore will not be rejected when configured on a router interface. If you think of a reason for this address/mask pair to be rejected, note those reasons on the following lines. In particular, check to ensure that

- The address is in the range of class A, B, and C addresses
- The address is not the subnet ID or subnet broadcast address of its subnet

_____

_____

Step 4. Repeat the previous step for both the second and third rows of the table, taking notes on the following lines.

_____

_____

Step 5. Enter global configuration mode using the **configure terminal** command.

Step 6. Configure the FastEthernet0/0 interface by issuing the **interface fa0/0** command.

Step 7. Set the IP address and mask for the first entry in the table at the beginning of this lab using the **ip address 222.222.222.222 255.255.255.224** command. Is the command rejected? If so, what does the error message tell you about the reason?

_____

_____

Step 8. Set the IP address and mask for the second entry in the table at the beginning of this lab. Record that IP address/mask on the following line. Is the command rejected? If so, what does the error message tell you about the reason?

_____

_____

Step 9. Set the IP address and mask for the last entry in the table at the beginning of this lab. Record that IP address/mask on the following line. Is the command rejected? If so, what does the error message tell you about the reason?

_____

_____

Hints and Answers

Table 2 lists hints and tips for any lab steps that do not supply all the details in the lab step, and for lab steps that ask questions about the lab.

Table 2   Hints

Step	Hint
3	Class A addresses begin with a first octet of 1 through 126, inclusive. Class B addresses begin with 128 through 191, and class C addresses begin with 192 through 223.
7	The number 222.222.222.222, with mask 255.255.255.224, is a valid IP address. It is in a subnet whose subnet ID is 222.222.222.192 with subnet broadcast address 222.222.222.223.
8	Use the **ip address 223.223.223.223 255.255.255.224** interface subcommand. In this case, number 223.223.223.223, when using mask 255.255.255.224, is a subnet broadcast address in a subnet with subnet ID 223.223.223.192. Router R1 rejects this **ip address** command because the subnet broadcast address cannot be used as an interface IP address.
9	Use the **ip address 224.224.224.224 255.255.255.224** interface subcommand. In this case, number 224.224.224.224 is actually a class D address because its first octet sits between 224 and 239, inclusive. Router R1 rejects this **ip address** command as a result.

Configuration Steps

Example 1 shows a sample of the lab exercise being completed from R1's CLI.

Example 1 Example of Performing This Lab

```
(Press enter)
Password: cs
R1> enable
Password: cs
R1#
R1# configure terminal
R1(config)# interface Fastethernet0/0
R1(config-if)#ip address 222.222.222.222 255.255.255.224
R1(config-if)#ip address 223.223.223.223 255.255.255.224
Bad mask /27 for address 223.223.223.223
R1(config-if)#ip address 224.224.224.224 255.255.255.224
Not a valid host address - 224.224.224.224
R1(config-if)# end
R1#
```

ICND1 Subnetting Exercises

Part 2: IP Address Rejection

Lab 6: IP Address Rejection VI

Overview

In this exercise, you begin by examining three IP addresses and masks. Each pair is a candidate to be configured on Router R1's FastEthernet0/0 interface. The question: Will R1 reject the IP address/mask combination as invalid for some reason? If rejected, what is the reason?

After you make your prediction in each case, you will configure the three IP addresses to see how the router reacts. The IP addresses to consider for this lab are as follows in Table 1.

Table 1   IP Address and Mask Reference

Address	Mask	Rejected? If so, why?
199.1.1.51	255.255.255.252	
199.1.1.61	255.255.255.252	
199.1.1.71	255.255.255.252	

Topology

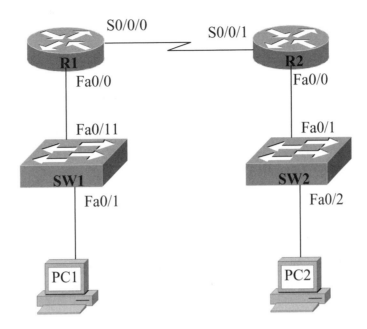

Figure 1   Topology for IP Address Configuration

Detailed Lab Steps

Step 1.   Connect to R1 from the simulator user interface. All passwords are **cs**.

Step 2.   Enter privileged exec ("enable") mode by issuing the **enable** command.

Step 3.   Examine the first of the three IP addresses and masks in the table at the beginning of this lab. Consider whether it is a valid unicast IP address and therefore will not be rejected when configured on a router interface. If you think of a reason for this address/mask pair to be rejected, note those reasons on the following lines. In particular, check to ensure that

-   The address is in the range of class A, B, and C addresses

-   The address is not the subnet ID or subnet broadcast address of its subnet

_____

_____

Step 4.   Repeat the previous step for both the second and third rows of the table, taking notes on the following lines.

_____

_____

Step 5.   Enter global configuration mode using the **configure terminal** command.

Step 6.   Configure the FastEthernet0/0 interface by issuing the **interface fa0/0** command.

Step 7. Set the IP address and mask for the first entry in the table at the beginning of this lab using the **ip address 199.1.1.51 255.255.255.252** command. Is the command rejected? If so, what does the error message tell you about the reason?

_____

_____

Step 8. Set the IP address and mask for the second entry in the table at the beginning of this lab. Record that IP address/mask on the following line. Is the command rejected? If so, what does the error message tell you about the reason?

_____

_____

Step 9. Set the IP address and mask for the last entry in the table at the beginning of this lab. Record that IP address/mask on the following line. Is the command rejected? If so, what does the error message tell you about the reason?

_____

_____

Hints and Answers

Table 2 lists hints and tips for any lab steps that do not supply all the details in the lab step, and for lab steps that ask questions about the lab.

Table 2   Hints

Step	Hint
3	Class A addresses begin with a first octet of 1 through 126, inclusive. Class B addresses begin with 128 through 191, and class C addresses begin with 192 through 223.
7	The number 199.1.1.51, when using mask 255.255.255.252, is a subnet broadcast address in a subnet with subnet ID 199.1.1.48. Router R1 rejects this **ip address** command because the subnet broadcast address cannot be used as an interface IP address.
8	Use the **ip address 199.1.1.61 255.255.255.252** interface subcommand. In this case, the number 199.1.1.61, with mask 255.255.255.252, is a valid IP address. It is in a subnet whose subnet ID is 199.1.1.60 with subnet broadcast address 199.1.1.63.
9	Use the **ip address 199.1.1.71 255.255.255.252** interface subcommand. In this case, number 199.1.1.71, when using mask 255.255.255.252, is a subnet broadcast address in a subnet with subnet ID 199.1.1.68. Router R1 rejects this **ip address** command because the subnet broadcast address cannot be used as an interface IP address.

Configuration Steps

Example 1 shows a sample of the lab exercise being completed from R1's CLI.

Example 1   Example of Performing This Lab

```
(Press enter)
Password: cs
R1> enable
Password: cs
R1#
R1# configure terminal
R1(config)# interface Fastethernet0/0
R1(config-if)#ip address 199.1.1.51 255.255.255.252
Bad mask /30 for address 199.1.1.51
R1(config-if)#ip address 199.1.1.61 255.255.255.252
R1(config-if)#ip address 199.1.1.71 255.255.255.252
Bad mask /30 for address 199.1.1.71
R1(config-if)# end
R1#
```

ICND1 Subnetting Exercises

Part 2: IP Address Rejection

Lab 7: IP Address Rejection VII

Overview

In this exercise, you begin by examining three IP addresses and masks. Each pair is a candidate to be configured on Router R1's FastEthernet0/0 interface. The question: Will R1 reject the IP address/mask combination as invalid for some reason? If rejected, what is the reason?

After you make your prediction in each case, you will configure the three IP addresses to see how the router reacts. The IP addresses to consider for this lab are as follows in Table 1.

Table 1   IP Address and Mask Reference

Address	Mask	Rejected? If so, why?
10.99.99.255	255.255.248.0	
10.199.199.255	255.255.248.0	
224.1.1.1	255.255.255.0	

Topology

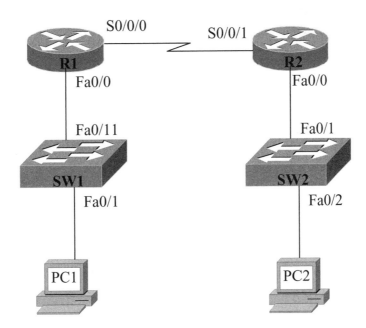

Figure 1   Topology for IP Address Configuration

Detailed Lab Steps

Step 1.   Connect to R1 from the simulator user interface. All passwords are **cs**.

Step 2.   Enter privileged exec ("enable") mode by issuing the **enable** command.

Step 3.   Examine the first of the three IP addresses and masks in the table at the beginning of this lab. Consider whether it is a valid unicast IP address and therefore will not be rejected when configured on a router interface. If you think of a reason for this address/mask pair to be rejected, note those reasons on the following lines. In particular, check to ensure that

- The address is in the range of class A, B, and C addresses

- The address is not the subnet ID or subnet broadcast address of its subnet

_____

_____

Step 4.   Repeat the previous step for both the second and third rows of the table, taking notes on the following lines.

_____

_____

Step 5.   Enter global configuration mode using the **configure terminal** command.

Step 6.   Configure the FastEthernet0/0 interface by issuing the **interface fa0/0** command.

Step 7. Set the IP address and mask for the first entry in the table at the beginning of this lab using the **ip address 10.99.99.255 255.255.248.0** command. Is the command rejected? If so, what does the error message tell you about the reason?

_____

_____

Step 8. Set the IP address and mask for the second entry in the table at the beginning of this lab. Record that IP address/mask on the following line. Is the command rejected? If so, what does the error message tell you about the reason?

_____

_____

Step 9. Set the IP address and mask for the last entry in the table at the beginning of this lab. Record that IP address/mask on the following line. Is the command rejected? If so, what does the error message tell you about the reason?

_____

_____

Hints and Answers

Table 2 lists hints and tips for any lab steps that do not supply all the details in the lab step, and for lab steps that ask questions about the lab.

Table 2   Hints

Step	Hint
3	Class A addresses begin with a first octet of 1 through 126, inclusive. Class B addresses begin with 128 through 191, and class C addresses begin with 192 through 223.
7	The number 10.99.99.255, with mask 255.255.248.0, is a valid IP address. It is in a subnet whose subnet ID is 10.99.96.0 with subnet broadcast address 10.99.103.255.
8	Use the **ip address 10.199.199.255 255.255.248.0** interface subcommand. In this case, the number 10.199.199.255, when using mask 255.255.248.0, is a subnet broadcast address in a subnet with subnet ID 10.199.192.0. Router R1 rejects this **ip address** command because the subnet broadcast address cannot be used as an interface IP address.
9	Use the **ip address 224.1.1.1 255.255.255.0** interface subcommand. In this case, the number 224.1.1.1 is illegal as an IP address to be assigned to an interface because the first octet is 224. Addresses that begin with 224 through 239 are class D multicast IP addresses; these addresses cannot be assigned as unicast IP addresses.

Configuration Steps

Example 1 shows a sample of the lab exercise being completed from R1's CLI.

Example 1   Example of Performing This Lab

```
(Press enter)
Password: cs
R1> enable
Password: cs
R1#
R1# configure terminal
R1(config)# interface Fastethernet0/0
R1(config-if)# ip address 10.99.99.255 255.255.248.0
R1(config-if)# ip address 10.199.199.255 255.255.248.0
Bad mask /21 for address 10.199.199.255
R1(config-if)# ip address 224.1.1.1 255.255.255.0
Not a valid host address - 224.1.1.1
R1(config-if)# end
R1#
```

ICND1 Subnetting Exercises

Part 2: IP Address Rejection

Lab 8: IP Address Rejection VIII

Overview

In this exercise, you begin by examining three IP addresses and masks. Each pair is a candidate to be configured on Router R1's FastEthernet0/0 interface. The question: Will R1 reject the IP address/mask combination as invalid for some reason? If rejected, what is the reason?

After you make your prediction in each case, you will configure the three IP addresses to see how the router reacts. The IP addresses to consider for this lab are as follows in Table 1.

Table 1   IP Address and Mask Reference

Address	Mask	Rejected? If so, why?
127.1.199.1	255.255.255.0	
191.255.255.100	255.255.255.128	
191.1.1.3	255.255.255.252	

Topology

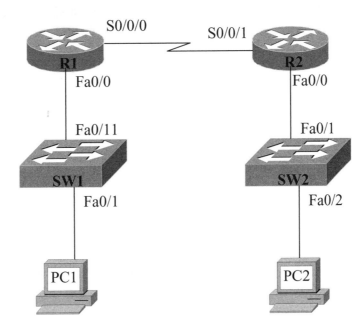

Figure 1   Topology for IP Address Configuration

Detailed Lab Steps

Step 1.   Connect to R1 from the simulator user interface. All passwords are **cs**.

Step 2.   Enter privileged exec ("enable") mode by issuing the **enable** command.

Step 3.   Examine the first of the three IP addresses and masks in the table at the beginning of this lab. Consider whether it is a valid unicast IP address and therefore will not be rejected when configured on a router interface. If you think of a reason for this address/mask pair to be rejected, note those reasons on the following lines. In particular, check to ensure that

- The address is in the range of class A, B, and C addresses

- The address is not the subnet ID or subnet broadcast address of its subnet

_____

_____

Step 4.   Repeat the previous step for both the second and third rows of the table, taking notes on the following lines.

_____

_____

Step 5.   Enter global configuration mode using the **configure terminal** command.

Step 6.   Configure the FastEthernet0/0 interface by issuing the **interface fa0/0** command.

Step 7. Set the IP address and mask for the first entry in the table at the beginning of this lab using the **ip address 127.1.199.1 255.255.255.0** command. Is the command rejected? If so, what does the error message tell you about the reason?

_____

_____

Step 8. Set the IP address and mask for the second entry in the table at the beginning of this lab. Record that IP address/mask on the following line. Is the command rejected? If so, what does the error message tell you about the reason?

_____

_____

Step 9. Set the IP address and mask for the last entry in the table at the beginning of this lab. Record that IP address/mask on the following line. Is the command rejected? If so, what does the error message tell you about the reason?

_____

_____

Hints and Answers

Table 2 lists hints and tips for any lab steps that do not supply all the details in the lab step, and for lab steps that ask questions about the lab.

Table 2   Hints

Step	Hint
3	Class A addresses begin with a first octet of 1 through 126, inclusive. Class B addresses begin with 128 through 191, and class C addresses begin with 192 through 223.
7	Use the **ip address 127.1.199.1 255.255.255.0** interface subcommand. In this case, the number 127.1.199.1 is illegal as an IP address to be assigned to an interface because the first octet is 127. IPv4 addressing rules reserves all addresses that begin with 127, and these addresses cannot be used as unicast IP addresses.
8	The number 191.255.255.100, with mask 255.255.255.128, is a valid IP address. It is in a subnet whose subnet ID is 191.255.255.0 with subnet broadcast address 191.255.255.127.
9	Use the **ip address 191.1.1.3 255.255.255.252** interface subcommand. In this case, number 191.1.1.3, when using mask 255.255.255.252, is a subnet broadcast address in a subnet with subnet ID 191.1.1.0. Router R1 rejects this **ip address** command because the subnet broadcast address cannot be used as an interface IP address.

Configuration Steps

Example 1 shows a sample of the lab exercise being completed from R1's CLI.

Example 1   Example of Performing This Lab

```
(Press enter)
Password: cs
R1> enable
Password: cs
R1#
R1# configure terminal
R1(config)# interface Fastethernet0/0
R1(config-if)# ip address 127.1.199.1 255.255.255.0
Not a valid host address - 127.1.199.1
R1(config-if)# ip address 191.255.255.100 255.255.255.128
R1(config-if)# ip address 191.1.1.3 255.255.255.252
Bad mask /30 for address 191.1.1.3
R1(config-if)# end
R1#
```

ICND1 Subnetting Exercises

Part 2: IP Address Rejection

Lab 9: IP Address Rejection IX

Overview

In this exercise, you begin by examining three IP addresses and masks. Each pair is a candidate to be configured on Router R1's FastEthernet0/0 interface. The question: Will R1 reject the IP address/mask combination as invalid for some reason? If rejected, what is the reason?

After you make your prediction in each case, you will configure the three IP addresses to see how the router reacts. The IP addresses to consider for this lab are as follows in Table 1.

Table 1   IP Address and Mask Reference

Address	Mask	Rejected? If so, why?
172.19.255.0	255.255.255.224	
172.19.255.0	255.255.254.0	
172.18.18.255	255.255.254.0	

Topology

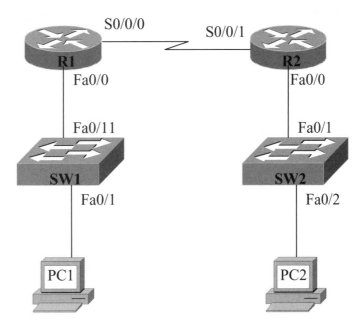

Figure 1   Topology for IP Address Configuration

Detailed Lab Steps

Step 1.   Connect to R1 from the simulator user interface. All passwords are **cs**.

Step 2.   Enter privileged exec ("enable") mode by issuing the **enable** command.

Step 3.   Examine the first of the three IP addresses and masks in the table at the beginning of this lab. Consider whether it is a valid unicast IP address and therefore will not be rejected when configured on a router interface. If you think of a reason for this address/mask pair to be rejected, note those reasons on the following lines. In particular, check to ensure that

- The address is in the range of class A, B, and C addresses

- The address is not the subnet ID or subnet broadcast address of its subnet

_____

_____

Step 4.   Repeat the previous step for both the second and third rows of the table, taking notes on the following lines.

_____

_____

Step 5.   Enter global configuration mode using the **configure terminal** command.

Step 6.   Configure the FastEthernet0/0 interface by issuing the **interface fa0/0** command.

Step 7. Set the IP address and mask for the first entry in the table at the beginning of this lab using the **ip address 172.19.255.0 255.255.255.224** command. Is the command rejected? If so, what does the error message tell you about the reason?

_____

_____

Step 8. Set the IP address and mask for the second entry in the table at the beginning of this lab. Record that IP address/mask on the following line. Is the command rejected? If so, what does the error message tell you about the reason?

_____

_____

Step 9. Set the IP address and mask for the last entry in the table at the beginning of this lab. Record that IP address/mask on the following line. Is the command rejected? If so, what does the error message tell you about the reason?

_____

_____

Hints and Answers

Table 2 lists hints and tips for any lab steps that do not supply all the details in the lab step, and for lab steps that ask questions about the lab.

Table 2   Hints

Step	Hint
3	Class A addresses begin with a first octet of 1 through 126, inclusive. Class B addresses begin with 128 through 191, and class C addresses begin with 192 through 223.
7	Use the **ip address 172.19.255.0 255.255.255.224** interface subcommand. In this case, number 172.19.255.0, when using mask 255.255.255.224, is a subnet ID. Router R1 rejects this **ip address** command as a result.
8	The number 172.19.255.0, with mask 255.255.254.0, is a valid IP address. It is in a subnet whose subnet ID is 172.19.254.0 with subnet broadcast address 172.19.255.255.
9	The number 172.18.18.255, with mask 255.255.254.0, is a valid IP address. It is in a subnet whose subnet ID is 172.18.18.0 with subnet broadcast address 172.18.19.255.

Configuration Steps

Example 1 shows a sample of the lab exercise being completed from R1's CLI.

Example 1 Example of Performing This Lab

```
(Press enter)
Password: cs
R1> enable
Password: cs
R1#
R1# configure terminal
R1(config)# interface Fastethernet0/0
R1(config-if)# ip address 172.19.255.0 255.255.255.224
Bad mask /27 for address 172.19.255.0
R1(config-if)# ip address 172.19.255.0 255.255.254.0
R1(config-if)# ip address 172.18.18.255 255.255.254.0
R1(config-if)# end
R1#
```

ICND1 Subnetting Exercises

Part 2: IP Address Rejection

Lab 10: IP Address Rejection X

Overview

In this exercise, you begin by examining three IP addresses and masks. Each pair is a candidate to be configured on Router R1's FastEthernet0/0 interface. The question: Will R1 reject the IP address/mask combination as invalid for some reason? If rejected, what is the reason?

After you make your prediction in each case, you will configure the three IP addresses to see how the router reacts. The IP addresses to consider for this lab are as follows in Table 1.

Table 1   IP Address and Mask Reference

Address	Mask	Rejected? If so, why?
10.10.10.10	255.255.255.252	
11.11.11.11	255.255.255.252	
12.12.12.12	255.255.255.252	

Topology

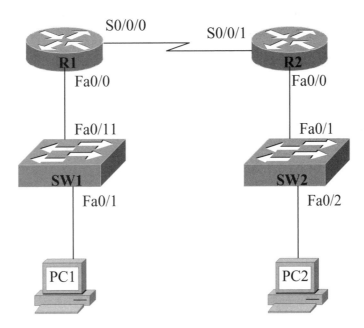

Figure 1   Topology for IP Address Configuration

Detailed Lab Steps

Step 1.   Connect to R1 from the simulator user interface. All passwords are **cs**.

Step 2.   Enter privileged exec ("enable") mode by issuing the **enable** command.

Step 3.   Examine the first of the three IP addresses and masks in the table at the beginning of this lab. Consider whether it is a valid unicast IP address and therefore will not be rejected when configured on a router interface. If you think of a reason for this address/mask pair to be rejected, note those reasons on the following lines. In particular, check to ensure that

- The address is in the range of class A, B, and C addresses

- The address is not the subnet ID or subnet broadcast address of its subnet

_____

_____

Step 4.   Repeat the previous step for both the second and third rows of the table, taking notes on the following lines.

_____

_____

Step 5.   Enter global configuration mode using the **configure terminal** command.

Step 6.   Configure the FastEthernet0/0 interface by issuing the **interface fa0/0** command.

Step 7. Set the IP address and mask for the first entry in the table at the beginning of this lab using the **ip address 10.10.10.10 255.255.255.252** command. Is the command rejected? If so, what does the error message tell you about the reason?

_____

_____

Step 8. Set the IP address and mask for the second entry in the table at the beginning of this lab. Record that IP address/mask on the following line. Is the command rejected? If so, what does the error message tell you about the reason?

_____

_____

Step 9. Set the IP address and mask for the last entry in the table at the beginning of this lab. Record that IP address/mask on the following line. Is the command rejected? If so, what does the error message tell you about the reason?

_____

_____

Hints and Answers

Table 2 lists hints and tips for any lab steps that do not supply all the details in the lab step, and for lab steps that ask questions about the lab.

Table 2   Hints

Step	Hint
3	Class A addresses begin with a first octet of 1 through 126, inclusive. Class B addresses begin with 128 through 191, and class C addresses begin with 192 through 223.
7	The number 10.10.10.10, with mask 255.255.255.252, is a valid IP address. It is in a subnet whose subnet ID is 10.10.10.8 with subnet broadcast address 10.10.10.11.
8	Use the **ip address 11.11.11.11 255.255.255.252** interface subcommand. In this case, the number 11.11.11.11, when using mask 255.255.255.252, is a subnet broadcast address in a subnet with subnet ID 11.11.11.8. Router R1 rejects this **ip address** command because the subnet broadcast address cannot be used as an interface IP address.
9	Use the **ip address 12.12.12.12 255.255.255.252** interface subcommand. In this case, number 12.12.12.12, when using mask 255.255.255.252, is a subnet ID. Router R1 rejects this **ip address** command as a result.

Configuration Steps

Example 1 shows a sample of the lab exercise being completed from R1's CLI.

Example 1   Example of Performing This Lab

```
(Press enter)
Password: cs
R1> enable
Password: cs
R1#
R1# configure terminal
R1(config)# interface Fastethernet0/0
R1(config-if)# ip address 10.10.10.10 255.255.255.252
R1(config-if)# ip address 11.11.11.11 255.255.255.252
Bad mask /30 for address 11.11.11.11
R1(config-if)# ip address 12.12.12.12 255.255.255.252
Bad mask /30 for address 12.12.12.12
R1(config-if)# end
R1#
```

ICND1 Subnetting Exercises

Part 2: IP Address Rejection

Lab 11: IP Address Rejection XI

Overview

In this exercise, you begin by examining three IP addresses and masks. Each pair is a candidate to be configured on Router R1's FastEthernet0/0 interface. The question: Will R1 reject the IP address/mask combination as invalid for some reason? If rejected, what is the reason?

After you make your prediction in each case, you will configure the three IP addresses to see how the router reacts. The IP addresses to consider for this lab are as follows in Table 1.

Table 1   **IP Address and Mask Reference**

Address	Mask	Rejected? If so, why?
210.210.210.210	255.255.255.128	
220.220.220.220	255.255.255.192	
230.230.230.230	255.255.255.224	

Topology

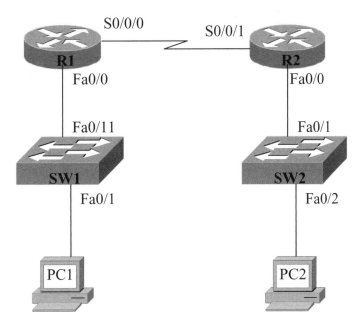

Figure 1   Topology for IP Address Configuration

Detailed Lab Steps

Step 1.   Connect to R1 from the simulator user interface. All passwords are **cs**.

Step 2.   Enter privileged exec ("enable") mode by issuing the **enable** command.

Step 3.   Examine the first of the three IP addresses and masks in the table at the beginning of this lab. Consider whether it is a valid unicast IP address and therefore will not be rejected when configured on a router interface. If you think of a reason for this address/mask pair to be rejected, note those reasons on the following lines. In particular, check to ensure that

- The address is in the range of class A, B, and C addresses

- The address is not the subnet ID or subnet broadcast address of its subnet

_____

_____

Step 4.   Repeat the previous step for both the second and third rows of the table, taking notes on the following lines.

_____

_____

Step 5.   Enter global configuration mode using the **configure terminal** command.

Step 6.   Configure the FastEthernet0/0 interface by issuing the **interface fa0/0** command.

Step 7. Set the IP address and mask for the first entry in the table at the beginning of this lab using the **ip address 210.210.210.210 255.255.255.128** command. Is the command rejected? If so, what does the error message tell you about the reason?

_____

_____

Step 8. Set the IP address and mask for the second entry in the table at the beginning of this lab. Record that IP address/mask on the following line. Is the command rejected? If so, what does the error message tell you about the reason?

_____

_____

Step 9. Set the IP address and mask for the last entry in the table at the beginning of this lab. Record that IP address/mask on the following line. Is the command rejected? If so, what does the error message tell you about the reason?

_____

_____

Hints and Answers

Table 2 lists hints and tips for any lab steps that do not supply all the details in the lab step, and for lab steps that ask questions about the lab.

Table 2   Hints

Step	Hint
3	Class A addresses begin with a first octet of 1 through 126, inclusive. Class B addresses begin with 128 through 191, and class C addresses begin with 192 through 223.
7	The number 210.210.210.210, with mask 255.255.255.128, is a valid IP address. It is in a subnet whose subnet ID is 210.210.210.128 with subnet broadcast address 210.210.210.255.
8	The number 220.220.220.220, with mask 255.255.255.192, is a valid IP address. It is in a subnet whose subnet ID is 220.220.220.192 with subnet broadcast address 220.220.220.255.
9	In this case, the number 230.230.230.230 is illegal as an IP address to be assigned to an interface because the first octet is 230. Addresses that begin with 224 through 239 are class D multicast IP addresses; these addresses cannot be assigned as unicast IP addresses.

Configuration Steps

Example 1 shows a sample of the lab exercise being completed from R1's CLI.

Example 1   Example of Performing This Lab

```
(Press enter)
Password: cs
R1> enable
Password: cs
R1#
R1# configure terminal
R1(config)# interface Fastethernet0/0
R1(config-if)# ip address 210.210.210.210 255.255.255.128
R1(config-if)# ip address 220.220.220.220 255.255.255.192
R1(config-if)# ip address 230.230.230.230 255.255.255.224
Not a valid host address - 230.230.230.230
R1(config-if)# end
R1#
```

Configuration Labs

Part 1: Router Configuration

Lab 2: Configuring Static Routes

Overview

The overall objective of this lab is to configure static routes on two routers so that there is a network connection between the computers in the two LANs. You will have to configure the computer's IP address, the gateway address, and the IP addresses for the appropriate router interfaces. This will require that the serial connection between routers be configured and enabled. In addition, you will configure static routing between the two networks.

Topology

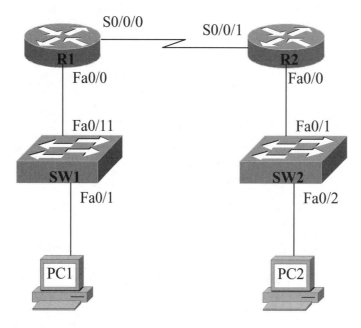

Figure 1   **Network Topology for This Lab**

Reference

The following simulator exercises provided with the CCNA 640-802 Network Simulator should be reviewed prior to starting this virtual laboratory exercise:

- Examining the IP Routing Table

- Using debug

- Connected Routes

- Testing Using Pings with Host Names

- Static Routes I–IV

- Default Routes

Key Concepts

The following concepts, terms, commands, and steps should have been mastered in this laboratory exercise. Verify your understanding of the material before taking the lab quiz.

- How to set the clock rate for the router.

- Which router controls the clock rate, DCE, or DTE?

- How to configure the IP address, subnet mask, and default gateway for the computers in your LAN.

- How is the gateway address for your LAN router configured?

- The steps for configuring the host name for your router.

- The steps for configuring the router interface's IP addresses and subnet masks.

- The commands for configuring a static route from your LAN router to the adjacent LAN router.

- List two commands that can be used to verify that the routes are configured on the router.

- Use the computers in your LAN to ping the computers in the adjacent LAN.

- Use the proper command on the router to trace the route from your router to a host in the other LAN.

- Use the router command that displays the network routes stored in your router's routing table.

- Use the command to save your router configuration to NVRAM.

- What command is used to verify the routing protocol being used? What are two commands that can be used to display the routing protocol?

Reference Tables

Table 1 provides the IP addresses and masks necessary for all interfaces used to complete this lab.

Table 1   Computer IP Addresses, Subnet Masks, and Gateway Addresses for Lab 2

Computer/Interface - R1	IP Address	Subnet Mask	Gateway Address
PC1	192.168.20.1	255.255.255.0	192.168.20.250
R1-Fa0/0	192.168.20.250	255.255.255.0	—
R1-S0/0/0	10.10.100.1	255.255.255.0	—

Computer/Interface – R2	IP Address	Subnet Mask	Gateway Address
PC2	172.16.75.65	255.255.255.0	172.16.75.250
R2-Fa0/0	172.16.75.250	255.255.255.0	—
R2-S0/0/1	10.10.100.2	255.255.255.0	—

Detailed Lab Steps

Task 1

Configure a static route to the adjacent LAN, LAN-A to LAN-B. Use the IP addresses provided in Table 1. You will be asked to verify that the computers in your LAN can ping the neighbor LAN. Note that a serial interface is being used to interconnect the LANs. You are configuring routing for both 192.168.20.0 and 172.16.75.0 networks. A subnet mask of 255.255.255.0 is being used. Use 1536000 for the clock rate on the serial link (DCE interface).

Step 1. Configure the gateway address for your LAN routers (R1 and R2) according to the addresses provided in Table 1. You will also need to enable the interfaces. List the commands used to configure the IP addresses and the subnet mask for your gateway, and list the command used to enable the interface.

_____

_____

Step 2. Configure the host name for your routers; R1 should be renamed LAN-A and R2 should be renamed LAN-B. List the router prompts and commands used to configure the router's host name.

_____

_____

Step 3. Configure the router interface's serial IP addresses and subnet masks according to the addresses specified in Table 1. Use the proper command to verify that the interfaces are properly configured. Set the clock rate on the serial interface interconnecting the two routers to 1536000. List the prompts and the commands used to accomplish this task.

_____

_____

_____

Step 4. Configure static routes from the LAN-A router to the LAN-B router and from LAN-B router back to the LAN-A router. Use two commands to verify that the routes are configured. List the commands used.

_____

_____

_____

Step 5. What does the statement "Gateway of last resort is not set" mean?

_____

_____

_____

Step 6. Use the computers in each LAN to ping the computers in the adjacent LAN.

_____

_____

_____

Step 7. Use the proper command to trace the route from a PC in LAN-A to a host in LAN-B. Your trace should pass through two routers. List the command used and record the trace information. How may hops did you record?

_____

_____

_____

Step 8. Use the command to open Telnet connectivity to the LAN-A router. Set the VTY password to ciscopress and enable remote login. List the commands used to establish the Telnet connection.

_____

_____

_____

Step 9. Use the router command that lists the network routes stored in the LAN-A router's routing table. List the routes. Are all the routes defined for your network?

_____

_____

_____

Step 10. Use the command to save your router configuration to the startup configuration. What command did you use? Use the proper command to verify that the configuration has been saved to NVRAM. What command did you use?

_____

_____

_____

Step 11. What command is used to verify the routing protocol being used? List two router commands.

_____

_____

_____

Task 2

Observe the following status and protocol states for the serial interfaces. If the routers are properly configured, explain what could cause the following conditions.

1. Serial 0/0/0 is up, line protocol is up

_____

_____

_____

2. Serial 0/0/0 is down, line protocol is down (DTE mode)

_____

_____

_____

3. Serial 0/0/0 is up, line protocol is down (DTE mode)

_____

_____

_____

4. Serial 0/0/0 is up, line protocol is down (DCE mode)

_____

_____

_____

5. Serial 0/0/0 is administratively down, line protocol is down

_____

_____

_____

Task 3: Configuration List

In this task you are to issue the **show running-configuration** command from the LANA# prompt.

The following is a partial list of the items displayed when you issue the **show running-configuration [sh run]** command. Your task is to define each item and its purpose. You might need to go to the Cisco website (http://www.cisco.com) and look up what each of these commands means.

1. no service password-encryption

_____

_____

_____

2. **boot-start-marker**

_____

_____

_____

3. **boot-end-marker**

_____

_____

_____

4. **enable secret 5 1KXED$S08d)zG3x3aiaeFjy7nCP**

_____

_____

_____

5. **no aaa new-model**

_____

_____

_____

6. **resource policy**

_____

_____

_____

Overview

The overall objective of this lab is to configure Routing Information Protocol (RIP) routing between two routers so that there is a routed network connection between computers in the two LANs. You will have to configure the computer's IP address, the gateway address, and the IP addresses for the appropriate router interfaces. This will require that the serial connection between routers be configured and enabled.

Topology

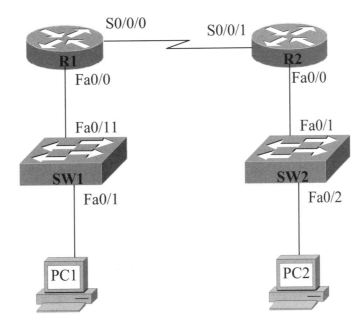

Figure 1   Network Topology for This Lab

Reference

The following simulator exercises provided with the CCNA 640-802 Network Simulator should be reviewed prior to starting this virtual laboratory exercise:

- RIP-2 Configuration I, II
- RIP Configuration I–VI
- RIP Auto-summary
- RIP Verification I
- Examining the IP Routing Table

Key Concepts

The following concepts, terms, commands, and steps should have been mastered in this laboratory exercise:

- How to set the clock rate for the router.
- Which router controls the clock rate, DCE, or DTE?
- How to configure the IP address, subnet mask, and default gateway for the computers in your LAN.
- How is the gateway address for your LAN router configured?
- The steps for configuring the host name for your router.
- The steps for configuring the router interface's IP addresses and subnet masks.
- The commands for configuring RIP routing from LAN-A to LAN-B.
- Two commands that can be used to verify that the routes are configured on the router.
- The steps to use the computers in your LAN to ping the computers in the adjacent LAN.
- Use the proper command to trace the route from a PC in LAN-A to the host in the connected LAN-B.
- Use the proper command to trace the route from your router in LAN-A to the host computer in LAN-B.
- Use the command to make a Telnet connection to your router. Know the steps to enable a Telnet connection to the router.
- Use the router command that displays the network routes stored in your router's routing table.
- Use the command to save your router configuration to NVRAM.

Reference Tables

Table 1 provides the IP addresses and masks of all necessary interfaces used to complete the lab.

Table 1   **Computer IP Addresses, Subnet Masks, and Gateway Addresses for Lab 3**

Computer/Interface - R1	IP Address	Subnet Mask	Gateway Address
PC1	10.10.12.1	255.255.255.0	10.10.12.250
R1-Fa0/0	10.10.12.250	255.255.255.0	—
R1-S0/0/0	10.20.200.1	255.255.255.0	—

Computer/Interface – R2	IP Address	Subnet Mask	Gateway Address
PC2	10.10.30.65	255.255.255.0	10.10.30.250
R2-Fa0/0	10.10.30.250	255.255.255.0	—
R2-S0/0/1	10.20.200.2	255.255.255.0	—

Detailed Lab Steps

Task 1

In this lab, you will configure a RIP V2 to the adjacent LANs, LAN-A to LAN-B, based on the network topology provided in Figure 1. You are to use the IP addresses provided in Table 1. You will be asked to verify that computers in your LAN can ping the neighbor LAN. You are configuring routing for both 10.10.12.0 and 10.10.30.0 networks. A subnet mask of 255.255.255.0 is being used. Note that a serial interface is being used to interconnect the LANs. Use 56000 for the clock rate on the serial link (DCE interface). The enable secret and line console 0 password should be set to **ciscopress**.

Step 1.   Configure the gateway address for your LAN routers according to the addresses listed in Table 1. List the prompts and the commands used to configure the gateway address and subnet mask on each of the routers.

Step 2.   Configure the host name for your routers; R1 should be renamed LAN-A and R2 should be renamed LAN-B. List the router prompts and commands used to configure the router's host name.

Step 3. Configure the routers' interfaces and include any relevant interface-specific commands and associated IP addresses and enable each of them; for this lab R1's S0/0/0 interface is the DCE with a rate of 56,000 kbps. Use the proper command to verify that the interfaces are properly configured. List the router prompts and commands used to accomplish this task.

_____

_____

_____

Step 4. Configure a RIP V2 route for both the LAN-A and LAN-B routers. Use two commands to verify that the routes are configured. List the router prompts and commands used to accomplish this.

_____

_____

_____

Step 5. Use the computers in each LAN to ping the computers in the adjacent LAN, PC1-PC2, and PC2-PC1. List the router prompts and commands used to accomplish this.

_____

_____

_____

Step 6. Use the proper command to trace the route from a PC in LAN-A to a host in LAN-B. Your trace should pass through two routers. List the router prompts and commands used and record the trace information. How may hops did you record?

_____

_____

_____

Step 7. Use the command to make a Telnet connection from the LAN-A router to the LAN-B router. Set the VTY password to **ciscopress** on the LAN-B router and enable remote login. List the prompts and the commands used to establish the Telnet connection. What IP address did you use? Repeat this so that a Telnet connection is established from the LAN-B router to the LAN-A router.

_____

_____

_____

Step 8. Use the router command that lists the network routes stored in the LAN-A router's routing table. List the prompts, the commands used, and the available routes. Are all the routes defined for your network? What does the statement "Gateway of last resort is not set" mean?

_____

_____

_____

Step 9. Use the command to save your router configuration to the startup configuration on the LAN-A router. What command did you use? Use the proper command to verify that the configuration has been saved to NVRAM. What command did you use?

_____

_____

_____

Task 2

In this task, you are to observe the status and protocol states for the FastEthernet interfaces provided and determine whether the routers are properly configured. Then explain what could cause the following conditions:

1.

```
Interface          status                 protocol
fastethernet 0/0   up                     up
```

_____

_____

_____

2.

```
Interface          status                 protocol
fastethernet 0/0   administratively down  down
```

_____

_____

_____

3.

```
Interface            status                protocol
fastethernet 0/0     administratively down up
```

_____

_____

_____

4.

```
Interface            status                protocol
fastethernet 0/0     down                  down
```

_____

_____

_____

Task 3: Configuration List

The following is a partial list of the items displayed when you issue the **show running-configuration [sh run]** command on a router. Your task is to define each item and its purpose. You might need to go to the Cisco website (http://www.cisco.com) and look up what each of these commands means.

1. **interface FastEthernet 0/0**

   What does 0/0 indicate? What is the difference between FastEthernet and Ethernet?

   _____

   _____

   _____

2. **ip address 10.10.20.0   255.255.255.224**

   How many host IP addresses are available in each subnet using this subnet mask?

   _____

   _____

3. **shutdown**

   What is the purpose of this command when it is applied to an interface?

   _____

   _____

   _____

4. **router rip**

What is the purpose of this command, and from what prompt is this command issued?

_____

_____

_____

5. **version 2**

What is the purpose of using this command, and from what prompt is this command issued?

_____

_____

_____

6. **network 10.0.0.0**

What is the purpose of this command, and from what prompt is this command issued?

_____

_____

_____

7. **ip http server**

What is the purpose of this command, and from what prompt is this command issued?

_____

_____

_____

8. **no ip http secure-server**

What is the purpose of using this command, and from what prompt is this command issued?

_____

_____

_____

IP Troubleshooting and EIGRP

Table 5-1 lists the labs for this unit. Check with your instructor or class syllabus to confirm what labs you should perform for class.

Table 5-1   Unit 5 Labs

Date	ICND1/ ICND2	Type	Part	Number	Name	Page
	ICND1	TS	1	6	IP Addressing and Routing	193
	ICND2	SB	3	1	EIGRP Serial Configuration I	204
	ICND2	SB	3	2	EIGRP Serial Configuration II	207
	ICND2	SB	3	12	EIGRP Route Tuning I	210
	ICND2	SB	3	16	EIGRP Neighbors I	213
	ICND2	CS	3	5	EIGRP Serial Configuration I	215
	Ungraded	CL	1	5	Configuring EIGRP Routing	226

ICND1 Troubleshooting Scenarios

Lab 6: IP Addressing and Routing

Overview

This lab uses a scenario in which you just took a job with a new company and are placed on a project that was recently planned and implemented. However, the internetwork is having some problems, and it is your job to solve the problems.

The network designer tried to be logical when planning the addressing and other details. Figure 1 shows the topology, along with the intended subnets. The design engineer has confirmed that the details in the figure are correct. Additionally, the following list details the conventions that the network design engineer would like to follow:

1. Routers are assigned the numerically smallest IP addresses in the respective subnets.

2. Hosts are assigned the numerically largest IP addresses in the respective subnets.

3. When assigning multiple router addresses in one subnet, the IP addresses should be given to the lowest-numbered device based on its hostname—for example, on serial links, R1 should be assigned IP addresses before R2, and R2 before R3.

4. RIP version 2 should be used on all routers.

5. PPP must be used on the R1-R3 serial link with default data link protocols on all other router interfaces.

> **Note:** You can find the problems in this lab by examining the configuration and looking for errors. In fact, for simulator questions on the exams, this strategy may be your fastest option. However, to practice for sim-let questions, which typically do not allow you to look at the configuration, you should purposefully avoid looking at the configuration, instead using other exec commands.

Topology

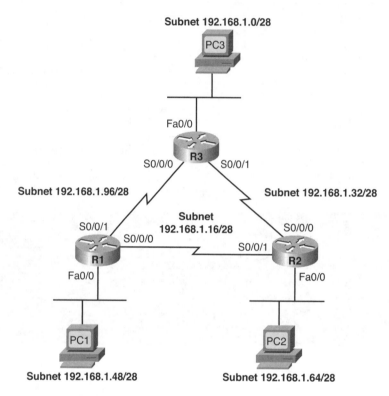

Figure 1   Network Topology for This Lab

Reference Tables

There are three root causes to the symptoms and issues you should find in this lab. Use the router and PC command lines to issue commands and find the problem symptoms, and record those symptoms in Table 1. Once you have found each of the root causes, record those in Table 2, along with the actions you took to fix the problem.

> **Note:** If you try to solve the problems without reading the specific lab steps, follow this convention when more than one solution exists for a single root cause: Change the lower-numbered device's configuration. If the change could be made on a router or PC with the same number, change the router.

Table 1   IP Addressing Reference (Planned)

Device	Interface	IP Address	Mask	Default Gateway
R1	S0/0/0			N/A
	S0/0/1			N/A
	Fa0/0			N/A
R2	S0/0/0			N/A
	S0/0/1			N/A
	Fa0/0			N/A
R3	S0/0/0			N/A
	S0/0/1			N/A
	Fa0/0			N/A
PC1	E0			
PC2	E0			
PC3	E0			

Table 2   Convenient Place to Record Root Causes and Solutions

Issue	Root Cause	Solution
1	_____	_____
	_____	_____
	_____	_____
	_____	_____
	_____	_____
	_____	_____
	_____	_____
2	_____	_____
	_____	_____
	_____	_____
	_____	_____
	_____	_____
	_____	_____

continues

Table 2   **Convenient Place to Record Root Causes and Solutions**   *continued*

Issue	Root Cause	Solution
3	_____	_____
	_____	_____
	_____	_____
	_____	_____
	_____	_____
	_____	_____

Detailed Lab Steps

You may perform this lab while ignoring all the detailed steps in this lab. The introductory material earlier in this lab gives you enough information to enable you to start testing with **ping** and **traceroute** commands and then work to discover why certain devices cannot ping each other. By following that general process, you should discover the three problems that exist at the beginning of this lab.

If you would like more guidance, follow the steps in this section. Regardless, the list of problems is included at the end of this lab.

Part 1 of the detailed lab steps provides a general inspection of what can and cannot be pinged from different locations in the internetwork. Parts 2, 3, and 4 each uncover one of the root causes that exist currently.

Note: All passwords are **ciscopress** unless otherwise noted.

Part 1: Ping All Devices from R1

You can start by pinging all IP addresses from one device. In this case, start with router R1.

Step 1.   Referring to Figure 1 and the network design information listed at the beginning of this lab, predict the IP addresses, masks, and default gateways assigned to the various router and PC interfaces. Record the values in Table 1 for reference.

Step 2.   From the simulator user interface, connect to router R1 and move into enable mode.

Step 3.   Use the **ping** command to test R1's ability to send packets to each IP address in Table 3. On the lines below, note the IP addresses that cannot be pinged. Also note which devices (and router interfaces, if the device is a router) use the addresses that cannot be pinged.

_____

_____

_____

Step 4. Connect to the devices that could not be pinged and verify that the correct IP addresses are configured. Record any devices whose IP addresses are incorrect.

_____

_____

_____

_____

Note: The simulator does not simulate cabling problems—all cables are in place and physically able to work.

Step 5. Step 3 may reveal that R1 could not ping some other routers' interfaces. Connect to each of those routers from the simulator user interface and examine the interface status for the interfaces that could not be pinged in Step 3. If the interface status is not "up and up," look for reasons why the interface is not up. Record any interface problems you have noticed. (Remember, it may be better for exam preparation to avoid looking at the configuration for now.)

_____

_____

_____

_____

Step 6. Repeat Steps 2, 3, and 4 from R2 and R3 to discover any problems pinging from those locations, and record your notes on the following lines.

_____

_____

_____

_____

Part 2: Investigate Why Some Pings of PC3 Did Not Work

Part 1 should have uncovered that many of the pings to PC3 fail. The testing should have shown that a ping of PC3 from R3 should work, but a ping to PC3 from other devices fails. In this part, you will look further at why R1 cannot ping PC3.

Step 7.   Connect to router R1 from the simulator user interface and use the **traceroute** command to determine the route taken when R1 sends packets to PC3. Record the last device listed in the output of the **traceroute** command output.

_____

_____

_____

_____

Step 8.   Compare the IP address found in the **traceroute** command in the previous step to Table 1 to find which device and which interface has been assigned that IP address. Whose IP address is it?

_____

Step 9.   Telnet to the IP address found in the previous step and use the **ping** and **traceroute** commands to test R3's connectivity to PC3. Do the commands show that R3 can send and receive packets with PC3?

_____

_____

The last few steps have shown that the forward route from R1 to PC3 actually works—R1 can deliver the packets to R3, which can in turn send them to PC3. The reason the **traceroute 192.168.1.14** command on R1 fails is that a problem exists with the reverse route from PC3 back to R1. The next few steps examine the reverse route from PC3 back to R1 to show that problem.

When the **ping 192.168.1.14** command was used on R1, R1 had to pick an IP address to use as the source of those packets. By default, routers pick the IP address of the outgoing interface used when forwarding the packet.

Step 10.   To find the IP address R1 currently uses when pinging PC3, first exit from your Telnet connection to R3 to move back to R1. Then use the **show ip route 192.168.1.14** command, which lists R1's route currently used when forwarding packets to 192.168.1.14. Look for the outgoing interface for this route and record that outgoing interface on the lines below.

_____

Step 11.   Record the IP address associated with R1's outgoing interface in the route examined in the previous step.

_____

Step 12.   From the simulator user interface, move to PC3 and ping R1's IP address recorded in the previous step. Does it work?

_____

_____

Step 13. From PC3, use the **tracert** command to find how far along the route the packets go before the next device cannot route the packet. What device IP addresses are listed in the output?

_____

_____

Step 14. Examine the default gateway setting on PC3 and confirm whether PC3 can ping the default gateway IP address. Record the IP address listed as PC3's default gateway as well.

_____

Step 15. Connect to R3 and confirm that R3's LAN IP address is the same address as configured for PC3's default gateway. Are they the same?

_____

Step 16. You have just found the first of three problems in this lab exercise. Record notes in Table 2 regarding the problem and the solution. Then go to PC3 and change its default gateway setting to 192.168.1.1 using the **gateway 192.168.1.1** command.

Part 3: General Examination of the IP Routing Table

This part uncovers an implementation error that is not uncovered by pinging other devices.

Step 17. From the network diagram and planning information, predict the IP subnets that you expect to see in the IP routing tables of the various routers. Take notes regarding the number of subnets and subnet numbers.

_____

_____

_____

_____

_____

_____

Step 18. On all three routers, use the **show ip route** command to discover which routes are known on each router. Note any missing or extra subnets for each router. Also, explain the presence of any subnets with a /32 prefix length.

_____

_____

_____

_____

One of the subnets in the previous step, 192.168.1.64/27, does not match the planning diagram shown in Figure 1. The planning diagram shows 192.168.1.64/28 off R2's Fa0/0 interface.

Step 19. Move to R2 using the simulator user interface and use the **show interfaces**, **show running-config**, and **show ip route** commands to confirm whether the IP address and mask have been configured correctly on R2. What IP address/mask is configured for R2's Fa0/0 interface?

_____

Step 20. The previous step should have uncovered the second of the three root causes of problems for this lab. Record the root cause in Table 2, along with your intended solution. Then fix the problem using the simulator.

Part 4: Examining An Extra Long Route

This final part of this lab examines a problem in which packets between PC1 and PC2 take the long route through R3.

Step 21. Connect to PC1 from the simulator user interface and ping PC2's IP address. Does the ping work?

_____

Step 22. Trace the route from PC1 to PC2. List the IP addresses from this command's output. Comparing these addresses to Table 1, what routers forward this packet?

_____

_____

Step 23. Move to router R1 from the simulator user interface and use the **show ip route 192.168.1.78** command to display the route R1 will use when forwarding packets to 192.168.1.78. What is the outgoing interface and next-hop IP address? Which router is the next-hop router?

_____

_____

Step 24. Use the **show ip protocols** command to display information about RIP on router R1. Look at the routing information sources. Which IP addresses are listed? Which routers use those IP addresses?

_____

_____

At this point, it appears that R2 is not sending routing updates to R1 over the R1-R2 serial link. The next step will be to look at RIP on router R2.

Step 25. From the simulator user interface, move to router R2 and enter enable mode.

Step 26. Use the **show ip protocols** command to display information about RIP on router R2. Look at the routing information sources. Which IP addresses are listed? Which routers use those IP addresses?

_____

_____

Step 27. Continue looking at the **show ip protocol** command output. Do you see any information about passive interfaces? What is listed?

_____

_____

_____

_____

Step 28. Display R2's running configuration. Look for the RIP section. Does R2 have any configuration commands configured that would prevent R2 from advertising routes to R1?

_____

_____

Step 29. The previous step should have uncovered the third of the three root causes of problems for this lab. Record the root cause in Table 2, along with your intended solution. Then fix the problem using the simulator.

Hints and Answers

Table 3 is a completed version of Table 1. Table 4 lists a completed version of Table 2, listing the three problems that exist in this lab and their solutions. Table 5 provides hints and tips for any lab steps that do not supply complete details and provides answers for any lab steps that ask questions.

Table 3 IP Addressing Reference (Planned)

Device	Interface	IP Address	Mask	Default Gateway
R1	S0/0/0	192.168.1.17	255.255.255.240	N/A
	S0/0/1	192.168.1.97	255.255.255.240	N/A
	Fa0/0	192.168.1.49	255.255.255.240	N/A
R2	S0/0/0	192.168.1.33	255.255.255.240	N/A
	S0/0/1	192.168.1.18	255.255.255.240	N/A
	Fa0/0	192.168.1.65	255.255.255.240	N/A
R3	S0/0/0	192.168.1.98	255.255.255.240	N/A
	S0/0/1	192.168.1.34	255.255.255.240	N/A
	Fa0/0	192.168.1.1	255.255.255.240	N/A
PC1	E0	192.168.1.62	255.255.255.240	192.168.1.49
PC2	E0	192.168.1.78	255.255.255.240	192.168.1.65
PC3	E0	192.168.1.14	255.255.255.240	192.168.1.1

Table 4 The Three Problems and Their Solutions

Issue	Root Cause	Solution
1	PC3 had been configured with IP address 192.168.1.15 as its default gateway. However, R3's Fa0/0 interface was correctly configured as 192.168.1.1. Address 192.168.1.15 is actually the subnet broadcast address in that subnet.	Reconfigure PC3's default gateway setting to be 192.168.1.1 using the **gateway 192.168.1.1** command on PC3.
2	R2's Fa0/0 interface was configured with address 192.168.1.65, which was correct, but with mask 255.255.255.224, which was incorrect according to the planning diagram. However, there were no outward symptoms, because PC2's IP address was in this larger subnet, and PC2 pointed to R2's 192.168.1.65 IP address as the default gateway.	Reconfigure R2 with the **interface fa0/0** and **ip address 192.168.1.65 255.255.255.240** commands.
3	R2 has a **passive-interface Serial0/0/1** command configured. This command tells R2 to not send RIP updates out that interface. As a result, R1 didn't learn any routes directly from R2. However, R1 learned of R2's LAN subnet (192.168.1.64/28) from R3. This route caused R1 to forward packets sent by PC1 to PC2 to take the longer path through R3.	Configure R2 with the **router rip** and **no passive-interface S0/0/1** commands.

Table 5   Hints and Answers

Step	Hint or Answer
1	Refer to Table 3 for a completed version of Table 1.
2	Once in user mode, use the **enable** command to move to enable mode. The password for accessible devices is **ciscopress**.
3	The only ping that does not work should be the ping of PC3.
4	On routers, use the **show ip interface brief**, **show interfaces**, and **show running-config** commands; on PCs, use the **ipconfig /all** command.
5	Use the **show ip interface brief** and **show interfaces** commands.
6	Most of the pings from R2 work, with these exceptions: Pings to/from PC3 from R2. All the pings from R3 work.
7	192.168.1.98
8	The last IP address should be R3's S0/0/0 IP address, 192.168.1.98.
9	R3 can successfully ping PC3's IP address (192.168.1.14).
10	The route lists 192.168.1.0/28 as the destination with an outgoing interface of S0/0/1.
11	The IP address is 192.168.1.97, as can be seen with the **show interfaces S0/0/1** and **show running-config** commands. Note in particular that you are looking for R1's S0/0/1 IP address, not the next-hop address listed in the route in the previous step.
12	The **ping 192.168.1.97** command on PC3 fails.
13	The **tracert 192.168.1.97** command does not list any IP addresses at all. PC3's **tracert** command in the previous step should not list any devices, meaning that PC3 cannot currently forward packets to its default gateway.
14	PC3 cannot ping its current default gateway, 192.168.1.15.
15	Use the **ipconfig /all** command to display PC3's IP address and gateway IP address. R3's Fa0/0 IP address is 192.168.1.1.
16	See Table 4 for a description of each of the three problems in this lab and their solutions.
18	The R1-R3 link uses PPP, which causes PPP to then advertise a /32 route for each serial interface's IP address. The two /32 routes should list R1's S0/0/1 IP address of 192.168.1.97 and R3's S0/0/0 IP address of 192.168.1.98.
19	The mask is configured as 255.255.255.224, instead of 255.255.255.240.
20	See Table 4 for a description of each of the three problems in this lab and their solutions.
21	The **ping 192.168.1.78** command should work.
22	The output lists 192.168.1.49, 192.168.1.98, 192.168.1.33, and 192.168.1.78. According to these IP addresses, the packets going from PC1 to PC2 go through R1, then R3, and then R2.

continues

Table 5   **Hints and Answers**   *continued*

Step	Hint or Answer
23	The output lists an outgoing interface of S0/0/1, next-hop address 192.168.1.98, which is R3.
24	The output only lists 192.168.1.98 (R3). It does not list R2's 192.168.1.18 IP address.
26	The output lists 192.168.1.17 (R1) and 192.168.1.34 (R3).
27	The output lists S0/0/1 as a passive interface.
28	R2 has a **passive-interface Serial0/0/1** command configured.
29	See Table 4 for a description of each of the three problems in this lab and their solutions.

Configuration

Example 1 shows the configuration commands added to PC3 and R2 during this lab.

Example 1   Configuration on PC3 and R2 During This Lab

```
PC3 IP settings:
Def. GW: 192.168.1.1
_____

On R2:


interface Fa0/0
 ip address 192.168.1.65 255.255.255.240
!
router rip
 no passive-interface S0/0/1
```

ICND2 Skill Builders

Part 3: IP Routing Protocols

Lab 1: EIGRP Serial Configuration I

Overview

In this lab you will gain valuable experience configuring the EIGRP routing protocol. The topology consists of two routers. The R1 router is already configured with EIGRP, but the R2 router is not. Your task is to configure EIGRP on R2 and verify that networks are being learned on R2.

Topology

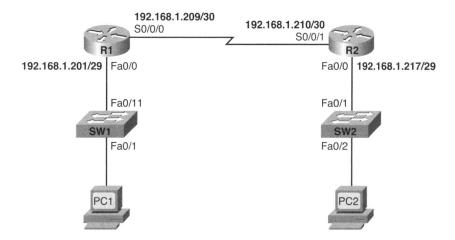

Figure 1   Network Topology for This Lab

Detailed Lab Steps

Step 1.   Log into R2 from the simulator user interface. Use the password **ciscopress**.

Step 2.   Enter privileged exec mode by issuing the **enable** command. Use the password **ciscopress**.

Step 3.   Issue the **show ip interface brief** command. Which interfaces are in an "up/up" state? Record those interfaces and their IP addresses on the lines below.

\
\
\

Step 4.   Enter global configuration mode by entering **configure terminal**.

Step 5.   Enter EIGRP configuration by entering **router eigrp 1**. What does the **1** represent in this command?

\
\
\

Step 6.   When in EIGRP subconfiguration mode, enter the **network 192.168.1.0** command. On which of R2's interfaces will this command enable EIGRP?

\
\
\

Step 7. With EIGRP configured, it is time to verify that router R2 is learning routes. Exit to the root of privileged exec mode by entering **end**.

Step 8. Verify your configuration by entering **show ip route**. Do you see any EIGRP-learned routes? What is the one-letter code for EIGRP routes listed on the far left of the output for that route?

_____

_____

_____

Step 9. Look at the output of the **show ip eigrp interfaces** command. Which interfaces are listed? Are these the same interfaces that you predicted in Step 6? Which interfaces show more than zero peers (neighbors)?

_____

_____

Hints and Answers

Table 1 provides hints and tips for any lab steps that do not supply complete details and provides answers for any lab steps that ask questions.

Table 1   **Hints and Answers**

Step	Hint or Answer
3	Interface S0/0/1 is up, with IP address 192.168.1.210. Fa0/0 also up, with IP address 192.168.1.217.
5	The **1** is the autonomous system number. This number must match the configured autonomous system number currently configured on R1.
6	This command activates EIGRP on Fa0/0 and S0/0/1 because both interfaces' IP addresses are part of Class C network 192.168.1.0. This causes R2 to begin advertising EIGRP routes and listening for EIGRP routes on those interfaces.
7	Alternatively, you could press **Ctrl-Z**.
8	If configured correctly, you should see the 192.168.1.200/29 subnet as an EIGRP route with letter "D" to the far left of the output.
9	The output lists interfaces S0/0/1 and Fa0/0, the same two interfaces that matched the **network 192.168.1.0** command in Step 6. The line for S0/0/1 lists one peer because R2 has formed a neighbor relationship with R1, which sits at the other end of the link connected to R2's S0/0/1 interface.

Configuration Steps

Example 1 shows a sample of the lab exercise being completed from R2.

Example 1   Example of Performing This Lab

```
R2#configure terminal
R2(config)#router eigrp 1
R2(config-router)#network 192.168.1.0
R2(config-router)#end
R2#
```

ICND2 Skill Builders

Part 3: IP Routing Protocols

Lab 2: EIGRP Serial Configuration II

Overview

In this lab, you will configure EIGRP in a case where a router connects to multiple classful networks. This will require you to determine what **network** statements should go into the configuration, configure those networks, and verify the configuration with the **show ip route** command.

Topology

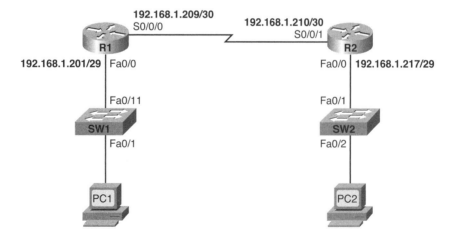

Figure 1   Network Topology for This Lab

Detailed Lab Steps

Step 1. Log into R2 from the simulator user interface. Use the password **ciscopress**.

Step 2. Enter privileged exec mode by issuing the **enable** command. Use the password **ciscopress**.

Step 3. Issue the **show ip interface brief** command. Which interfaces are in an "up/up" state? Record those interfaces and their IP addresses on the lines below.

_____

_____

_____

Step 4. Plan the EIGRP configuration's **network** command(s). To do so, write down the **network** command(s) you would configure to enable EIGRP on all of R2's interfaces that are both up and have an IP address configured. Record these commands on the lines below.

_____

_____

_____

Step 5. Enter global configuration mode by entering **configure terminal**.

Step 6. Enter EIGRP configuration by entering **router eigrp 1**. What does the **1** represent in this command?

_____

_____

_____

Step 7. While still in EIGRP subconfiguration mode, enter the **network 192.168.82.0** command. On which of R2's interfaces will this command enable EIGRP?

_____

Step 8. Enter the **network 172.16.0.0** command. On which of R2's interfaces will this command enable EIGRP?

_____

Step 9. With EIGRP configured, it is time to verify that router R2 is learning routes. Exit privileged exec mode by entering **end**.

Step 10. Verify your configuration by entering **show ip route**. Do you see any EIGRP-learned routes? What is the one-letter code for EIGRP routes listed on the far left of the output for that route?

_____

_____

Step 11. Look at the output of the **show ip eigrp interfaces** command. Which interfaces are listed? Are these the same interfaces that you predicted in Step 4? Which interfaces show more than zero peers (neighbors)?

_____

_____

Step 12. Examine the output of the **show ip eigrp neighbors** command. How many neighbors does R2 have? What IP address is listed as the neighbor? What device uses this IP address (according to Figure 1)?

_____

_____

Hints and Answers

Table 1 provides hints and tips for any lab steps that do not supply complete details and provides answers for any lab steps that ask questions.

Table 1   Hints and Answers

Step	Hint or Answer
3	Interface S0/0/1 is up, with IP address 192.168.82.10. Fa0/0 also up, with IP address 172.16.132.1.
4	Because R2 has interfaces in two different classful networks, R2 needs two different **network** commands. The commands are **network 192.168.82.0** **network 172.16.0.0**
6	The **1** is the autonomous system number. This number must match the configured autonomous system number currently configured on R1.
7	This command activates EIGRP on S0/0/1 because only S0/0/1 has an IP address in Class C network 192.168.82.0. This causes R2 to begin advertising EIGRP routes and listening for EIGRP routes on those interfaces.

continues

Table 1   Hints and Answers   *continued*

Step	Hint or Answer
8	This command activates EIGRP on Fa0/0 because only Fa0/0 has an IP address in Class B network 172.16.0.0.
9	Alternatively, you could press **Ctrl-Z**.
10	If configured correctly, you should see the 172.16.64.0/18 subnet as an EIGRP route with letter "D" to the far left of the output advertised from R1.
11	The output lists interfaces S0/0/1 and Fa0/0. The line for S0/0/1 lists one peer, because R2 has formed a neighbor relationship with R1, which sits at the other end of the link connected to R2's S0/0/1 interface.
12	R2 has a single neighbor, 192.168.82.9. According to Figure 1, this IP address is R1's S0/0/0 IP address.

Configuration Steps

Example 1 shows a sample of the lab exercise being completed from R2.

Example 1   Example of Performing This Lab

```
R2#configure terminal
R2(config)#router eigrp 1
R2(config-router)#network 192.168.82.0
R2(config-router)#network 172.16.0.0
R2(config-router)#end
R2#
```

ICND2 Skill Builders

Part 3: IP Routing Protocols

Lab 12: EIGRP Route Tuning I

Overview

This lab begins with a working internetwork, with valid IP addresses on all routers and PCs, and with EIGRP fully enabled on R1, R2, and R3. This lab guides you through a configuration utilizing EIGRP route tuning by influencing the bandwidth of the route that traffic takes. This lab then shows the resulting different route table.

Topology

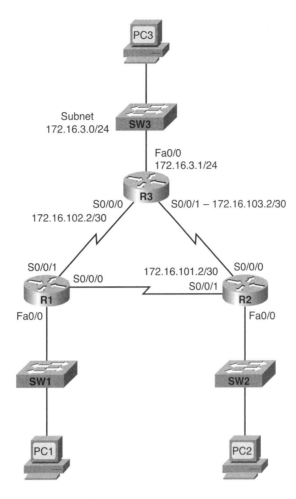

Figure 1   Network Topology for This Lab

Detailed Lab Steps

Step 1. Connect to R1 from the simulator user interface using the password **ciscopress**.

Step 2. Issue the **show ip route 172.16.3.1** command. Examine the output and note the outgoing interface and next-hop IP address listed for this route.

_____

_____

Step 3. Use the **show interfaces** command to display information about each of R1's interfaces. Note the current bandwidth settings on each interface.

_____

_____

The bandwidth setting on the other routers' serial interfaces has also defaulted to 1544 (kbps). Next, you will configure R1's S0/0/1 interface with a lower bandwidth, which makes the EIGRP metric through that direct path to R3 larger than the metric for the seemingly longer route through R2.

Step 4. Enter privileged exec mode using the **enable** command (password **ciscopress**) and then move to global configuration mode using the **configure terminal** command.

Step 5. Enter interface configuration mode for interface S0/0/1 by entering the **interface Se0/0/1** command.

Step 6. Lower the bandwidth configured to 10 kbps by entering the **bandwidth 10** command.

Step 7. Exit from configuration mode using the **end** command.

Step 8. Display the interface bandwidth of each interface again using the **show interfaces** command. What is the bandwidth setting on S0/0/1?

_____

_____

Step 9. Issue the **show ip route 172.16.3.1** command again. Just as you did in Step 2, examine the output and note the outgoing interface and next-hop IP address listed for this route. Is it the same route as before?

_____

_____

_____

Hints and Answers

Table 1 provides hints and tips for any lab steps that do not supply complete details and provides answers for any lab steps that ask questions.

Table 1   Hints and Answers

Step	Hint or Answer
2	The next-hop address is R3's S0/0/0 IP address of 172.16.102.2. The outgoing interface is R1's S0/0/1 interface.
3	S0/0/0 and S0/0/1 both have bandwidths of 1544, and the Fa0/0 lists 100,000. Both numbers represent the number of kilobits per second.
8	The bandwidth setting on S0/0/1 is now 10, meaning 10 Kbps.
9	The next-hop address is 172.16.101.2 (R2), with an outgoing interface of R1's S0/0/0 interface. The route has changed since Step 2, with the route now causing R1 to send packets destined to subnet 172.16.3.0/24 to R2 instead of to R3.

Configuration Steps

Example 1 shows a sample of the lab exercise being completed on R1's CLI.

Example 1   Example of Performing This Lab

```
R1#configure terminal
R1(config)#interface S0/0/1
R1(config-if)#bandwidth 10
R1(config-if)#end
R1#
```

ICND2 Skill Builders

Part 3: IP Routing Protocols

Lab 16: EIGRP Neighbors I

Overview

This lab begins with a working internetwork, with valid IP addresses on all routers and PCs, and with
EIGRP fully enabled on R1, R2, R3, and R4. This lab guides you through the manual configuration
of the EIGRP Hello timer on R1 and shows the affect on R1's EIGRP neighbors when it is changed.

Topology

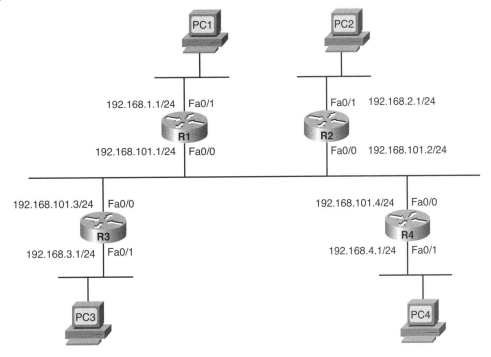

Figure 1   Network Topology for This Lab

Detailed Lab Steps

Step 1. Connect to R1 from the simulator user interface using the password **ciscopress**.

Step 2. View the existing EIGRP neighbor information by issuing the **show ip eigrp neighbors** command. Write down each neighbor's and how long each neighbor has been up. Also, compare the neighbor IP addresses to Figure 1 and determine which routers (R2, R3, and R4) are currently R1's EIGRP neighbors.

_____

_____

_____

Step 3. Enter privileged exec mode using the **enable** command (password **ciscopress**) and then move to global configuration mode using the **configure terminal** command.

Step 4. Enter Fa0/0 interface configuration mode by entering the **interface Fa0/0** command.

Step 5. Shut down the Fa0/0 interface by entering the **shutdown** command.

Step 6. Change the EIGRP Hello timer interval from 10 seconds to 30 seconds by entering the **ip hello-interval eigrp 10 30** command. Note that the number 10 represents the EIGRP AS number, as configured in the **router eigrp** command.

Step 7. Re-enable the Fa0/0 interface by entering the **no shutdown** command.

Step 8. Exit into enable mode by entering the **end** command.

Step 9. View the existing EIGRP neighbor information by issuing the **show ip eigrp neighbors** command. Are the same neighbors listed again?

_____

_____

_____

Step 10. Wait 10 seconds and then view the existing EIGRP neighbor information again by issuing the **show ip eigrp neighbors** command. Write down each neighbor and how long each has been up.

_____

_____

_____

Hints and Answers

Table 1 provides hints and tips for any lab steps that do not supply complete details and provides answers for any lab steps that ask questions.

Table 1   Hints and Answers

Step	Hint or Answer
2	R1's current EIGRP neighbors: 192.168.101.2 (R2) 192.168.101.3 (R3) 192.168.101.4 (R4)
9	All the same neighbors are listed again.
10	The neighbors do not have issues due to the Hello timer mismatch. The reason is that R1 advertises its Hello timer setting, and the neighbors then expect to receive Hello messages only from R1 on that interval.

Configuration Steps

Example 1 shows a sample of the lab exercise being completed from R1's CLI.

Example 1   Example of Performing This Lab

```
R1#configure terminal
R1(config)#interface Fa0/0
R1(config-if)#shutdown
R1(config-if)#ip hello-interval eigrp 10 30
R1(config-if)#no shutdown
R1(config-if)#end
```

ICND2 Configuration Scenarios
Part 3: IP Routing Protocols

Lab 5: EIGRP Serial Configuration I

Overview

Imagine that you just took a new job replacing another engineer that left the company unexpectedly right in the middle of a network implementation. Your new boss tells you that all the routers and PCs have been configured correctly with IP addresses, masks, and default gateways, but that the engineer left before enabling EIGRP on the routers. Your job is to become familiar with the internetwork and then enable EIGRP on all router interfaces.

Note: When auto-summary is enabled on a router that is on the boundary between multiple classful networks, that router's EIGRP process adds summary routes for those classful networks. Those summary routes have a destination of "null0". As a result, if there are not any more specific routes listed in the routing table, packets sent to destinations in those networks are discarded. This lab will generally ignore these summary null routes.

Reference Tables

For convenience, Table 1 provides a place to record the IP address, mask, and current state of the most important interfaces used in this lab. The specific lab instructions will direct you to find the information to complete this table.

Table 1   IP Address Table

Device	Interface	IP Address	Mask	Status
R1	Fa0/0			
	S0/0/0			
	S0/0/1			
R2	Fa0/0			
	S0/0/0			
	S0/0/1			
R3	Fa0/0			
	S0/0/0			
	S0/0/1			

Table 2 provides space to list the subnet numbers and masks in each subnet.

Table 2   IP Subnet Table

Location	Subnet Number	Mask
R1's LAN		
R2's LAN		
R3's LAN		
R1-R2 serial		
R1-R3 serial		
R2-R3 serial		

Topology

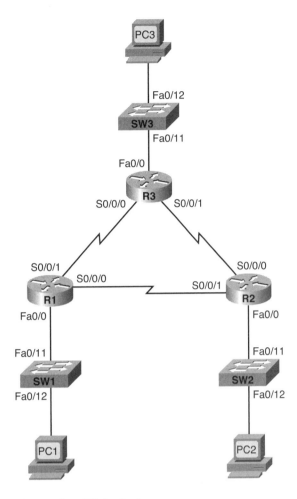

Figure 1   Network Topology for This Lab

Detailed Lab Steps

Part 1: Discover the IP Addresses Used in the Internetwork

Step 1.   Connect to R1 from the simulator user interface and enter user mode by using the console password **ciscopress**.

Step 2.   Use the **show ip interface brief** command to determine the IP address of each working interface. Record the addresses and the interface states of each interface in Table 1.

Step 3.   Use the **show interfaces** command to find the subnet mask used on each interface. Record this information in Table 1.

Step 4.   Repeat Steps 1 through 3 on router R2 and on router R3, completing the details in Table 1.

Step 5.   Based on the information already gathered in Table 1, calculate the subnet number for each of the subnets in this internetwork. Record those subnet numbers in Table 2.

Step 6. Confirm your calculations from the previous step by using the **show ip route connected** command on routers R1, R2, and R3. These commands list the connected routes with each route listing the subnet number.

Part 2: Configure EIGRP on R1

Step 7. Connect to R1's console from the simulator user interface and log in using the password **ciscopress**.

Step 8. Plan your EIGRP configuration on R1 so that EIGRP is enabled on all three of R1's interfaces shown in Figure 1. Use an AS number of 99, and do not use wildcard masks on the EIGRP **network** command. List your intended configuration on the lines below.

_____

_____

_____

_____

_____

_____

Step 9. Enter configuration mode on router R1 and configure the EIGRP commands you planned in the previous step.

Step 10. Exit configuration mode and issue the **show ip route eigrp** command. Do you see any EIGRP-learned routes (other than summary routes with a destination of null0)?

_____

_____

Step 11. Issue the **show ip eigrp interfaces** command. On which interfaces has EIGRP been enabled on this router? How many peers are listed off each interface?

_____

_____

_____

Step 12. Issue the **show ip eigrp neighbors** command. How many neighbors does R1 have? What are their IP addresses?

_____

_____

_____

Part 3: Configure EIGRP on R2

At this point, R1 may be configured correctly for EIGRP, but until at least one of the other routers has been configured for EIGRP, R1 cannot learn any routes. Part 3 of this lab guides you through the configuration process, pointing out some interesting facts along the way.

Step 13. Connect to R2's console from the simulator user interface and log in using the password **ciscopress**.

Step 14. Plan your EIGRP configuration on R2 so that EIGRP is enabled on all three of R1's interfaces shown in Figure 1. Use an AS number of 99, and do not use wildcard masks on the EIGRP **network** command. List your intended configuration on the lines below.

_____

_____

_____

_____

Step 15. Enter configuration mode on router R2 and configure EIGRP. However, do not enable EIGRP on R2's Fa0/0 interface. List the commands you configured on the lines below.

_____

_____

_____

_____

Step 16. Exit configuration mode and issue the **show ip route eigrp** command. Do you see any EIGRP-learned routes? List the subnet/prefix length for that route. Why isn't this route a route for R1's LAN subnet of 192.168.1.0/25?

_____

_____

Step 17. Issue the **show ip eigrp interfaces** command. On which interfaces has EIGRP been enabled on this router? How many peers are listed off each interface?

_____

_____

_____

Step 18. Issue the **show ip eigrp neighbors** command. How many neighbors does R2 have? What are their IP addresses?

_____

_____

_____

Step 19. Connect to R1's console using the simulator user interface, and then issue the **show** command that lists only EIGRP-learned routes. Do you see any EIGRP-learned routes (other than summary routes with a destination of null0)?

_____

_____

Step 20. Again from R1, issue the **show** command that lists EIGRP neighbors. How many neighbors does R1 have? What are their IP addresses?

_____

_____

_____

Step 21. R1 has not learned a route that matches the IP addresses on R2's LAN interface. Explain why.

_____

_____

Step 22. Return to R2's console and enter configuration mode on router R2.

Step 23. Complete the EIGRP configuration on R2 by enabling EIGRP on interface Fa0/0. List the commands you configured.

_____

_____

_____

Step 24. Exit configuration mode and issue the **show** command that lists only EIGRP-learned routes on R2. Do you see any EIGRP-learned routes? Are any of these routes new since the previous time you looked at R2's IP routes (other than summary routes with a destination of null0)?

_____

_____

Step 25. Connect to R1's console using the simulator user interface, and then issue the **show** command that lists only EIGRP-learned routes. Do you see any EIGRP-learned routes? Are any of these new since the previous time you looked at R1's IP routes (other than summary routes with a destination of null0)?

_____

_____

Part 4: Configure EIGRP on R3

At this point, R1 and R2 should be configured correctly for EIGRP. The last part has you complete the configuration of R3 and examine EIGRP on R3 to confirm EIGRP is working.

Step 26. Connect to R3's console from the simulator user interface and log in using the password **ciscopress**.

Step 27. Plan your EIGRP configuration on R3 so that EIGRP is enabled on all three of R3's interfaces shown in Figure 1. Use an AS number of 99, and do not use wildcard masks on the EIGRP **network** command. List your intended configuration on the lines below.

_____

_____

_____

_____

_____

Step 28. Enter configuration mode on router R3 and configure EIGRP as planned in the previous step.

Step 29. Exit configuration mode and issue the **show** command that lists only EIGRP-learned routes. Do you see any EIGRP-learned routes (other than summary routes with a destination of null0)? List the routes on the lines below.

_____

_____

_____

_____

Step 30. Issue the **show** command on R3 that lists the interfaces on which EIGRP has been enabled. On which interfaces has EIGRP been enabled on this router? How many peers are listed off each interface?

_____

_____

_____

Step 31. Issue the **show** command on R3 that lists all EIGRP neighbors. How many neighbors does R3 have? What are their IP addresses?

_____

_____

_____

Step 32. Go back to R1's console and then issue the **show ip route** command. Does this command list a route for all six subnets? Are three of the routes learned using EIGRP? What is the one-letter code on the far left of the output of the **show ip route** command that means "EIGRP"?

_____

_____

_____

Step 33. Go back to R2's console and then issue the **show ip route** command. Does this command list a route for all six subnets (other than summary routes with a destination of null0)? Are three of the routes learned using EIGRP?

_____

_____

_____

Hints and Answers

Table 3 is a completed version of the IP address reference table, Table 1, and Table 4 is a completed version of the IP subnet planning table, Table 2. Table 5 provides hints and tips for any lab steps that do not supply complete details and provides answers for any lab steps that ask questions.

Table 3   Completed IP Address Table

Device	Interface	IP Address	Mask	Status
R1	Fa0/0	192.168.1.126	/25	up/up
	S0/0/0	192.168.4.1	/30	up/up
	S0/0/1	192.168.4.5	/30	up/up
R2	Fa0/0	192.168.3.62	/26	up/up
	S0/0/0	192.168.4.9	/30	up/up
	S0/0/1	192.168.4.2	/30	up/up
R3	Fa0/0	192.168.2.158	/27	up/up
	S0/0/0	192.168.4.6	/30	up/up
	S0/0/1	192.168.4.10	/30	up/up
PC1		192.168.1.1	/25	up
PC2		192.168.3.1	/26	up
PC3		192.168.2.129	/27	up

Table 4   Completed IP Subnet Table

Location	Subnet Number	Mask
R1's LAN	192.168.1.0	255.255.255.128
R2's LAN	192.168.3.0	255.255.255.192
R3's LAN	192.168.2.128	255.255.255.224
R1-R2 serial	192.168.4.0	255.255.255.252
R1-R3 serial	192.168.4.4	255.255.255.252
R2-R3 serial	192.168.4.8	255.255.255.252

Table 5   Hints and Answers

Step	Hint or Answer
2	The **show ip interface brief** command will not list the subnet mask information, but the **show interfaces** command will.
5	The subnets will be 192.168.1.0/25, 192.168.2.128/27, 192.168.3.0/26, 192.168.4.0/30, 192.168.4.4/30, and 192.168.4.8/30.

continues

Table 5   **Hints and Answers**   *continued*

Step	Hint or Answer

8	The configuration should be as follows:
	
	router eigrp 99
	
	  network 192.168.1.0
	
	  network 192.168.4.0

10	You should not see any EIGRP-learned routes. The **show ip route eigrp** command lists only the routes learned by this router using EIGRP.
11	The **show ip eigrp interfaces** command lists the interfaces on which the router has enabled EIGRP and the number of peers (routers) known off each interface.
12	Neither of the other two routers has been configured for EIGRP yet, so R1 cannot have an EIGRP neighbor relationship with either R2 or R3.

14	The configuration should be as follows:
	
	router eigrp 99
	
	  network 192.168.3.0
	
	  network 192.168.4.0

15	Configure the **router eigrp 99** and **network 192.168.4.0** commands. Do not configure the **network 192.168.3.0** command yet.
16	R2 should now list two EIGRP-learned routes: a route for 192.168.1.0/24, and the serial subnet between R1-R3, namely 192.168.4.4/30. Instead of its LAN subnet of 192.168.1.0/25, R1 advertises to R2 the entire Class C network's route of 192.168.1.0/24 because of R1's default setting of auto-summary. R2's routing table will also show two local EIGRP summary routes for the 192.168.3.0/24 and 192.168.4.0/24 networks.
17	This command should list S0/0/0 and S0/0/1, with one peer off R2's S0/0/1 interface (namely, R1), and zero peers off R2's S0/0/0 interface.
18	R2 will list one neighbor, namely 192.168.4.1, which is R1's serial IP address on their common link.
19	R1's **show ip route eigrp** command should list one EIGRP-learned route: the serial subnet between R2-R3, namely 192.168.4.8/30.
20	The **show ip eigrp neighbors** command list R1 as having one neighbor, R2, listed as IP address 192.168.4.2.
21	Because R2's configuration omitted the **network 192.168.3.0** command, R2's EIGRP configuration does not match R2's Fa0/0 interface. As a result, R2 does not attempt to listen for EIGRP messages in that interface, send EIGRP messages out that interface, and, most importantly in this case, advertise about the subnet connected to that interface.
23	Configure the **router eigrp 99** and **network 192.168.3.0** commands. This step completes the configuration of EIGRP on R2 for all three interfaces.
24	The **show ip route eigrp** command on R2 should list the same two routes shown in Step 16: a route for 192.168.1.0/24, and the serial subnet between R1-R3, namely 192.168.4.4/30. (Additional summary routes, with outgoing interface null0, may also exist.)

Step	Hint or Answer
25	Now that R2 has enabled EIGRP on R2's Fa0/0 interface (in Step 23), R2 advertises its LAN subnet to R1. However, due to the default setting of auto-summary, because the link between R1 and R2 is in a different classful network (192.168.4.0) from R2's LAN interface (192.168.3.0), R2 automatically summarizes the route into a route for the entire Class C network of 192.168.3.0/24. As a result, the **show ip route eigrp** command on R1 now has two EIGRP-learned routes: the serial subnet between R2-R3, namely 192.168.4.8/30, and the newly learned 192.168.3.0/24.
27	The configuration should be as follows: **router eigrp 99** **network 192.168.2.0** **network 192.168.4.0**
29	The **show ip route eigrp** command on R3 should have learned three routes (other than summary routes with a destination of null0). Of the six subnets in this internetwork, three are directly connected to R3; R3 will now learn routes to the other three subnets using EIGRP. 192.168.1.0/24 192.168.3.0/24 192.168.4.0/30
30	The **show ip eigrp interface** command on R3 should list all three interfaces on R3. R3 should list one peer off interface S0/0/0 (R1, 192.168.4.5), one peer off interface S0/0/1 (R2, 192.168.4.9), and zero peers off interface Fa0/0.
31	The **show ip eigrp neighbors** command on R3 should list two neighbors, R1 and R2.
32	R1 should list routes for three connected routes and three EIGRP-learned routes (other than summary routes with a destination of null0). The EIGRP routes have a letter *D* on the far left of the output.
33	R2 should list routes for three connected routes and three EIGRP-learned routes (other than summary routes with a destination of null0). The EIGRP routes have a letter *D* on the far left of the output.

Configuration

Example 1 shows the configuration commands added to R1, R2, and R3 during this lab.

Example 1 Configuration Added During This Lab

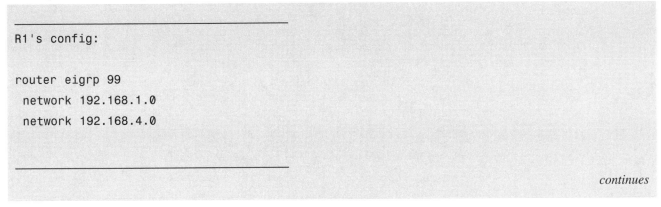

```
R1's config:


router eigrp 99
 network 192.168.1.0
 network 192.168.4.0
```

continues

Example 1   Configuration Added During This Lab   *continued*

```
R2's config:
router eigrp 99
 network 192.168.3.0
 network 192.168.4.0



R3's config:

router eigrp 99
 network 192.168.2.0
 network 192.168.4.0
```

Configuration Labs

Part 1: Router Configuration

Lab 5: Configuring EIGRP Routing

Overview

The overall objective of this laboratory exercise is to configure Enhanced IGRP (EIGRP) routing between two routers so that there is a routed network connection between computers in the two LANs. You will have to configure the computer's IP address, the gateway address, and the IP addresses for the appropriate router interfaces. You will have to configure and enable the serial connection between the routers to establish a connection.

Topology

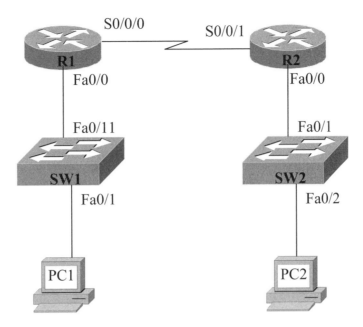

Figure 1   Network Topology for This Lab

Reference

The following simulator exercises provided with the CCNA 640-802 Network Simulator should be reviewed prior to starting this virtual laboratory exercise:

- EIGRP Configuration I, II
- EIGRP Serial Configuration I–VI
- EIGRP Neighbors I–V

Key Concepts

The following concepts, terms, commands, and steps should have been mastered in this laboratory exercise:

- How to configure the IP address, subnet mask, and default gateway for the computers in your LAN.
- How is the gateway address for your LAN router configured?
- The steps for configuring the host name for your router.
- The steps for configuring the router interface's IP addresses and subnet masks.
- The commands for configuring EIGRP routing from LAN-A to LAN-B.
- List two commands that can be used to verify that the routes are configured on the router.
- Use the computers in your LAN to ping the computers in the adjacent LAN.

- Use the proper command to trace the route from a PC in LAN-A to the host in the connected LAN-B.

- Use the proper command to trace the route from your router in LAN-A to the host computer in LAN-B.

- The steps to establish a Telnet connection to your router.

- Use the router command that displays the network routes stored in your router's routing table.

- Use the command to save your router configuration to NVRAM.

- What command is used to verify the routing protocol being used? What are two commands that can be used to display the routing protocol?

- What command displays only the EIGRP routes?

- What are wildcard bits or inverse mask bits?

Reference Tables

Table 1 provides the IP addresses and subnet masks of all interfaces used to complete this lab.

Table 1   Computer IP Addresses, Subnet Masks, and Gateway Addresses for Lab 5

Computer/Interface - R1	IP Address	Subnet Mask	Gateway Address
PC1	192.168.21.18	255.255.255.240	192.168.21.17
R1-Fa0/0	192.168.21.17	255.255.255.240	—
R1-S0/0/0	10.30.1.1	255.255.255.252	—
Computer/Interface – R2	IP Address	Subnet Mask	Gateway Address
PC2	192.168.85.21	255.255.255.240	192.168.85.18
R2-Fa0/0	192.168.85.18	255.255.255.240	—
R2-S0/0/1	10.30.1.2	255.255.255.252	—

Detailed Lab Steps

Task 1

In this lab, you are configuring EIGRP routing to the adjacent LAN for the network shown in Figure 1. You will be required to verify that computers in your LAN can ping the neighbor LAN. Note that a serial interface is being used to interconnect the LANs. You are configuring routing for both 172.20.15.0 and 192.168.25.0 networks. A subnet mask of 255.255.255.240 is being used. Use 56000 for the clock rate on the serial link (DCE interface).

Step 1. Configure the gateway address for FastEthernet 0/0 and the serial s0/0/0 interfaces on Router R1. You also need to configure the IP and gateway address for computer PC1. Use the IP address and subnet mask specified in Table 1. You will need to enable each interface and set the clock rate on the serial interface to 56000. List the router prompts and commands used to configure the interfaces.

_____

_____

_____

Step 2. Configure the gateway address for FastEthernet 0/0 and the serial s0/0/1 interfaces on Router R2. You also need to configure the IP and gateway address for computer PC2. Use the IP address and subnet mask specified in Table 1. List the router prompts and commands used to configure the interfaces.

_____

_____

_____

Step 3. Configure the host name for your routers (R1 should be renamed LAN-A and R2 should be renamed LAN-B). List the router prompts and commands used to configure the router's host name.

_____

_____

_____

Step 4. Use the proper command to verify that the router interfaces are properly configured. List the router prompts and commands used to verify the interfaces.

_____

_____

_____

Step 5. Configure an EIGRP route from the LAN-A router to the LAN-B router. Use an autonomous system number of 100. List the router prompts and commands used to configure EIGRP routing.

_____

_____

_____

Step 6. List the router prompts and commands used to verify that EIGRP routing has been configured on the LAN-A router. Are there routes configured to all the networks?

_____

_____

_____

Step 7. Use the computers in each LAN to ping the computers in the adjacent LAN.

_____

_____

_____

Step 8. Use the proper command to trace the route from a PC in LAN-A to a host in LAN-B. Your trace should pass through two routers. List the command used and record the trace information. How many hops did you record?

_____

_____

_____

Step 9. Use the command to list the EIGRP neighbors off the LAN-A router.

_____

_____

_____

Step 10. Use the command to make a Telnet connection from the LAN-A router to the LAN-B router. Set the VTY password to **ciscopress** and enable remote login. List the commands used to establish the Telnet connection. What IP address did you use?

_____

_____

_____

Step 11. Use the command to save your router configuration to the startup configuration. What command did you use? Use the proper command to verify that the configuration has been saved to NVRAM. List the router prompts and the commands used.

_____

_____

_____

Task 2

The following is a partial list of the items displayed when you issue the **show running-configuration [sh run]** command. Your task is to define each item and its purpose. You may need to go to the Cisco website (http://www.cisco.com) and look up what each of these commands means.

1. **shutdown**

_____

_____

_____

2. **log-adjacency changes**

_____

_____

_____

3. **control-plane**

_____

_____

_____

4. **scheduler allocate 20000 1000**

_____

_____

_____

5. scheduler allocate interrupt-time process-time

_____

_____

_____

6. login local

_____

_____

_____

7. line con 0

_____

_____

_____

8. line aux 0

_____

_____

_____

9. line vty 0 4

_____

_____

_____

Answer the following router questions:

1. What is the purpose of the wildcard bits?

_____

_____

_____

2. How many IP addresses are available using a 255.255.255.240 subnet mask?

_____

_____

_____

3. How many IP addresses are available using a 255.255.255.252 subnet mask?

_____

_____

_____

4. What command is used to determine your EIGRP neighbors?

_____

_____

_____

Subnet Design

Table 6-1 lists the labs for this unit. Check with your instructor or class syllabus to confirm what labs you should perform for class.

Table 6-1   Unit 6 Labs

Date	ICND1/ ICND2	Type	Part	Number	Name	Page
	ICND1	CS	3	1	Subnetting and Addressing I	235
	ICND1	CS	3	2	Subnetting and Addressing II	242
	ICND1	CS	3	3	Subnetting and Addressing III	251
	ICND1	SE	3	1–10	IP Route Selection I–X	261

ICND1 Configuration Scenarios

Part 3: IP Addressing, Routing, and WANs

Lab 1: Subnetting and Addressing I

Overview

For this lab, you will plan the subnetting scheme used in a small internetwork. Then, you will choose IP addresses for the routers and hosts in the internetwork, and configure those addresses. Throughout the lab, you will test the network using **ping** commands to discover if the interfaces are working.

Note: All passwords are **ciscopress** unless otherwise noted.

Topology

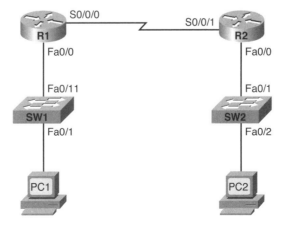

Figure 1   Network Lab Topology for This Lab

Detailed Lab Steps

Part 1: Subnet Planning

In Part 1, you will plan the IP subnets used for the topology shown in Figure 1.

Step 1.   Plan the three subnets you will use for the internetwork shown in this lab, using the following criteria:

- Subnet Class C network 192.168.20.0.

- Use the numerically lowest subnet numbers.

- Assign the lowest subnet number to the subnet on the left LAN, the next highest subnet number to the LAN on the right, and the next highest subnet numbers for any remaining subnets.

- Use a static-length mask for all subnets.

- Choose the mask that has the fewest host bits that allows the LANs to include 50 IP addresses.

Step 2.   Record the subnet numbers in Table 1. You can check your work using Table 3 in the "Hints and Answers" section at the end of this lab.

Table 1   Subnet Planning Table

Location	Subnet Number	Prefix Length
R1 LAN		
R1-R2 serial link		
R2 LAN		

Part 2: Configure and Verify the Router Interface IP Addresses

In Part 2, you will configure the IP addresses and masks on the two routers to match the design goals in Part 1.

Step 3.   Connect to R2's user interface from the simulator user interface and move to configuration mode.

Step 4.   Configure R2's two interfaces with the lowest possible IP address values in the subnets planned in Part 1 (and as summarized in Table 1). What commands did you use on each interface?

Step 5. Connect to R1's user interface from the simulator user interface and move to configuration mode.

Step 6. Configure R1's two interfaces with the lowest remaining possible IP address values in the subnets planned in Part 1 (and as summarized in Table 1). What commands did you use on each interface?

_____

_____

_____

Step 7. Move to interface configuration mode for interface S0/0/0 if you are not already in that mode.

Step 8. Because R1's S0/0/0 interface has a DCE cable installed, it needs a **clock rate** command for the link to work, so configure a **clock rate 1536000** command.

Step 9. Use the **end** command or press **Ctrl-Z** to exit back to enable mode.

Step 10. From R1, ping R1's own IP addresses. Do the pings work? If any of the pings fail, troubleshoot and fix problems until R1 can ping its own IP addresses.

_____

_____

_____

Step 11. Connect to R2's user interface from the simulator user interface and move to enable mode.

Step 12. Ping R2's own IP addresses. Do the pings work? If any of the pings fail, troubleshoot and fix problems until R2 can ping its own IP addresses.

_____

_____

_____

Part 3: Plan and Configure IP Addressing for PC1 and PC2

Now that the routers have valid IP addresses, Part 3 will guide you through the process of planning and configuring IP addresses for PC1 and PC2.

Step 13. Plan IP addresses for PC1 and PC2, using the following criteria:

- Choose the largest available IP address in each subnet for each PC.

- Choose an appropriate mask per the earlier subnet planning rules.

- Choose an appropriate default gateway IP address.

Step 14. Record the IP address, mask, and default gateway information in Table 2. You can check your work using Table 4 in the "Hints and Answers" section at the end of this lab.

Table 2   IP Addresses for PC1 and PC2

Device	IP Address	Mask	Default Gateway
PC1			
PC2			

Step 15. Connect to PC1's user interface from the simulator user interface.

Step 16. On PC1, use the **ip address** *ip-address mask* command and **gateway** *gw-address* commands to configure the IP address, mask, and default gateway planned in Table 2.

Step 17. From PC1, ping R1's LAN IP address. Record the command you used below. Does the ping work? Should the ping work? Explain why it works or does not work.

_____

_____

_____

_____

_____

Step 18. From PC1, ping R1's serial link IP address. Record the command you used below. Does the ping work? Should the ping work? Explain why it works or does not work.

_____

_____

_____

_____

_____

Step 19. From PC1, ping R2's serial link IP address. Record the command you used below. Does the ping work? Should the ping work? Explain why it works or does not work.

_____

_____

_____

_____

_____

_____

Step 20. Connect to PC2's user interface from the simulator user interface.

Step 21. On PC2, use the **ip address** *ip-address mask* command and **gateway** *gw-address* commands to configure the IP address, mask, and default gateway planned in Table 2.

Step 22. From PC2, ping R2's LAN IP address. Record the command you used below. Does the ping work? Should the ping work? Explain why it works or does not work.

_____

_____

_____

_____

_____

_____

Step 23. From PC2, ping R2's serial link IP address. Record the command you used below. Does the ping work? Should the ping work? Explain why it works or does not work.

_____

_____

_____

_____

_____

_____

Step 24. From PC2, ping R1's serial link IP address. Record the command you used below. Does the ping work? Should the ping work? Explain why it works or does not work.

_____

_____

_____

_____

_____

_____

Hints and Answers

Table 3 is a completed subnet planning table from Step 2 in the lab, and Table 4 shows a complete list of IP addresses for PC1 and PC2 from Step 14 in the lab. Table 5 provides hints and tips for any lab steps that do not supply complete details and provides answers for any lab steps that ask questions.

Table 3   Completed Subnet Planning Table

Location	Subnet Number	Prefix Length
R1 LAN	192.168.20.0	/26
R1-R2 serial link	192.168.20.128	/26
R2 LAN	192.168.20.64	/26

Table 4   Completed IP Addresses for PC1 and PC2

Device	IP Address	Mask	Default Gateway
PC1	192.168.20.62	255.255.255.192	192.168.20.1
PC2	192.168.20.126	255.255.255.192	192.168.20.65

Table 5   Hints and Answers

Step	Hint or Answer
2	See Table 3 for a completed version of Table 1.
3	Log in using the **ciscopress** password, use the **enable** command to move to enable mode, and then use the **configure terminal** command to move to configuration mode.
4	Fa0/0 will be configured with the **ip address 192.168.20.65 255.255.255.192** command, and S0/0/1 will be configured with the **ip address 192.168.20.129 255.255.255.192** command. To use these two commands, you first need to move into interface configuration mode; for example, use **interface fastethernet 0/0** before configuring Fa0/0's IP address/mask.

Step	Hint or Answer
5	Use the same process as in Step 3.
6	Fa0/0 will be configured with the **ip address 192.168.20.1 255.255.255.192** command, and S0/0/0 will be configured with the **ip address 192.168.20.130 255.255.255.192** command.
7	Use the **interface serial0/0/0** command from any part of configuration mode.
10 & 12	The pings should work at this point, assuming the configuration was completed correctly.
13	The PCs should both use the same mask calculated in Part 1 (255.255.255.192, or /26). The IP addresses should be 192.168.20.62 on PC1 and 192.168.20.126 on PC2. They should also refer to the IP addresses of their respective local routers as each PC's default gateway: 192.168.20.1 and 192.168.20.65.
14	See Table 4 for a completed version of Table 2.
16	Use the **ip address 192.168.20.62 255.255.255.192** and **gateway 192.168.20.1** commands.
17	The command will be **ping 192.168.20.1**. The ping should work in part because you already know that R1's Fa0/0 interface is configured and up, and you just configured PC1's IP address to be in the same subnet.
18	The command will be **ping 192.168.20.130**. The ping should work in part because PC1 knows a valid default gateway (192.168.20.1), and once the ping packet gets to R1, R1 knows how to forward the packet back to PC1's subnet (192.168.20.0/26).
19	The command will be **ping 192.168.20.129**. The ping should not work. PC1 should send the packet to its default gateway (192.168.20.1), and R1 knows how to forward the packet to R2's serial IP address (192.168.20.130). However, R2 does not have a route pointing back to PC1's subnet because no routing protocol has been configured yet. So, the ping should fail.
21	Use the **ip address 192.168.20.126 255.255.255.192** and **gateway 192.168.20.65** commands.
22	The command will be **ping 192.168.20.65**. The ping should work in part because you already know that R2's Fa0/0 is configured and up, and you just configured PC2's IP address to be in the same subnet.
23	The command will be **ping 192.168.20.129**. The ping should work in part because PC2 knows a valid default gateway (192.168.20.65) and, once the ping packet gets to R2, R2 knows how to forward the packet back to PC2's subnet (192.168.20.64/26).
24	The command will be **ping 192.168.20.130**. The ping should not work. PC2 should send the packet to its default gateway (192.168.20.65), and R2 knows how to forward the packet to R1's serial IP address (192.168.20.129). However, R1 does not have a route pointing back to PC2's subnet because no routing protocol has been configured yet. So, the ping should fail.

Configuration

Example 1 shows the configuration commands added to R1 and R2 during this lab.

Example 1   Configuration on R1 and R2 Added During This Lab

```
R1 Config:

interface fastethernet0/0
 ip address 192.168.20.1 255.255.255.192
interface serial 0/0/0
 ip address 192.168.20.130 255.255.255.192

R2 config:

interface fastethernet0/0
 ip address 192.168.20.65 255.255.255.192
interface serial 0/0/1
 ip address 192.168.20.129 255.255.255.192
```

ICND1 Configuration Scenarios

Part 3: IP Addressing, Routing, and WANs

Lab 2: Subnetting and Addressing II

Overview

For this lab, you will plan the subnetting scheme used in a small internetwork. Then, you will choose IP addresses for the routers and hosts in the internetwork, and configure those addresses. Throughout the lab, you will test the network using **ping** commands to discover if the interfaces are working.

Note: All passwords are **ciscopress** unless otherwise noted.

Topology

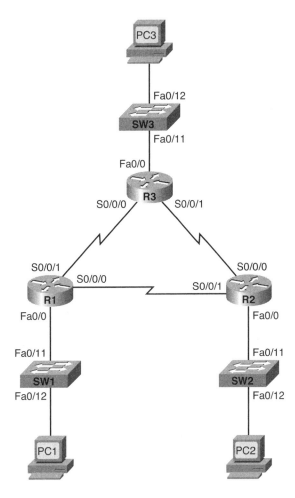

Figure 1   Network Lab Topology for This Lab

Detailed Lab Steps

Part 1: Plan the IP Subnets

In Part 1, you will plan the IP subnets used for the topology shown in Figure 1.

Step 1.   Plan the three subnets you will use for the internetwork shown in this lab, using the following criteria:

- Subnet Class B network 172.25.0.0.

- Use the numerically largest subnet numbers.

- Assign the subnets from highest to lowest to the following locations: R1's LAN, R2's LAN, R3's LAN, the R1-R2 serial link, the R2-R3 serial link, and the R1-R3 serial link.

- Use a static-length mask for all subnets.

- Choose the mask that has the fewest host bits that allows the LANs to include 120 IP addresses.

Step 2. Record the subnet numbers in Table 1. You can check your work using Table 3 in the "Hints and Answers" section at the end of this lab.

Table 1   Subnet Planning Table

Location	Subnet Number	Prefix Length
R1 LAN		
R2 LAN		
R3 LAN		
R1-R2 serial link		
R2-R3 serial link		
R1-R3 serial link		

Part 2: Configure and Verify the Router Interface IP Addresses

In Part 2, you will configure the IP addresses and masks on the two routers to match the design goals in Part 1.

Step 3. Connect to R1's user interface from the simulator user interface and move to configuration mode.

Step 4. Configure R1's three interfaces with the lowest possible IP address values in the subnets planned in Part 1 (and as summarized in Table 1). What commands did you use on each interface?

_____

_____

_____

_____

_____

_____

Step 5. Use the **end** command or press **Ctrl-Z** to exit back to enable mode.

Step 6. Connect to R2's user interface from the simulator user interface and move to configuration mode.

Step 7.   Configure R2's three interfaces with the lowest remaining possible IP address values in the subnets planned in Part 1 (and as summarized in Table 1). What commands did you use on each interface?

_____

_____

_____

_____

_____

_____

Step 8.   Use the **end** command or press **Ctrl-Z** to exit back to enable mode.

Step 9.   Connect to R3's user interface from the simulator user interface and move to configuration mode.

Step 10.   Configure R3's three interfaces with the lowest remaining possible IP address values in the subnets planned in Part 1 (and as summarized in Table 1). What commands did you use on each interface?

_____

_____

_____

_____

_____

_____

Step 11.   Use the **end** command or press **Ctrl-Z** to exit back to enable mode.

Step 12.   From R3, ping R3's own IP addresses. Do the pings work? If any of the pings fail, troubleshoot and fix problems until R1 can ping its own IP addresses.

_____

_____

_____

Step 13.   Connect to R2's user interface from the simulator user interface and move to enable mode.

Step 14.   Ping R2's own IP addresses. Do the pings work? If any of the pings fail, troubleshoot and fix problems until R2 can ping its own IP addresses.

_____

_____

_____

Step 15.   Connect to R1's user interface from the simulator user interface and move to enable mode.

Step 16.   Ping R1's own IP addresses. Do the pings work? If the ping fails, troubleshoot and fix problems until R1 can ping its own IP addresses.

_____

_____

_____

Part 3: Plan and Configure IP Addressing for Hosts

Now that the routers have valid IP addresses, Part 3 will guide you through the process of planning and configuring IP addresses for PC1, PC2, and PC3.

Step 17.   Plan IP addresses for the PCs using the following criteria:

  - Choose the largest available IP address in each subnet for each PC.

  - Choose an appropriate mask per the earlier subnet planning rules.

  - Choose an appropriate default gateway IP address

Step 18.   Record the IP address, mask, and default gateway information in Table 2. You can check your work using Table 4 in the "Hints and Answers" section at the end of this lab.

Table 2   IP Addresses for PC1 and PC2

Device	IP Address	Mask	Default Gateway
PC1			
PC2			
PC3			

Step 19.   Connect to PC1's user interface from the simulator user interface.

Step 20.   Use the PC **ip address** _ip-addr mask_ and **gateway** _gw-addr_ commands to configure the IP address, mask, and default gateway planned in Table 2.

Step 21. From PC1, ping R1's LAN IP address. Record the command you used below. Does the ping work? Should the ping work? Explain why it works or does not work.

_____

_____

_____

_____

_____

_____

Step 22. From PC1, ping R2's S0/0/1 IP address (172.25.254.2). Record the command you used below. Does the ping work? Should the ping work? Explain why it works or does not work.

_____

_____

_____

_____

_____

_____

Step 23. Connect to PC2's user interface from the simulator user interface.

Step 24. Use the PC **ip address** _ip-addr mask_ and **gateway** _gw-addr_ commands to configure the IP address, mask, and default gateway planned in Table 2.

Step 25. From PC2, ping R2's LAN IP address. Record the command you used below. Does the ping work? Should the ping work? Explain why it works or does not work.

_____

_____

_____

_____

_____

Step 26. From PC2, ping R3's S0/0/1 IP address of 172.25.253.130. Does the ping work? Should the ping work? Explain why it works or does not work.

_____

_____

_____

_____

_____

Step 27. Connect to PC3's user interface from the simulator user interface.

Step 28. Use the PC **ip address** *ip-addr mask* and **gateway** *gw-addr* commands to configure the IP address, mask, and default gateway planned in Table 2.

Step 29. From PC3, ping R3's LAN IP address. Record the command you used below. Does the ping work? Should the ping work? Explain why it works or does not work.

_____

_____

_____

_____

_____

Hints and Answers

Table 3 is a completed subnet planning table from Step 2 in the lab, and Table 4 shows a complete list of IP addresses for PC1 and PC2 from Step 18 in the lab. Table 5 provides hints and tips for any lab steps that do not supply complete details and provides answers for any lab steps that ask questions.

Table 3   Completed Subnet Planning Table

Location	Subnet Number	Prefix Length
R1 LAN	172.25.255.128	/25
R2 LAN	172.25.255.0	/25
R3 LAN	172.25.254.128	/25
R1-R2 serial link	172.25.254.0	/25
R2-R3 serial link	172.25.253.128	/25
R1-R3 serial link	172.25.253.0	/25

Table 4   Completed IP Addresses for PC1 and PC2

Device	IP Address	Mask	Default Gateway
PC1	172.25.255.254	255.255.255.128	172.25.255.129
PC2	172.25.255.126	255.255.255.128	172.25.255.1
PC3	172.25.254.254	255.255.255.128	172.25.254.129

Table 5   Hints and Answers

Step	Hint or Answer
2	See Table 3 for a completed version of Table 1.
3	Log in using the **ciscopress** password, use the **enable** command to move to enable mode, and then use the **configure terminal** command to move to configuration mode.
4	The configuration should be as follows: **interface fastethernet0/0** **ip address 172.25.255.129 255.255.255.128** **interface serial 0/0/0** **ip address 172.25.254.1 255.255.255.128** **interface serial 0/0/1** **ip address 172.25.253.1 255.255.255.128**
6	Use the same process as in Step 3.
7	The configuration should be as follows: **interface fastethernet0/0** **ip address 172.25.255.1 255.255.255.128** **interface serial 0/0/0** **ip address 172.25.253.129 255.255.255.128** **interface serial 0/0/1** **ip address 172.25.254.2 255.255.255.128**
9	Use the same process as in Step 3.
10	The configuration should be as follows: **interface fastethernet0/0** **ip address 172.25.254.129 255.255.255.128** **interface serial 0/0/0** **ip address 172.25.253.2 255.255.255.128** **interface serial 0/0/1** **ip address 172.25.253.130 255.255.255.128**
12, 14, 16	The pings should work at this point, assuming the configuration was completed correctly.

continues

Table 5 **Hints and Answers** *continued*

Step	Hint or Answer
18	See Table 4 for a completed version of Table 2.
20	Use the **ip address 172.25.255.254 255.255.255.128** and **gateway 172.25.255.129** commands.
21	The command will be **ping 172.25.255.129**. The ping should work in part because you already know that R1's Fa0/0 is configured and up, and you just configured PC1's IP address to be in the same subnet.
22	The command will be **ping 172.25.254.2**. The ping should not work. PC1 should send the packet to its default gateway (172.25.255.129), and R1 knows how to forward the packet to R2's serial IP address (172.25.254.2). However, R2 does not have a route pointing back to PC1's subnet because no routing protocol has been configured yet. So, the ping should fail.
24	Use the **ip address 172.25.255.126 255.255.255.128** and **gateway 172.25.255.1** commands.
25	The command will be **ping 172.25.255.1**. The ping should work in part because you already know that R2's Fa0/0 is configured and up, and you just configured PC2's IP address to be in the same subnet.
26	The command will be **ping 172.25.253.130**. The ping should not work. PC2 should send the packet to its default gateway (172.25.255.1), and R2 knows how to forward the packet to R3's S0/0/1 IP address because that IP address is on a common subnet with R2. However, R3 does not have a route pointing back to PC2's subnet because no routing protocol has been configured yet. So, the ping should fail.
28	Use the **ip address 172.25.254.254 255.255.255.128** and **gateway 172.25.254.129** commands.
29	The command will be **ping 172.25.254.129**. The ping should work in part because you already know that R3's Fa0/0 is configured and up, and you just configured PC3's IP address to be in the same subnet.

Configuration

Example 1 shows the configuration commands added to R1, R2, and R3 during this lab.

Example 1   Configuration on R1, R2, and R3 Added During This Lab

```
R1 config:


interface fastethernet0/0
 ip address 172.25.255.129 255.255.255.128
interface serial 0/0/0
```

```
 ip address 172.25.254.1 255.255.255.128
interface serial 0/0/1
 ip address 172.25.253.1 255.255.255.128


R2 config:


interface fastethernet0/0
 ip address 172.25.255.1 255.255.255.128
 interface serial 0/0/0
ip address 172.25.253.129 255.255.255.128
interface serial 0/0/1
 ip address 172.25.254.2 255.255.255.128


R3 config:


interface fastethernet0/0
 ip address 172.25.254.129 255.255.255.128
interface serial 0/0/0
 ip address 172.25.253.2 255.255.255.128
interface serial 0/0/1
 ip address 172.25.253.130 255.255.255.128
```

ICND1 Configuration Scenarios
Part 3: IP Addressing, Routing, and WANs

Lab 3: Subnetting and Addressing III

Overview

This lab begins with two of the four routers already having IP addresses configured. Your job will be to discover the IP addresses and calculate the subnet numbers used in each case. Then, you will do some additional subnet planning, choose two additional subnets to use, and configure IP addresses on the two remaining routers.

In this case, all four routers will be preconfigured with a valid RIP-2 configuration that will work on all interfaces, once the IP addresses have been configured on all interfaces. So, at the end of the lab, all hosts and routers should be able to ping all other IP addresses in the internetwork.

Reference Tables

Tables 1 and 2 provide a convenient place to record the subnet numbers (Table 1) and router IP addresses (Table 2) found and calculated in this lab.

Table 1   **Subnet Planning Table**

Location	Subnet Number	Prefix Length
Central LAN		
R1 Fa0/1 LAN		
R2 Fa0/1 LAN		
R3 Fa0/1 LAN		
R4 Fa0/1 LAN		

Table 2   **Router IP Addresses and Masks**

Device	Interface	IP Address	Mask
R1	Fa0/0		
R1	Fa0/1		
R2	Fa0/0		
R2	Fa0/1		
R3	Fa0/0		
R3	Fa0/1		
R4	Fa0/0		
R4	Fa0/1		

Topology

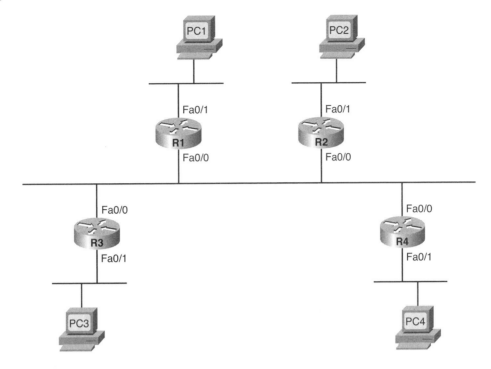

Figure 1   **Network Topology for This Lab**

Detailed Lab Steps

Part 1: Discover Existing Subnets and IP Addresses

Part 1 of this lab lists steps to examine the current configuration of the various routers to find any existing IP addresses configured on the routers.

Step 1.   Connect to R1's user interface from the simulator user interface and move to enable mode.

Step 2.   Use the **show ip interface brief** command to list a summary that shows each interface and IP address. What interfaces have IP addresses assigned? What addresses? What masks? Record as much information as is possible in Tables 1 and 2.

Step 3. List the IP address and mask of each interface using the **show interfaces** command. What mask is used on each "up/up" interface? Record as much information as is possible in Tables 1 and 2.

_____

_____

Step 4. Based on the IP addresses and masks found in the previous two steps, calculate the subnet numbers for any subnets connected to R1. Record these subnet numbers in Table 1.

Step 5. List the connected routes on R1 using the **show ip route connected** command. Are the listed subnet numbers the same values that you calculated in Step 4 and recorded in Table 1? (If not, check your math from Step 4.)

_____

_____

Step 6. Connect to R2's user interface from the simulator user interface and move to enable mode.

Step 7. Use the **show ip interface brief** command to list a summary that shows each interface and IP address. What interfaces have IP addresses assigned? What addresses? What masks? Record as much information as is possible in Tables 1 and 2.

_____

_____

_____

_____

Step 8. List the IP address and mask of each interface using the **show interfaces** command. What mask is used on each "up/up" interface? Record as much information as is possible in Tables 1 and 2.

_____

_____

Step 9. Based on the IP addresses and masks found in the previous two steps, calculate the subnet numbers for any subnets connected to R2. Record these subnet numbers in Table 1.

Step 10. List the connected routes on R2 using the **show ip route connected** command. Are the listed subnet numbers the same values that you calculated in Step 9 and recorded in Table 1? (If not, check your math from Step 4.)

_____

_____

Step 11. Connect to R3's user interface from the simulator user interface and move to enable mode.

Step 12. Use the **show ip interface brief** command to list a summary that shows each interface and IP address. What interfaces have IP addresses assigned? What addresses? What masks? Record as much information as is possible into Tables 1 and 2.

_____

_____

_____

_____

Step 13. Connect to R4's user interface from the simulator user interface and move to enable mode.

Step 14. Use the **show ip interface brief** command to list a summary that shows each interface and IP address. What interfaces have IP addresses assigned? What addresses? What masks? Record as much information as is possible in Tables 1 and 2.

_____

_____

_____

_____

Part 2: Plan the IP Subnets and Addresses

After Part 1 of this lab, Table 1 should list three of the five subnets required in this internetwork. Table 2 should also list the IP addresses used on the two LAN interfaces of both R1 and R2. In this part of the lab, you will complete the subnet and address planning by choosing two additional subnets, and then choosing IP addresses for the two LAN interfaces on both R3 and R4.

For the two remaining subnets, you will choose the two numerically smallest subnets that have not already been allocated, while avoiding use of the zero subnet.

Step 15. Calculate the first eight possible subnets (in other words, the eight numerically smallest subnet numbers) of Class C network 192.168.8.0 when using mask 255.255.255.240. Record those subnets in Table 3.

Table 3   **Possible Subnets of Class C Network 192.168.8.0 with Mask 255.255.255.240**

Subnet	Location
192.168.8._____	
192.168.8._____	
192.168.8._____	
192.168.8._____	
192.168.8._____	
192.168.8._____	
192.168.8._____	
192.168.8._____	

Step 16.   In Table 3, note which three subnets are currently in use.

Step 17.   Additionally, note which of these subnets is the zero subnet in the Location column of Table 3.

Step 18.   Pick the two numerically smallest subnet numbers from Table 3 that are not already in use. Do not use the zero subnet. What are those subnet numbers?

_____

_____

Step 19.   Of the two subnet numbers chosen in the previous step, use the lower numeric value as R3's Fa0/1 subnet and use the higher numeric value as R4's Fa0/1 subnet. Record your choices by noting them in the Location column of Table 3 and in Table 2 at the beginning of this lab.

Step 20.   Choose an IP address for R3's Fa0/0 and Fa0/1 interfaces. Use the lowest numeric IP addresses that have not already been assigned to other routers in those subnets. Tables 1 and 2 should list the subnets and all known IP addresses. What addresses did you choose? Record your answers below as well as in Table 2.

_____

_____

Step 21.   Choose an IP address for R4's Fa0/0 and Fa0/1 interfaces. Use the lowest numeric IP addresses that have not already been assigned to other routers in those subnets. Tables 1 and 2 should list the subnets and all known IP addresses. What addresses did you choose? Record your answers below as well as in Table 2.

_____

_____

Part 3: Configure Router IP Addresses

Next, you will configure R3 and R4 with the IP addresses you chose and listed in Table 2.

Step 22. Connect to R3's user interface from the simulator user interface and move to configuration mode.

Step 23. Configure R3's two interfaces with the lowest possible IP address values in the subnets planned in Part 1 (and as summarized in Table 1). What commands did you use on each interface?

Step 24. Use the **end** command or press **Ctrl-Z** to exit back to enable mode.

Step 25. Connect to R4's user interface from the simulator user interface and move to configuration mode.

Step 26. Configure R4's two interfaces with the lowest possible IP address values in the subnets planned in Part 1 (and as summarized in Table 1). What commands did you use on each interface?

Step 27. Use the **end** command or press **Ctrl-Z** to exit back to enable mode.

Part 4: Test the IP Addresses

All four routers have been preconfigured with RIP 2 so that they should all now have routes to all five subnets. Additionally, all four PCs have been configured with appropriate IP addresses/masks and default gateways. This lab ends with some ping tests to ensure that you configured the lab per the instructions.

Step 28. Connect to PC1 from the simulator user interface.

Step 29. Ping each of the eight router IP addresses from PC1 per the address referenced in Table 4. Note that Table 4 lists the IP addresses that should have been configured if you followed the preceding lab steps, so if a ping fails, it could be that you have a different IP address configured.

Table 4   Ping Test Reference

Device	IP Address	Ping from PC1 Worked?	Ping from PC3 Worked?
R1 Fa0/0	192.168.8.18		
R1 Fa0/1	192.168.8.33		
R2 Fa0/0	192.168.8.19		
R2 Fa0/1	192.168.8.65		
R3 Fa0/0	192.168.8.17		
R3 Fa0/1	192.168.8.49		
R4 Fa0/0	192.168.8.20		
R4 Fa0/1	192.168.8.81		

Step 30. Connect to PC3 from the simulator user interface.

Step 31. Repeat the ping tests from Step 29, listing in Table 4 which pings worked and which did not. Note that all pings should work at this point.

Hints and Answers

Table 5 is the completed version of Table 1, the subnet planning chart. Table 6 is the completed version of Table 2, with the IP addresses and masks configured for the four routers in this lab. Table 7 lists the subnets used in this lab, plus a few others, and their locations or status. Finally, Table 8 provides hints and tips for any lab steps that do not supply complete details and provides answers for any lab steps that ask questions.

Table 5   Completed Subnet Planning Table

Location	Subnet Number	Prefix Length
Central LAN	192.168.8.16	/28
R1 Fa0/1 LAN	192.168.8.32	/28
R2 Fa0/1 LAN	192.168.8.64	/28
R3 Fa0/1 LAN	192.168.8.48	/28
R4 Fa0/1 LAN	192.168.8.80	/28

Table 6   Completed Router IP Addresses and Masks

Device	Interface	IP Address	Mask
R1	Fa0/0	192.168.8.18	255.255.255.240
R1	Fa0/1	192.168.8.33	255.255.255.240
R2	Fa0/0	192.168.8.19	255.255.255.240
R2	Fa0/1	192.168.8.65	255.255.255.240
R3	Fa0/0	192.168.8.17	255.255.255.240
R3	Fa0/1	192.168.8.49	255.255.255.240
R4	Fa0/0	192.168.8.20	255.255.255.240
R4	Fa0/1	192.168.8.81	255.255.255.240

Table 7   Completed Table of Possible Subnets of Class C Network 192.168.8.0 with Mask 255.255.255.240

Subnet	Location
192.168.8.0	Zero subnet
192.168.8.16	Preconfigured as subnet to which all routers are connected
192.168.8.32	Preconfigured as R1's Fa0/1 subnet
192.168.8.48	Chosen during this lab as R3's Fa0/1 subnet
192.168.8.64	Preconfigured as R2's Fa0/1 LAN subnet
192.168.8.80	Chosen during this lab as R4's Fa0/1 subnet
192.168.8.96	Currently unused
192.168.8.112	Currently unused

Table 8   Hints and Answers

Step	Hint or Answer
1	Log in using the **ciscopress** password and use the **enable** command to move to enable mode.
2	This command lists IP addresses for Fa0/0 and Fa0/1. However, this command does not list mask information.
3	Interfaces Fa0/0 and Fa0/1 should be in an "up/up" state. They should be assigned IP addresses 192.168.8.18 and 192.168.8.33, respectively.
4	The subnets are 192.168.8.16/28 and 192.168.8.32/28.
5	The subnets should be the same. If not, check your math from step 4.
6	Log in using the **ciscopress** password and use the **enable** command to move to enable mode.

continues

Table 8   Hints and Answers   *continued*

Step	Hint or Answer
7	This command lists IP addresses for Fa0/0 and Fa0/1. However, this command does not list mask information.
8	Interfaces Fa0/0 and Fa0/1 should be in an "up/up" state. They should be assigned IP addresses 192.168.8.19 and 192.168.8.65, respectively.
9	The subnets are 192.168.8.16/28 and 192.168.8.64/28.
10	The subnets should be the same. If not, check your math from step 4.
12	R3 does not have any interfaces that have IP addresses assigned.
14	R4 does not have any interfaces that have IP addresses assigned.
18	The subnet numbers are 192.168.8.48 and 192.168.8.80.
20	Fa0/0: 192.168.8.17 Fa0/1: 192.168.8.49
21	Fa0/0: 192.168.8.20 Fa0/1: 192.168.8.81
22	Log in using the **ciscopress** password, use the **enable** command to move to enable mode, and then use the **configure terminal** command to move to configuration mode.

23	The configuration should be as follows:
	 interface fastethernet0/0
	  ip address 192.168.8.17 255.255.255.240
	 interface fastethernet0/1
	  ip address 192.168.8.49 255.255.255.240

26	The configuration should be as follows:
	 interface fastethernet0/0
	  ip address 192.168.8.20 255.255.255.240
	 interface fastethernet0/1
	  ip address 192.168.8.81 255.255.255.240

Configuration

Example 1 shows the configuration commands added to R3 and R4 during this lab.

Example 1   Configuration on R1 and R2 Added During This Lab

```
R3 config:

interface fastethernet0/0
 ip address 192.168.8.17 255.255.255.240
interface fastethernet0/1
 ip address 192.168.8.49 255.255.255.240


R4 config:

interface fastethernet0/0
 ip address 192.168.8.20 255.255.255.240
interface fastethernet0/1
 ip address 192.168.8.81 255.255.255.240
```

ICND1 Subnetting Exercises

Part 3: IP Route Selection

Lab 1: IP Route Selection I

Overview

In this exercise, you focus on the routes known by Router R1. This lab essentially guides you to ask and then answer a question about three different IP addresses. The question: If a packet arrived at R1 destined for a particular IP address, which of R1's routes, if any, would R1 use when forwarding the packet?

During this lab, you look at R1's routing table and make your prediction. You then use commands to confirm which route R1 would use. The IP addresses to consider for this lab are as follows in Table 1.

Table 1   Destinations and Matching Route Info (to Be Completed)

Destination Address	Matching Route's Subnet/Mask	Matching Route's Outgoing Interface
10.99.110.2		
10.99.130.2		
10.99.70.2		

Topology

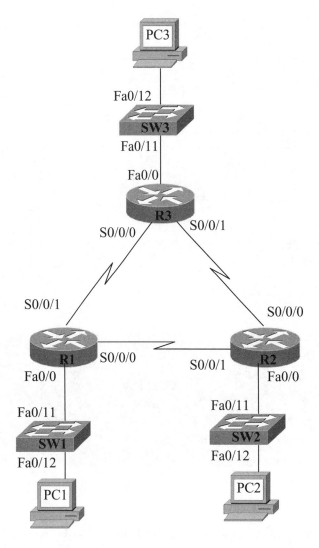

Figure 1   Topology for IP Address Configuration

Detailed Lab Steps

Step 1.   Connect to R1 from the simulator user interface. All passwords are **cs**.

Step 2.   Enter privileged exec ("enable") mode by issuing the **enable** command.

Step 3.   Use the output from the **show cdp neighbors detail** command, along with the diagram in this lab, to discover key facts about R1's outgoing interfaces for its routes. What local interfaces does R1 have? What other routers are neighbors of R1? Per the command output, what IP address does R2 use on the other end of the serial link? R3? Record your answers on the following lines.

_____

_____

_____

Step 4. Display the IP routing table using the **show ip route** exec command.

Step 5. Examine the first three IP addresses in the table at the beginning of this lab compared to the routing table displayed in the previous step. Imagine that a packet arrives at R1 with a destination IP address of the IP address listed in the table. Using any math you know to examine the existing routes, decide whether any routes match the packet. If so, complete the table's last two columns for that IP address.

The **show ip route** *address* command, where *address* is some IP address, lists details about a route. Specifically, it lists details about the route that a router would match when processing a packet destined for the IP address in the command. For example, the **show ip route 1.1.1.1** command lists information about the route used to forward packets destined for 1.1.1.1. If the router does not match any routes, the output either lists nothing or lists an error message.

Step 6. Issue the **show ip route** *address* command, where *address* is the first IP address listed in the table. Does this command confirm that the router does indeed match a route for this packet destination? Does the output list the same subnet ID, and same outgoing interface, that you predicted and recorded in the table per Step 5?

Step 7. Issue the **traceroute** *address* command, where *address* is the first IP address listed in the table. Does the command show either R2's IP address or R3's IP address? Does it show a series of asterisks, signifying that no route existed?

Step 8. Similar to Step 5, examine the second IP address in the table at the beginning of this lab, and make predictions about which of R1's routes this packet will match. Complete the appropriate row of the table at the beginning of this lab.

Step 9. Similar to Step 6, confirm whether you made the correct prediction using the **show ip route** *address* command, where *address* is the second IP address listed in the table. Does the output list the same subnet ID, and same outgoing interface, that you predicted and recorded in the table per the previous step?

Step 10. Issue the **traceroute** *address* command, where *address* is the second IP address listed in the table. Does the command show a first entry with either R2's IP address or R3's IP address?

_____

_____

Step 11. Similar to Step 5, examine the third IP address in the table at the beginning of this lab, and make predictions about which of R1's routes this packet will match. Complete the appropriate row of the table at the beginning of this lab.

_____

_____

Step 12. Similar to Step 6, confirm whether you made the correct prediction using the **show ip route** *address* command, where *address* is the third IP address listed in the table. Does the output list the same subnet ID, and same outgoing interface, that you predicted and recorded in the table per the previous step?

_____

_____

Step 13. Issue the **traceroute** *address* command, where *address* is the IP address listed in the table. Does the command show a first entry with either R2's IP address or R3's IP address?

_____

_____

Hints and Answers

Table 2 lists hints and tips for any lab steps that do not supply all the details in the lab step, and for lab steps that ask questions about the lab.

Table 2 Hints

Step	Hint
3	The **show cdp neighbors detail** command lists a group of messages per neighbor. For each neighbor, the output lists the local router interface, the neighbor's host name, and the neighbor's IP address.
5	The method used to determine the matching route is to look at each subnet in the routing table and mentally calculate the range of addresses in the subnet. Then choose the route whose subnet range includes the IP address in question. If more than one route's subnet range matches the IP address, choose the route with the more specific match; that is, the longer prefix mask.

continues

Table 2   **Hints**   *continued*

Step	Hint
6	The output of the **show ip route 10.99.110.2** command should list subnet 10.99.104.0/21 (/21 is equal to 255.255.248.0). It should also list R2's IP address 10.1.12.2 as the next-hop, with R1's outgoing interface of S0/0/0.
7	It lists a single line, 10.1.12.2, which is R2's IP address. So the **traceroute 10.99.110.2** command confirms that the next-hop router in the route is R2.
9	The output of the **show ip route 10.99.130.2** command should list subnet 10.99.128.0/21 (/21 is equal to 255.255.248.0). It should also list R3's IP address 10.1.3.2 as the next-hop, with R1's outgoing interface of S0/0/1.
10	It lists a single line, 10.1.3.2, which is R3's IP address. So the **traceroute 10.99.130.2** command confirms that the next-hop router in the route is R3.
12	The output of the **show ip route 10.99.70.2** command lists a message which means that R1 matches no routes.
13	It lists three lines of three asterisks, which in the simulator means that the command would not complete and did not even get a response from the next router. In this case, the **traceroute 10.99.70.2** command confirms that R1 has no matching route for 10.99.70.2.

Configuration Steps

This lab requires no configuration.

ICND1 Subnetting Exercises

Part 3: IP Route Selection

Lab 2: IP Route Selection 2

Overview

In this exercise, you focus on the routes known by Router R1. This lab essentially guides you to ask and then answer a question about three different IP addresses. The question: If a packet arrived at R1 destined for a particular IP address, which of R1's routes, if any, would R1 use when forwarding the packet?

During this lab, you look at R1's routing table and make your prediction. You then use commands to confirm which route R1 would use. The IP addresses to consider for this lab are as follows in Table 1.

Table 1   Destinations and Matching Route Info (to Be Completed)

Destination Address	Matching Route's Subnet/Mask	Matching Route's Outgoing Interface
10.8.21.2		
10.8.23.2		
10.8.25.2		

Topology

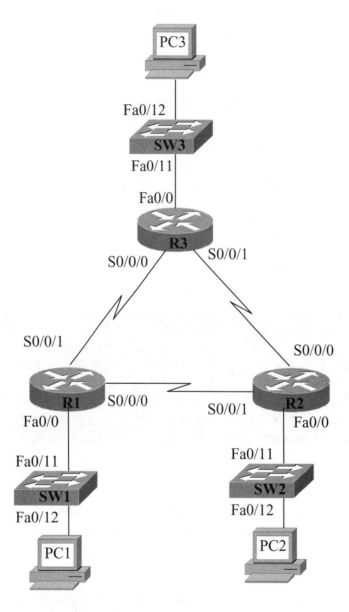

Figure 1   Topology for IP Address Configuration

Detailed Lab Steps

Step 1. Connect to R1 from the simulator user interface. All passwords are **cs**.

Step 2. Enter privileged exec ("enable") mode by issuing the **enable** command.

Step 3. Use the output from the **show cdp neighbors detail** command, along with the diagram in this lab, to discover key facts about R1's outgoing interfaces for its routes. What local interfaces does R1 have? What other routers are neighbors of R1? Per the command output, what IP address does R2 use on the other end of the serial link? R3? Record your answers on the following lines.

Step 4. Display the IP routing table using the **show ip route** exec command.

Step 5. Examine the first of the three IP addresses in the table at the beginning of this lab compared to the routing table displayed in the previous step. Imagine that a packet arrives at R1 with a destination IP address of the IP address listed in the table. Using any math you know to examine the existing routes, decide whether any routes match the packet. If so, complete the table's last two columns for that IP address.

The **show ip route** *address* command, where *address* is some IP address, lists details about a route. Specifically, it lists details about the route that a router would match when processing a packet destined for the IP address in the command. For example, the **show ip route 1.1.1.1** command lists information about the route used to forward packets destined for 1.1.1.1. If the router does not match any routes, the output either lists nothing or lists an error message.

Step 6. Issue the **show ip route** *address* command, where *address* is the first IP address listed in the table. Does this command confirm that the router does indeed match a route for this packet destination? Does the output list the same subnet ID, and same outgoing interface, that you predicted and recorded in the table per Step 5?

Step 7. Issue the **traceroute** *address* command, where *address* is the first IP address listed in the table. Does the command show either R2's IP address or R3's IP address? Does it show a series of asterisks, signifying that no route existed?

Step 8. Similar to Step 5, examine the second IP address in the table at the beginning of this lab, and make predictions about which of R1's routes this packet will match. Complete the appropriate row of the table at the beginning of this lab.

_____

_____

Step 9. Similar to Step 6, confirm whether you made the correct prediction using the **show ip route** *address* command, where *address* is the second IP address listed in the table. Does the output list the same subnet ID, and same outgoing interface, that you predicted and recorded in the table per the previous step?

_____

_____

Step 10. Issue the **traceroute** *address* command, where *address* is the second IP address listed in the table. Does the command show a first entry with either R2's IP address or R3's IP address?

_____

_____

Step 11. Similar to Step 5, examine the third IP address in the table at the beginning of this lab, and make predictions about which of R1's routes this packet will match. Complete the appropriate row of the table at the beginning of this lab.

_____

_____

Step 12. Similar to Step 6, confirm whether you made the correct prediction using the **show ip route** *address* command, where *address* is the third IP address listed in the table. Does the output list the same subnet ID, and same outgoing interface, that you predicted and recorded in the table per the previous step?

_____

_____

Step 13. Issue the **traceroute** *address* command, where *address* is the IP address listed in the table. Does the command show a first entry with either R2's IP address or R3's IP address?

_____

_____

Hints and Answers

Table 2 lists hints and tips for any lab steps that do not supply all the details in the lab step, and for lab steps that ask questions about the lab.

Table 2   Hints

Step	Hint
3	The **show cdp neighbors detail** command lists a group of messages per neighbor. For each neighbor, the output lists the local router interface, the neighbor's host name, and the neighbor's IP address.
5	The method used to determine the matching route is to look at each subnet in the routing table and mentally calculate the range of addresses in the subnet. Then choose the route whose subnet range includes the IP address in question. If more than one route's subnet range matches the IP address, choose the route with the more specific match; that is, the longer prefix mask.
6	The output of the **show ip route 10.8.21.2** command should list subnet 10.8.20.0/23 (/23 is equal to 255.255.254.0). It should also list R2's IP address 10.1.12.2 as the next-hop, with R1's outgoing interface of S0/0/0.
7	It lists a single line, 10.1.12.2, which is R2's IP address. So the **traceroute 10.8.21.2** command confirms that the next-hop router in the route is R2.
9	The output of the **show ip route 10.8.23.2** command lists a message which means that R1 matches no routes.
10	It lists three lines of three asterisks, which in the simulator means that the command would not complete and did not even get a response from the next router. In this case, the **traceroute 10.8.23.2** command confirms that R1 has no matching route for 10.8.23.2.
12	The output of the **show ip route 10.8.25.2** command should list subnet 10.8.24.0/23 (/23 is equal to 255.255.254.0). It should also list R3's IP address 10.1.3.2 as the next-hop, with R1's outgoing interface of S0/0/1.
13	It lists a single line, 10.1.3.2, which is R3's IP address. So the **traceroute 10.8.25.2** command confirms that the next-hop router in the route is R3.

Configuration Steps

This lab requires no configuration.

Overview

In this exercise, you focus on the routes known by Router R1. This lab essentially guides you to ask and then answer a question about three different IP addresses. The question: If a packet arrived at R1 destined for a particular IP address, which of R1's routes, if any, would R1 use when forwarding the packet?

During this lab, you look at R1's routing table and make your prediction. You then use commands to confirm which route R1 would use. The IP addresses to consider for this lab are as follows in Table 1.

Table 1   Destinations and Matching Route Info (to Be Completed)

Destination Address	Matching Route's Subnet/Mask	Matching Route's Outgoing Interface
172.25.1.122		
172.25.1.222		
172.25.2.222		

Topology

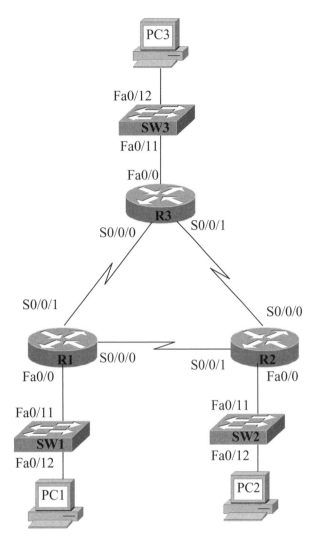

Figure 1   **Topology for IP Address Configuration**

Detailed Lab Steps

Step 1.   Connect to R1 from the simulator user interface. All passwords are **cs**.

Step 2.   Enter privileged exec ("enable") mode by issuing the **enable** command.

Step 3.   Use the output from the **show cdp neighbors detail** command, along with the diagram in this lab, to discover key facts about R1's outgoing interfaces for its routes. What local interfaces does R1 have? What other routers are neighbors of R1? Per the command output, what IP address does R2 use on the other end of the serial link? R3? Record your answers on the following lines.

_____

_____

_____

Step 4. Display the IP routing table using the **show ip route** exec command.

Step 5. Examine the first of the three IP addresses in the table at the beginning of this lab compared to the routing table displayed in the previous step. Imagine that a packet arrives at R1 with a destination IP address of the IP address listed in the table. Using any math you know to examine the existing routes, decide whether any routes match the packet. If so, complete the table's last two columns for that IP address.

_____

_____

The **show ip route** _address_ command, where _address_ is some IP address, lists details about a route. Specifically, it lists details about the route that a router would match when processing a packet destined for the IP address in the command. For example, the **show ip route 1.1.1.1** command lists information about the route used to forward packets destined for 1.1.1.1. If the router does not match any routes, the output either lists nothing or lists an error message.

Step 6. Issue the **show ip route** _address_ command, where _address_ is the first IP address listed in the table. Does this command confirm that the router does indeed match a route for this packet destination? Does the output list the same subnet ID, and same outgoing interface, that you predicted and recorded in the table per Step 5?

_____

_____

Step 7. Issue the **traceroute** _address_ command, where _address_ is the first IP address listed in the table. Does the command show either R2's IP address or R3's IP address? Does it show a series of asterisks, signifying that no route existed?

_____

_____

Step 8. Similar to Step 5, examine the second IP address in the table at the beginning of this lab, and make predictions about which of R1's routes this packet will match. Complete the appropriate row of the table at the beginning of this lab.

_____

_____

Step 9. Similar to Step 6, confirm whether you made the correct prediction using the **show ip route** _address_ command, where _address_ is the second IP address listed in the table. Does the output list the same subnet ID, and same outgoing interface, that you predicted and recorded in the table per the previous step?

_____

_____

Step 10. Issue the **traceroute** *address* command, where *address* is the second IP address listed in the table. Does the command show a first entry with either R2's IP address or R3's IP address?

_____

_____

Step 11. Similar to Step 5, examine the third IP address in the table at the beginning of this lab, and make predictions about which of R1's routes this packet will match. Complete the appropriate row of the table at the beginning of this lab.

_____

_____

Step 12. Similar to Step 6, confirm whether you made the correct prediction using the **show ip route** *address* command, where *address* is the third IP address listed in the table. Does the output list the same subnet ID, and same outgoing interface, that you predicted and recorded in the table per the previous step?

_____

_____

Step 13. Issue the **traceroute** *address* command, where *address* is the IP address listed in the table. Does the command show a first entry with either R2's IP address or R3's IP address?

_____

_____

Hints and Answers

Table 2 lists hints and tips for any lab steps that do not supply all the details in the lab step, and for lab steps that ask questions about the lab.

Table 2   Hints

Step	Hint
3	The **show cdp neighbors detail** command lists a group of messages per neighbor. For each neighbor, the output lists the local router interface, the neighbor's host name, and the neighbor's IP address.
5	The method used to determine the matching route is to look at each subnet in the routing table and mentally calculate the range of addresses in the subnet. Then choose the route whose subnet range includes the IP address in question. If more than one route's subnet range matches the IP address, choose the route with the more specific match; that is, the longer prefix mask.

continues

Table 2   **Hints**   *continued*

Step	Hint
6	The output of the **show ip route 172.25.1.122** command should list subnet 172.25.1.64/26 (/26 is equal to 255.255.255.192). It should also list R3's IP address 172.25.3.2 as the next-hop, with R1's outgoing interface of S0/0/1.
7	It lists a single line, 172.25.3.2, which is R3's IP address. So the **traceroute 172.25.1.122** command confirms that the next-router in the route is R3.
9	The output of the **show ip route 172.25.1.222** command should list subnet 172.25.1.192/26 (/26 is equal to 255.255.255.192). It should also list R3's IP address 172.25.3.2 as the next-hop, with R1's outgoing interface of S0/0/1.
10	It lists a single line, 172.25.3.2, which is R3's IP address. So the **traceroute 172.25.1.222** command confirms that the next-router in the route is R3.
12	The output of the **show ip route 172.25.2.222** command lists a message which means that R1 matches no routes.
13	It lists three lines of three asterisks, which in the simulator means that the command would not complete and did not even get a response from the next router. In this case, the **traceroute 172.25.2.222** command confirms that R1 has no matching route for 172.25.2.222.

Configuration Steps

This lab requires no configuration.

ICND1 Subnetting Exercises

Part 3: IP Route Selection

Lab 4: IP Route Selection IV

Overview

In this exercise, you focus on the routes known by Router R1. This lab essentially guides you to ask and then answer a question about three different IP addresses. The question: If a packet arrived at R1 destined for a particular IP address, which of R1's routes, if any, would R1 use when forwarding the packet?

During this lab, you look at R1's routing table and make your prediction. You then use commands to confirm which route R1 would use. The IP addresses to consider for this lab are as follows in Table 1.

Table 1　Destinations and Matching Route Info (to Be Completed)

Destination Address	Matching Route's Subnet/Mask	Matching Route's Outgoing Interface
172.25.0.22		
172.25.0.122		
172.25.0.222		

Topology

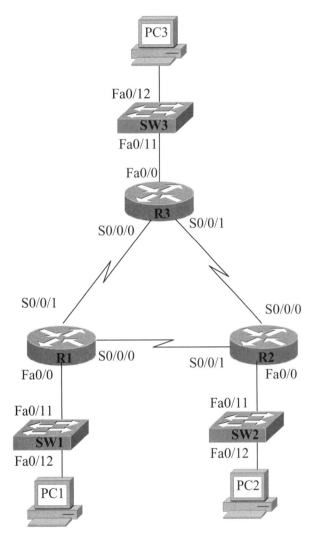

Figure 1　Topology for IP Address Configuration

Detailed Lab Steps

Step 1.   Connect to R1 from the simulator user interface. All passwords are **cs**.

Step 2.   Enter privileged exec ("enable") mode by issuing the **enable** command.

Step 3.   Use the output from the **show cdp neighbors detail** command, along with the diagram in this lab, to discover key facts about R1's outgoing interfaces for its routes. What local interfaces does R1 have? What other routers are neighbors of R1? Per the command output, what IP address does R2 use on the other end of the serial link? R3? Record your answers on the following lines.

_____

_____

_____

Step 4.   Display the IP routing table using the **show ip route** exec command.

Step 5.   Examine the first of the three IP addresses in the table at the beginning of this lab compared to the routing table displayed in the previous step. Imagine that a packet arrives at R1 with a destination IP address of the IP address listed in the table. Using any math you know to examine the existing routes, decide whether any routes match the packet. If so, complete the table's last two columns for that IP address.

_____

_____

The **show ip route** *address* command, where *address* is some IP address, lists details about a route. Specifically, it lists details about the route that a router would match when processing a packet destined for the IP address in the command. For example, the **show ip route 1.1.1.1** command lists information about the route used to forward packets destined for 1.1.1.1. If the router does not match any routes, the output either lists nothing or lists an error message.

Step 6.   Issue the **show ip route** *address* command, where *address* is the first IP address listed in the table. Does this command confirm that the router does indeed match a route for this packet destination? Does the output list the same subnet ID, and same outgoing interface, that you predicted and recorded in the table per Step 5?

_____

_____

Step 7.   Issue the **traceroute** *address* command, where *address* is the first IP address listed in the table. Does the command show either R2's IP address or R3's IP address? Does it show a series of asterisks, signifying that no route existed?

_____

_____

Step 8. Similar to Step 5, examine the second IP address in the table at the beginning of this lab, and make predictions about which of R1's routes this packet will match. Complete the appropriate row of the table at the beginning of this lab.

_____

_____

Step 9. Similar to Step 6, confirm whether you made the correct prediction using the **show ip route** *address* command, where *address* is the second IP address listed in the table. Does the output list the same subnet ID, and same outgoing interface, that you predicted and recorded in the table per the previous step?

_____

_____

Step 10. Issue the **traceroute** *address* command, where *address* is the second IP address listed in the table. Does the command show a first entry with either R2's IP address or R3's IP address?

_____

_____

Step 11. Similar to Step 5, examine the third IP address in the table at the beginning of this lab, and make predictions about which of R1's routes this packet will match. Complete the appropriate row of the table at the beginning of this lab.

_____

_____

Step 12. Similar to Step 6, confirm whether you made the correct prediction using the **show ip route** *address* command, where *address* is the third IP address listed in the table. Does the output list the same subnet ID, and same outgoing interface, that you predicted and recorded in the table per the previous step?

_____

_____

Step 13. Issue the **traceroute** *address* command, where *address* is the IP address listed in the table. Does the command show a first entry with either R2's IP address or R3's IP address?

_____

_____

Hints and Answers

Table 2 lists hints and tips for any lab steps that do not supply all the details in the lab step, and for lab steps that ask questions about the lab.

Table 2   Hints

Step	Hint
3	The **show cdp neighbors detail** command lists a group of messages per neighbor. For each neighbor, the output lists the local router interface, the neighbor's host name, and the neighbor's IP address.
5	The method used to determine the matching route is to look at each subnet in the routing table and mentally calculate the range of addresses in the subnet. Then choose the route whose subnet range includes the IP address in question. If more than one route's subnet range matches the IP address, choose the route with the more specific match; that is, the longer prefix mask.
6	The output of the **show ip route 172.25.0.22** command should list subnet 172.25.0.0/27 (/27 is equal to 255.255.255.224). It should also list R2's IP address 172.25.12.2 as the next-hop, with R1's outgoing interface of S0/0/0.
7	It lists a single line, 172.25.12.2, which is R2's IP address. So the **traceroute 172.25.0.22** command confirms that the next-hop router in the route is R2.
9	The output of the **show ip route 172.25.0.122** command lists a message which means that R1 matches no routes.
10	It lists three lines of three asterisks, which in the simulator means that the command would not complete and did not even get a response from the next router. In this case, the **traceroute 172.25.0.122** command confirms that R1 has no matching route for 172.25.0.122.
12	The output of the **show ip route 172.25.0.222** command should list subnet 172.25.0.192/27 (/27 is equal to 255.255.255.224). It should also list R3's IP address 172.25.3.2 as the next-hop, with R1's outgoing interface of S0/0/1.
13	It lists a single line, 172.25.3.2, which is R3's IP address. So the **traceroute 172.25.0.222** command confirms that the next-hop router in the route is R3.

Configuration Steps

This lab requires no configuration.

ICND1 Subnetting Exercises

Part 3: IP Route Selection

Lab 5: IP Route Selection V

Overview

In this exercise, you focus on the routes known by Router R1. This lab essentially guides you to ask and then answer a question about three different IP addresses. The question: If a packet arrived at R1 destined for a particular IP address, which of R1's routes, if any, would R1 use when forwarding the packet?

During this lab, you look at R1's routing table and make your prediction. You then use commands to confirm which route R1 would use. The IP addresses to consider for this lab are as follows in Table 1.

Table 1   Destinations and Matching Route Info (to Be Completed)

Destination Address	Matching Route's Subnet/Mask	Matching Route's Outgoing Interface
172.25.3.72		
172.25.3.92		
172.25.3.102		

Topology

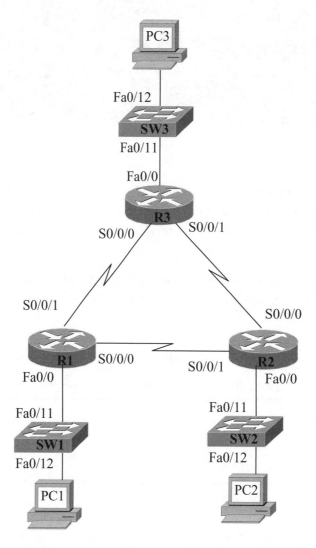

Figure 1 **Topology for IP Address Configuration**

Detailed Lab Steps

Step 1. Connect to R1 from the simulator user interface. All passwords are **cs**.

Step 2. Enter privileged exec ("enable") mode by issuing the **enable** command.

Step 3. Use the output from the **show cdp neighbors detail** command, along with the diagram in this lab, to discover key facts about R1's outgoing interfaces for its routes. What local interfaces does R1 have? What other routers are neighbors of R1? Per the command output, what IP address does R2 use on the other end of the serial link? R3? Record your answers on the following lines.

_____

_____

_____

Step 4. Display the IP routing table using the **show ip route** exec command.

Step 5. Examine the first of the three IP addresses in the table at the beginning of this lab compared to the routing table displayed in the previous step. Imagine that a packet arrives at R1 with a destination IP address of the IP address listed in the table. Using any math you know to examine the existing routes, decide whether any routes match the packet. If so, complete the table's last two columns for that IP address.

_____

_____

The **show ip route** *address* command, where *address* is some IP address, lists details about a route. Specifically, it lists details about the route that a router would match when processing a packet destined for the IP address in the command. For example, the **show ip route 1.1.1.1** command lists information about the route used to forward packets destined for 1.1.1.1. If the router does not match any routes, the output either lists nothing or lists an error message.

Step 6. Issue the **show ip route** *address* command, where *address* is the first IP address listed in the table. Does this command confirm that the router does indeed match a route for this packet destination? Does the output list the same subnet ID, and same outgoing interface, that you predicted and recorded in the table per Step 5?

_____

_____

Step 7. Issue the **traceroute** *address* command, where *address* is the first IP address listed in the table. Does the command show either R2's IP address or R3's IP address? Does it show a series of asterisks, signifying that no route existed?

_____

_____

Step 8. Similar to Step 5, examine the second IP address in the table at the beginning of this lab, and make predictions about which of R1's routes this packet will match. Complete the appropriate row of the table at the beginning of this lab.

_____

_____

Step 9. Similar to Step 6, confirm whether you made the correct prediction using the **show ip route** *address* command, where *address* is the second IP address listed in the table. Does the output list the same subnet ID, and same outgoing interface, that you predicted and recorded in the table per the previous step?

_____

_____

Step 10. Issue the **traceroute** *address* command, where *address* is the second IP address listed in the table. Does the command show a first entry with either R2's IP address or R3's IP address?

_____

_____

Step 11. Similar to Step 5, examine the third IP address in the table at the beginning of this lab, and make predictions about which of R1's routes this packet will match. Complete the appropriate row of the table at the beginning of this lab.

_____

_____

Step 12. Similar to Step 6, confirm whether you made the correct prediction using the **show ip route** *address* command, where *address* is the third IP address listed in the table. Does the output list the same subnet ID, and same outgoing interface, that you predicted and recorded in the table per the previous step?

_____

_____

Step 13. Issue the **traceroute** *address* command, where *address* is the IP address listed in the table. Does the command show a first entry with either R2's IP address or R3's IP address?

_____

_____

Hints and Answers

Table 2 lists hints and tips for any lab steps that do not supply all the details in the lab step, and for lab steps that ask questions about the lab.

Table 2   **Hints**

Step	Hint
3	The **show cdp neighbors detail** command lists a group of messages per neighbor. For each neighbor, the output lists the local router interface, the neighbor's host name, and the neighbor's IP address.
5	The method used to determine the matching route is to look at each subnet in the routing table and mentally calculate the range of addresses in the subnet. Then choose the route whose subnet range includes the IP address in question. If more than one route's subnet range matches the IP address, choose the route with the more specific match; that is, the longer prefix mask.

continues

Table 2 **Hints** *continued*

Step	Hint
6	The output of the **show ip route 172.25.3.72** command should list subnet 172.25.3.64/28 (/28 is equal to 255.255.255.240). It should also list R3's IP address 172.25.3.2 as the next-hop, with R1's outgoing interface of S0/0/1.
7	It lists a single line, 172.25.3.2, which is R3's IP address. So the **traceroute 172.25.3.72** command confirms that the next-hop router in the route is R3.
9	The output of the **show ip route 172.25.3.92** command should list subnet 172.25.3.80 (/28 is equal to 255.255.255.240). It should also list R2's IP address 172.25.12.2 as the next-hop, with R1's outgoing interface of S0/0/0.
10	It lists a single line, 172.25.12.2, which is R2's IP address. So the **traceroute 172.25.3.92** command confirms that the next-hop router in the route is R2.
12	The output of the **show ip route 172.25.3.102** command lists a message which means that R1 matches no routes.
13	It lists three lines of three asterisks, which in the simulator means that the command would not complete and did not even get a response from the next router. In this case, the **traceroute 172.25.3.102** command confirms that R1 has no matching route for 172.25.3.102.

Configuration Steps

This lab requires no configuration.

ICND1 Subnetting Exercises

Part 3: IP Route Selection

Lab 6: IP Route Selection VI

Overview

In this exercise, you focus on the routes known by Router R1. This lab essentially guides you to ask and then answer a question about three different IP addresses. The question: If a packet arrived at R1 destined for a particular IP address, which of R1's routes, if any, would R1 use when forwarding the packet?

During this lab, you look at R1's routing table and make your prediction. You then use commands to confirm which route R1 would use. The IP addresses to consider for this lab are as follows in Table 1.

Table 1   Destinations and Matching Route Info (to Be Completed)

Destination Address	Matching Route's Subnet/Mask	Matching Route's Outgoing Interface
172.16.12.110		
172.16.12.130		
172.16.12.150		

Topology

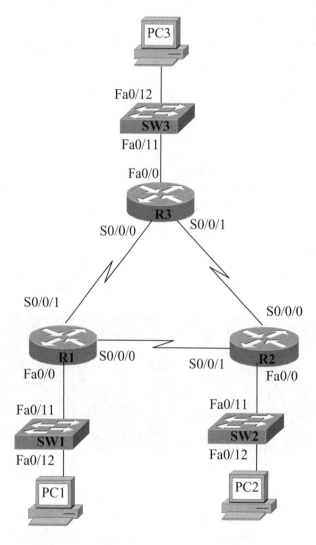

Figure 1   Topology for IP Address Configuration

Detailed Lab Steps

Step 1. Connect to R1 from the simulator user interface. All passwords are **cs**.

Step 2. Enter privileged exec ("enable") mode by issuing the **enable** command.

Step 3. Use the output from the **show cdp neighbors detail** command, along with the diagram in this lab, to discover key facts about R1's outgoing interfaces for its routes. What local interfaces does R1 have? What other routers are neighbors of R1? Per the command output, what IP address does R2 use on the other end of the serial link? R3? Record your answers on the following lines.

_____

_____

_____

Step 4. Display the IP routing table using the **show ip route** exec command.

Step 5. Examine the first of the three IP addresses in the table at the beginning of this lab compared to the routing table displayed in the previous step. Imagine that a packet arrives at R1 with a destination IP address of the IP address listed in the table. Using any math you know to examine the existing routes, decide whether any routes match the packet. If so, complete the table's last two columns for that IP address.

_____

_____

The **show ip route** *address* command, where *address* is some IP address, lists details about a route. Specifically, it lists details about the route that a router would match when processing a packet destined for the IP address in the command. For example, the **show ip route 1.1.1.1** command lists information about the route used to forward packets destined for 1.1.1.1. If the router does not match any routes, the output either lists nothing or lists an error message.

Step 6. Issue the **show ip route** *address* command, where *address* is the first IP address listed in the table. Does this command confirm that the router does indeed match a route for this packet destination? Does the output list the same subnet ID, and same outgoing interface, that you predicted and recorded in the table per Step 5?

_____

_____

Step 7. Issue the **traceroute** *address* command, where *address* is the first IP address listed in the table. Does the command show either R2's IP address or R3's IP address? Does it show a series of asterisks, signifying that no route existed?

_____

_____

Step 8. Similar to Step 5, examine the second IP address in the table at the beginning of this lab, and make predictions about which of R1's routes this packet will match. Complete the appropriate row of the table at the beginning of this lab.

_____

_____

Step 9. Similar to Step 6, confirm whether you made the correct prediction using the **show ip route** *address* command, where *address* is the second IP address listed in the table. Does the output list the same subnet ID, and same outgoing interface, that you predicted and recorded in the table per the previous step?

_____

_____

Step 10. Issue the **traceroute** *address* command, where *address* is the second IP address listed in the table. Does the command show a first entry with either R2's IP address or R3's IP address?

_____

_____

Step 11. Similar to Step 5, examine the third IP address in the table at the beginning of this lab, and make predictions about which of R1's routes this packet will match. Complete the appropriate row of the table at the beginning of this lab.

_____

_____

Step 12. Similar to Step 6, confirm whether you made the correct prediction using the **show ip route** *address* command, where *address* is the third IP address listed in the table. Does the output list the same subnet ID, and same outgoing interface, that you predicted and recorded in the table per the previous step?

_____

_____

Step 13. Issue the **traceroute** *address* command, where *address* is the IP address listed in the table. Does the command show a first entry with either R2's IP address or R3's IP address?

_____

_____

Hints and Answers

Table 2 lists hints and tips for any lab steps that do not supply all the details in the lab step, and for lab steps that ask questions about the lab.

Table 2   **Hints**

Step	Hint
3	The **show cdp neighbors detail** command lists a group of messages per neighbor. For each neighbor, the output lists the local router interface, the neighbor's host name, and the neighbor's IP address.
5	The method used to determine the matching route is to look at each subnet in the routing table and mentally calculate the range of addresses in the subnet. Then choose the route whose subnet range includes the IP address in question. If more than one route's subnet range matches the IP address, choose the route with the more specific match; that is, the longer prefix mask.
6	The output of the **show ip route 172.16.12.110** command should list subnet 172.16.12.104/29 (/29 is equal to 255.255.255.248). It should also list R2's IP address 172.16.10.2 as the next-hop, with R1's outgoing interface of S0/0/0.
7	It lists a single line, 172.16.10.2, which is R2's IP address. So the **traceroute 172.16.12.110** command confirms that the next-hop router in the route is R2.
9	The output of the **show ip route 172.16.12.130** command should list subnet 172.16.12.128 (/29 is equal to 255.255.255.248). It should also list R2's IP address 172.16.10.2 as the next-hop, with R1's outgoing interface of S0/0/0.
10	It lists a single line, 172.16.10.2, which is R2's IP address. So the **traceroute 172.16.12.130** command confirms that the next-hop router in the route is R2.
12	The output of the **show ip route 172.16.12.150** command should list subnet 172.16.12.144/29 (/29 is equal to 255.255.255.248). It should also list R3's IP address 172.16.11.3 as the next-hop, with R1's outgoing interface of S0/0/1.
13	It lists a single line, 172.16.11.3, which is R3's IP address. So the **traceroute 172.16.12.150** command confirms that the next-hop router in the route is R3.

Configuration Steps

This lab requires no configuration.

ICND1 Subnetting Exercises

Part 3: IP Route Selection

Lab 7: IP Route Selection VII

Overview

In this exercise, you focus on the routes known by Router R1. This lab essentially guides you to ask and then answer a question about three different IP addresses. The question: If a packet arrived at R1 destined for a particular IP address, which of R1's routes, if any, would R1 use when forwarding the packet?

During this lab, you look at R1's routing table and make your prediction. You then use commands to confirm which route R1 would use. The IP addresses to consider for this lab are as follows in Table 1.

Table 1   Destinations and Matching Route Info (to Be Completed)

Destination Address	Matching Route's Subnet/Mask	Matching Route's Outgoing Interface
172.16.30.1		
172.16.28.150		
172.16.31.100		

Topology

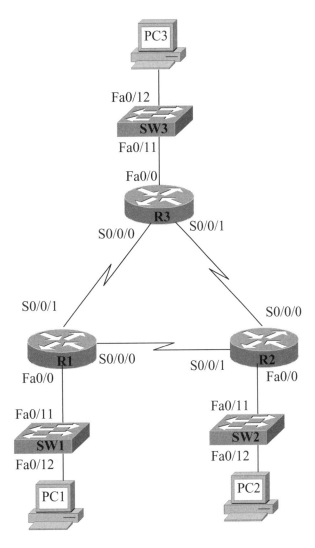

PC3

Fa0/12

SW3

Fa0/11

Fa0/0

R3

S0/0/0   S0/0/1

S0/0/1   S0/0/0

R1   S0/0/0   S0/0/1   R2

Fa0/0   Fa0/0

Fa0/11   Fa0/11

SW1   SW2

Fa0/12   Fa0/12

PC1   PC2

Figure 1   Topology for IP Address Configuration

Detailed Lab Steps

Step 1.   Connect to R1 from the simulator user interface. All passwords are **cs**.

Step 2.   Enter privileged exec ("enable") mode by issuing the **enable** command.

Step 3.   Use the output from the **show cdp neighbors detail** command, along with the diagram in this lab, to discover key facts about R1's outgoing interfaces for its routes. What local interfaces does R1 have? What other routers are neighbors of R1? Per the command output, what IP address does R2 use on the other end of the serial link? R3? Record your answers on the following lines.

_____

_____

_____

Step 4. Display the IP routing table using the **show ip route** exec command.

Step 5. Examine the first of the three IP addresses in the table at the beginning of this lab compared to the routing table displayed in the previous step. Imagine that a packet arrives at R1 with a destination IP address of the IP address listed in the table. Using any math you know to examine the existing routes, decide whether any routes match the packet. If so, complete the table's last two columns for that IP address.

_____

_____

The **show ip route** *address* command, where *address* is some IP address, lists details about a route. Specifically, it lists details about the route that a router would match when processing a packet destined for the IP address in the command. For example, the **show ip route 1.1.1.1** command lists information about the route used to forward packets destined for 1.1.1.1. If the router does not match any routes, the output either lists nothing or lists an error message.

Step 6. Issue the **show ip route** *address* command, where *address* is the first IP address listed in the table. Does this command confirm that the router does indeed match a route for this packet destination? Does the output list the same subnet ID, and same outgoing interface, that you predicted and recorded in the table per Step 5?

_____

_____

Step 7. Issue the **traceroute** *address* command, where *address* is the first IP address listed in the table. Does the command show either R2's IP address or R3's IP address? Does it show a series of asterisks, signifying that no route existed?

_____

_____

Step 8. Similar to Step 5, examine the second IP address in the table at the beginning of this lab, and make predictions about which of R1's routes this packet will match. Complete the appropriate row of the table at the beginning of this lab.

_____

_____

Step 9. Similar to Step 6, confirm whether you made the correct prediction using the **show ip route** *address* command, where *address* is the second IP address listed in the table. Does the output list the same subnet ID, and same outgoing interface, that you predicted and recorded in the table per the previous step?

_____

_____

Step 10. Issue the **traceroute** *address* command, where *address* is the second IP address listed in the table. Does the command show a first entry with either R2's IP address or R3's IP address?

_____

_____

Step 11. Similar to Step 5, examine the third IP address in the table at the beginning of this lab, and make predictions about which of R1's routes this packet will match. Complete the appropriate row of the table at the beginning of this lab.

_____

_____

Step 12. Similar to Step 6, confirm whether you made the correct prediction using the **show ip route** *address* command, where *address* is the third IP address listed in the table. Does the output list the same subnet ID, and same outgoing interface, that you predicted and recorded in the table per the previous step?

_____

_____

Step 13. Issue the **traceroute** *address* command, where *address* is the IP address listed in the table. Does the command show a first entry with either R2's IP address or R3's IP address?

_____

_____

Hints and Answers

Table 2 lists hints and tips for any lab steps that do not supply all the details in the lab step, and for lab steps that ask questions about the lab.

Table 2   Hints

Step	Hint
3	The **show cdp neighbors detail** command lists a group of messages per neighbor. For each neighbor, the output lists the local router interface, the neighbor's host name, and the neighbor's IP address.
5	The method used to determine the matching route is to look at each subnet in the routing table and mentally calculate the range of addresses in the subnet. Then choose the route whose subnet range includes the IP address in question. If more than one route's subnet range matches the IP address, choose the route with the more specific match; that is, the longer prefix mask.

continues

Table 2   Hints   *continued*

Step	Hint
6	The output of the **show ip route 172.16.30.1** command lists a message which means that R1 matches no routes.
7	It lists three lines of three asterisks, which in the simulator means that the command would not complete and did not even get a response from the next router. In this case, the **traceroute 172.16.30.1** command confirms that R1 has no matching route for 172.16.30.1.
9	The output of the **show ip route 172.16.28.150** command should list subnet 172.16.28.128/25 (/25 is equal to 255.255.255.128). It should also list R3's IP address 172.16.11.3 as the next-hop, with R1's outgoing interface of S0/0/1.
10	It lists a single line, 172.16.11.3, which is R3's IP address. So the **traceroute 172.16.28.150** command confirms that the next-hop router in the route is R3.
12	The output of the **show ip route 172.16.31.100** command should list subnet 172.16.31.0/25 (/25 is equal to 255.255.255.128). It should also list R2's IP address 172.16.10.2 as the next-hop, with R1's outgoing interface of S0/0/0.
13	It lists a single line, 172.16.10.2, which is R2's IP address. So the **traceroute 172.16.31.100** command confirms that the next-hop router in the route is R2.

Configuration Steps

This lab requires no configuration.

ICND1 Subnetting Exercises
Part 3: IP Route Selection

Lab 8: IP Route Selection VIII

Overview

In this exercise, you focus on the routes known by Router R1. This lab essentially guides you to ask and then answer a question about three different IP addresses. The question: If a packet arrived at R1 destined for a particular IP address, which of R1's routes, if any, would R1 use when forwarding the packet?

During this lab, you look at R1's routing table and make your prediction. You then use commands to confirm which route R1 would use. The IP addresses to consider for this lab are as follows in Table 1.

Table 1　Destinations and Matching Route Info (to Be Completed)

Destination Address	Matching Route's Subnet/Mask	Matching Route's Outgoing Interface
172.16.115.100		
172.16.100.100		
172.16.105.100		

Topology

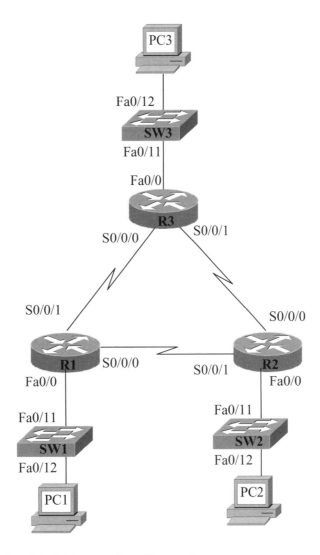

Figure 1　Topology for IP Address Configuration

Detailed Lab Steps

Step 1. Connect to R1 from the simulator user interface. All passwords are **cs**.

Step 2. Enter privileged exec ("enable") mode by issuing the **enable** command.

Step 3. Use the output from the **show cdp neighbors detail** command, along with the diagram in this lab, to discover key facts about R1's outgoing interfaces for its routes. What local interfaces does R1 have? What other routers are neighbors of R1? Per the command output, what IP address does R2 use on the other end of the serial link? R3? Record your answers on the following lines.

_____

_____

_____

Step 4. Display the IP routing table using the **show ip route** exec command.

Step 5. Examine the first of the three IP addresses in the table at the beginning of this lab compared to the routing table displayed in the previous step. Imagine that a packet arrives at R1 with a destination IP address of the IP address listed in the table. Using any math you know to examine the existing routes, decide whether any routes match the packet. If so, complete the table's last two columns for that IP address.

_____

_____

The **show ip route** *address* command, where *address* is some IP address, lists details about a route. Specifically, it lists details about the route that a router would match when processing a packet destined for the IP address in the command. For example, the **show ip route 1.1.1.1** command lists information about the route used to forward packets destined for 1.1.1.1. If the router does not match any routes, the output either lists nothing or lists an error message.

Step 6. Issue the **show ip route** *address* command, where *address* is the first IP address listed in the table. Does this command confirm that the router does indeed match a route for this packet destination? Does the output list the same subnet ID, and same outgoing interface, that you predicted and recorded in the table per Step 5?

_____

_____

Step 7. Issue the **traceroute** *address* command, where *address* is the first IP address listed in the table. Does the command show either R2's IP address or R3's IP address? Does it show a series of asterisks, signifying that no route existed?

_____

_____

Step 8. Similar to Step 5, examine the second IP address in the table at the beginning of this lab, and make predictions about which of R1's routes this packet will match. Complete the appropriate row of the table at the beginning of this lab.

_____

_____

Step 9. Similar to Step 6, confirm whether you made the correct prediction using the **show ip route** *address* command, where *address* is the second IP address listed in the table. Does the output list the same subnet ID, and same outgoing interface, that you predicted and recorded in the table per the previous step?

_____

_____

Step 10. Issue the **traceroute** *address* command, where *address* is the second IP address listed in the table. Does the command show a first entry with either R2's IP address or R3's IP address?

_____

_____

Step 11. Similar to Step 5, examine the third IP address in the table at the beginning of this lab, and make predictions about which of R1's routes this packet will match. Complete the appropriate row of the table at the beginning of this lab.

_____

_____

Step 12. Similar to Step 6, confirm whether you made the correct prediction using the **show ip route** *address* command, where *address* is the third IP address listed in the table. Does the output list the same subnet ID, and same outgoing interface, that you predicted and recorded in the table per the previous step?

_____

_____

Step 13. Issue the **traceroute** *address* command, where *address* is the IP address listed in the table. Does the command show a first entry with either R2's IP address or R3's IP address?

_____

_____

Hints and Answers

Table 2 lists hints and tips for any lab steps that do not supply all the details in the lab step, and for lab steps that ask questions about the lab.

Table 2   Hints

Step	Hint
3	The **show cdp neighbors detail** command lists a group of messages per neighbor. For each neighbor, the output lists the local router interface, the neighbor's host name, and the neighbor's IP address.
5	The method used to determine the matching route is to look at each subnet in the routing table and mentally calculate the range of addresses in the subnet. Then choose the route whose subnet range includes the IP address in question. If more than one route's subnet range matches the IP address, choose the route with the more specific match; that is, the longer prefix mask.
6	The output of the **show ip route 172.16.115.100** command should list subnet 172.16.112.0/22 (/22 is equal to 255.255.252.0). It should also list R2's IP address 172.16.10.2 as the next-hop, with R1's outgoing interface of S0/0/0.
7	It lists a single line, 172.16.10.2, which is R2's IP address. So the **traceroute 172.16.115.100** command confirms that the next-hop router in the route is R2.
9	The output of the **show ip route 172.16.100.100** command should list subnet 172.16.100.0/22 (/22 is equal to 255.255.252.0). It should also list R3's IP address 172.16.5.3 as the next-hop, with R1's outgoing interface of S0/0/1.
10	It lists a single line, 172.16.5.3, which is R3's IP address. So the **traceroute 172.16.100.100** command confirms that the next-hop router in the route is R3.
12	The output of the **show ip route 172.16.105.100** command lists a message which means that R1 matches no routes.
13	It lists three lines of three asterisks, which in the simulator means that the command would not complete and did not even get a response from the next router. In this case, the **traceroute 172.16.105.100** command confirms that R1 has no matching route for 172.16.105.100.

Configuration Steps

This lab requires no configuration.

ICND1 Subnetting Exercises

Part 3: IP Route Selection

Lab 9: IP Route Selection IX

Overview

In this exercise, you focus on the routes known by Router R1. This lab essentially guides you to ask and then answer a question about three different IP addresses. The question: If a packet arrived at R1 destined for a particular IP address, which of R1's routes, if any, would R1 use when forwarding the packet?

During this lab, you look at R1's routing table and make your prediction. You then use commands to confirm which route R1 would use. The IP addresses to consider for this lab are as follows in Table 1.

Table 1   Destinations and Matching Route Info (to Be Completed)

Destination Address	Matching Route's Subnet/Mask	Matching Route's Outgoing Interface
10.50.1.1		
10.60.1.1		
10.70.1.1		

Topology

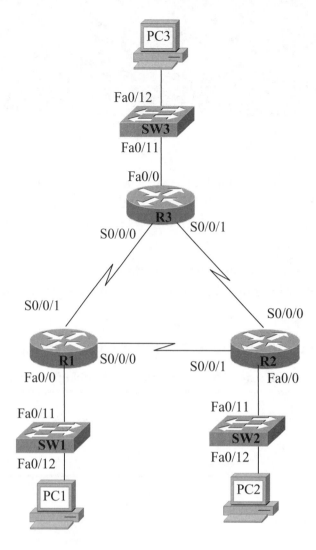

Figure 1   Topology for IP Address Configuration

Detailed Lab Steps

Step 1.   Connect to R1 from the simulator user interface. All passwords are **cs**.

Step 2.   Enter privileged exec ("enable") mode by issuing the **enable** command.

Step 3.   Use the output from the **show cdp neighbors detail** command, along with the diagram in this lab, to discover key facts about R1's outgoing interfaces for its routes. What local interfaces does R1 have? What other routers are neighbors of R1? Per the command output, what IP address does R2 use on the other end of the serial link? R3? Record your answers on the following lines.

_____

_____

_____

Step 4. Display the IP routing table using the **show ip route** exec command.

Step 5. Examine the first of the three IP addresses in the table at the beginning of this lab compared to the routing table displayed in the previous step. Imagine that a packet arrives at R1 with a destination IP address of the IP address listed in the table. Using any math you know to examine the existing routes, decide whether any routes match the packet. If so, complete the table's last two columns for that IP address.

_____

_____

The **show ip route** *address* command, where *address* is some IP address, lists details about a route. Specifically, it lists details about the route that a router would match when processing a packet destined for the IP address in the command. For example, the **show ip route 1.1.1.1** command lists information about the route used to forward packets destined for 1.1.1.1. If the router does not match any routes, the output either lists nothing or lists an error message.

Step 6. Issue the **show ip route** *address* command, where *address* is the first IP address listed in the table. Does this command confirm that the router does indeed match a route for this packet destination? Does the output list the same subnet ID, and same outgoing interface, that you predicted and recorded in the table per Step 5?

_____

_____

Step 7. Issue the **traceroute** *address* command, where *address* is the first IP address listed in the table. Does the command show either R2's IP address or R3's IP address? Does it show a series of asterisks, signifying that no route existed?

_____

_____

Step 8. Similar to Step 5, examine the second IP address in the table at the beginning of this lab, and make predictions about which of R1's routes this packet will match. Complete the appropriate row of the table at the beginning of this lab.

_____

_____

Step 9. Similar to Step 6, confirm whether you made the correct prediction using the **show ip route** *address* command, where *address* is the second IP address listed in the table. Does the output list the same subnet ID, and same outgoing interface, that you predicted and recorded in the table per the previous step?

_____

_____

Step 10. Issue the **traceroute** *address* command, where *address* is the second IP address listed in the table. Does the command show a first entry with either R2's IP address or R3's IP address?

_____

_____

Step 11. Similar to Step 5, examine the third IP address in the table at the beginning of this lab, and make predictions about which of R1's routes this packet will match. Complete the appropriate row of the table at the beginning of this lab.

_____

_____

Step 12. Similar to Step 6, confirm whether you made the correct prediction using the **show ip route** *address* command, where *address* is the third IP address listed in the table. Does the output list the same subnet ID, and same outgoing interface, that you predicted and recorded in the table per the previous step?

_____

_____

Step 13. Issue the **traceroute** *address* command, where *address* is the IP address listed in the table. Does the command show a first entry with either R2's IP address or R3's IP address?

_____

_____

Hints and Answers

Table 2 lists hints and tips for any lab steps that do not supply all the details in the lab step, and for lab steps that ask questions about the lab.

Table 2   Hints

Step	Hint
3	The **show cdp neighbors detail** command lists a group of messages per neighbor. For each neighbor, the output lists the local router interface, the neighbor's host name, and the neighbor's IP address.
5	The method used to determine the matching route is to look at each subnet in the routing table and mentally calculate the range of addresses in the subnet. Then choose the route whose subnet range includes the IP address in question. If more than one route's subnet range matches the IP address, choose the route with the more specific match; that is, the longer prefix mask.

continues

Table 2   Hints   *continued*

Step	Hint
6	The output of the **show ip route 10.50.1.1** command should list subnet 10.48.0.0/13 (/13 is equal to 255.248.0.0). It should also list R2's IP address 10.1.1.2 as the next-hop, with R1's outgoing interface of S0/0/0.
7	It lists a single line, 10.1.1.2, which is R2's IP address. So the **traceroute 10.50.1.1** command confirms that the next-hop router in the route is R2.
9	The output of the **show ip route 10.60.1.1** command lists a message which means that R1 matches no routes.
10	It lists three lines of three asterisks, which in the simulator means that the command would not complete and did not even get a response from the next router. In this case, the **traceroute 10.60.1.1** command confirms that R1 has no matching route for 10.60.1.1.
12	The output of the **show ip route 10.70.1.1** command should be a blank line, meaning that R1 matches no routes.
13	It lists three lines of three asterisks, which in the simulator means that the command would not complete and did not even get a response from the next router. In this case, the **traceroute 10.70.1.1** command confirms that R1 has no matching route for 10.70.1.1.

Configuration Steps

This lab requires no configuration.

ICND1 Subnetting Exercises
Part 3: IP Route Selection

Lab 10: IP Route Selection X

Overview

In this exercise, you focus on the routes known by Router R1. This lab essentially guides you to ask and then answer a question about three different IP addresses. The question: If a packet arrived at R1 destined for a particular IP address, which of R1's routes, if any, would R1 use when forwarding the packet?

During this lab, you look at R1's routing table and make your prediction. You then use commands to confirm which route R1 would use. The IP addresses to consider for this lab are as follows in Table 1.

Table 1   Destinations and Matching Route Info (to Be Completed)

Destination Address	Matching Route's Subnet/Mask	Matching Route's Outgoing Interface
10.7.101.1		
10.7.151.1		
10.7.201.1		

Topology

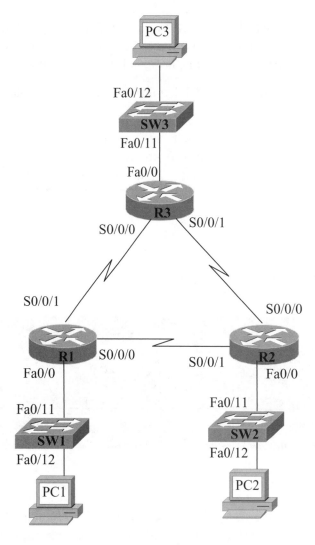

Figure 1   Topology for IP Address Configuration

Detailed Lab Steps

Step 1. Connect to R1 from the simulator user interface. All passwords are **cs**.

Step 2. Enter privileged exec ("enable") mode by issuing the **enable** command.

Step 3. Use the output from the **show cdp neighbors detail** command, along with the diagram in this lab, to discover key facts about R1's outgoing interfaces for its routes. What local interfaces does R1 have? What other routers are neighbors of R1? Per the command output, what IP address does R2 use on the other end of the serial link? R3? Record your answers on the following lines.

_____

_____

_____

Step 4. Display the IP routing table using the **show ip route** exec command.

Step 5. Examine the first of the three IP addresses in the table at the beginning of this lab compared to the routing table displayed in the previous step. Imagine that a packet arrives at R1 with a destination IP address of the IP address listed in the table. Using any math you know to examine the existing routes, decide whether any routes match the packet. If so, complete the table's last two columns for that IP address.

_____

_____

The **show ip route** *address* command, where *address* is some IP address, lists details about a route. Specifically, it lists details about the route that a router would match when processing a packet destined for the IP address in the command. For example, the **show ip route 1.1.1.1** command lists information about the route used to forward packets destined for 1.1.1.1. If the router does not match any routes, the output either lists nothing or lists an error message.

Step 6. Issue the **show ip route** *address* command, where *address* is the first IP address listed in the table. Does this command confirm that the router does indeed match a route for this packet destination? Does the output list the same subnet ID, and same outgoing interface, that you predicted and recorded in the table per Step 5?

_____

_____

Step 7. Issue the **traceroute** *address* command, where *address* is the first IP address listed in the table. Does the command show either R2's IP address or R3's IP address? Does it show a series of asterisks, signifying that no route existed?

_____

_____

Step 8. Similar to Step 5, examine the second IP address in the table at the beginning of this lab, and make predictions about which of R1's routes this packet will match. Complete the appropriate row of the table at the beginning of this lab.

_____

_____

Step 9. Similar to Step 6, confirm whether you made the correct prediction using the **show ip route** *address* command, where *address* is the second IP address listed in the table. Does the output list the same subnet ID, and same outgoing interface, that you predicted and recorded in the table per the previous step?

_____

_____

Step 10. Issue the **traceroute** *address* command, where *address* is the second IP address listed in the table. Does the command show a first entry with either R2's IP address or R3's IP address?

_____

_____

Step 11. Similar to Step 5, examine the third IP address in the table at the beginning of this lab, and make predictions about which of R1's routes this packet will match. Complete the appropriate row of the table at the beginning of this lab.

_____

_____

Step 12. Similar to Step 6, confirm whether you made the correct prediction using the **show ip route** *address* command, where *address* is the third IP address listed in the table. Does the output list the same subnet ID, and same outgoing interface, that you predicted and recorded in the table per the previous step?

_____

_____

Step 13. Issue the **traceroute** *address* command, where *address* is the IP address listed in the table. Does the command show a first entry with either R2's IP address or R3's IP address?

_____

_____

Hints and Answers

Table 2 lists hints and tips for any lab steps that do not supply all the details in the lab step, and for lab steps that ask questions about the lab.

Table 2   Hints

Step	Hint
3	The **show cdp neighbors detail** command lists a group of messages per neighbor. For each neighbor, the output lists the local router interface, the neighbor's host name, and the neighbor's IP address.
5	The method used to determine the matching route is to look at each subnet in the routing table and mentally calculate the range of addresses in the subnet. Then choose the route whose subnet range includes the IP address in question. If more than one route's subnet range matches the IP address, choose the route with the more specific match; that is, the longer prefix mask.
6	The output of the **show ip route 10.7.101.1** command should list subnet 10.7.64.0/18 (/18 is equal to 255.255.192.0). It should also list R3's IP address 10.33.1.3 as the next-hop, with R1's outgoing interface of S0/0/1.
7	It lists a single line, 10.33.1.3, which is R3's IP address. So the **traceroute 10.7.101.1** command confirms that the next-hop router in the route is R3.
9	The output of the **show ip route 10.7.151.1** command lists a message which means that R1 matches no routes.
10	It lists three lines of three asterisks, which in the simulator means that the command would not complete and did not even get a response from the next router. In this case, the **traceroute 10.7.151.1** command confirms that R1 has no matching route for 10.7.151.1.
12	The output of the **show ip route 10.7.201.1** command should list subnet 10.7.192.0/18 (/18 is equal to 255.255.192.0). It should also list R3's IP address 10.33.1.3 as the next-hop, with R1's outgoing interface of S0/0/1.
13	It lists a single line, 10.33.1.3, which is R3's IP address. So the **traceroute 10.7.201.1** command confirms that the next-hop router in the route is R3.

Configuration Steps

This lab requires no configuration.

Advanced IP Routing Topics and OSPF

Table 7-1 lists the labs for this unit. Check with your instructor or class syllabus to confirm what labs you should perform for class.

Table 7-1 Unit 7 Labs

Date	ICND1/ ICND2	Type	Part	Number	Name	Page
	ICND2	CS	2	1	IP Addressing and Configuration I	307
	ICND2	SB	3	19	OSPF Serial Configuration I	319
	ICND2	SB	3	25	OSPF Router ID I	322
	ICND2	SB	3	32	OSPF Metric Tuning I	325
	ICND2	SB	3	35	OSPF Neighbors I	327
	ICND2	TS	1	10	Routing Analysis III	329
	ICND2	TS	1	13	IP Routing II	340
	ICND2	SE	1	1–11	VLSM Overlaps I–XI	351
	ICND2	SE	2	1–7	Selecting VLSM Routes I–VII	395
	Ungraded	CL	1	4	Configuring OSPF Routing	430

ICND2 Configuration Scenarios
Part 2: IP Addressing and Routing

Lab 1: IP Addressing and Configuration I

Overview

You are to plan and implement the multilocation internetwork based on some incomplete work from a fellow network engineer. First, you will choose the subnet numbers to use, and then the addresses to use for the devices shown in Figure 1. Following that, you will configure the router LAN interfaces, followed by the configuration of the router WAN interfaces. Finally, once all the configuration is complete, you need to establish a routing protocol between the routers to share the routes. Once the configuration is complete, you will need to perform network testing and correct any issues.

At the beginning of this lab, the PCs have been fully configured. The routers have their device names applied and passwords configured, and the console and vty lines are configured. The switches also do not require any further configuration and will essentially be ignored for the purposes of this lab.

Topology

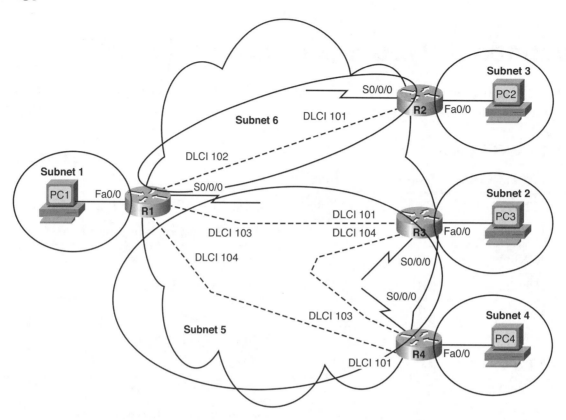

Figure 1   Network Topology for This Lab

Reference Tables

Table 1 provides a place to record the results of your subnet planning process, as requested by various steps in this lab. Table 2 is a place to record the IP address, mask, and default gateway information you choose during the lab.

Table 1   IP Subnet Address Planning

Generic Subnet Number	Network	Number of Host Addresses	Subnet Number	Mask	Lowest Address	Highest Address
1	R1 LAN	200				
2	R3 LAN	70				
3	R2 LAN	25				
4	R4 LAN	12				
5	R1-R3-R4 WAN	3				
6	R1-R2 WAN	2				

Table 2   **IP Addressing Reference**

Device	Interface	IP Address	Mask	Default Gateway
R1	S0/0/0.2			
	S0/0/0.34			
	Fa0/0			
R2	S0/0/0.1			
	Fa0/0			
R3	S0/0/0.14			
	Fa0/0			
R4	S0/0/0.13			
	Fa0/0			
PC1				
PC2				
PC3				
PC4				

Detailed Lab Steps

Part 1: Address Planning

In the first part of this lab, you will plan the subnet numbers you will configure during this lab, based on subnetting requirements and plans made by another engineer.

Note: Tables 3 and 4, in the "Hints and Answers" section of this lab, show the completed versions of Tables 1 and 2. To receive a passing score on this lab, you must use the addresses suggested in Tables 3 and 4.

Step 1. Examine Figure 1, noting the six subnets planned for a small internetwork. For each subnet, Table 1 lists the generic subnet numbers to match the figure, along with the required number of hosts in each of the subnets. In this step, choose the mask to support each subnet so that the mask has the least number of host bits that supports the required number of hosts, and record those masks in Table 1.

Step 2. Choose subnet numbers to use for each subnet. When making your choices, assign the lowest possible subnet numbers; the zero subnet is allowed to be used. Assign the subnets in the order listed in Table 1 (subnet 1 first, then subnet 2, and so forth).

Step 3. Plan the specific addresses to be used by router interfaces and the PCs. By convention, assign the routers the highest IP address(es) in each subnet, and the hosts the lowest IP address. In the cases of more than one router interface in the same subnetwork, begin the addressing with the highest address applied to the interface of the lowest-numbered router. For example, R1 would get the highest address in the subnet, R2 would receive the next lower address in the subnet. Table 2 has been provided for planning this addressing scheme.

Part 2: Configure the Router LAN Interfaces

In Part 1, you created the addressing plan for the devices in the internetwork. In Part 2, you will begin the router configuration. With the routers preconfigured with the basic device information, you can concentrate on the configuration of the interface and the routing protocol.

Beginning with R1, you should add the address to the LAN interfaces. After all the LAN interfaces are operational, you will configure the Frame Relay subinterfaces for the WAN connections.

Step 4. From the simulator user interface, connect to R1 and move into enable mode.

Step 5. Add the IP address to the FastEthernet 0/0 interface of R1. What commands are used to add the address to Fa0/0 of R1? Exit configuration mode when finished.

_____

_____

Step 6. After adding the address to Fa0/0 of R1, examine the routing table to determine if the route of the network connected to this interface has been added to the routing table. Was the route added? Why or why not?

_____

_____

_____

Step 7. Move back into interface configuration mode to enable the Fa0/0 interface. Exit configuration mode when finished.

Step 8. Re-examine the routing table to verify that the connected route for Fa0/0 is present.

Step 9. To verify the operation of the Fa0/0 interface, ping the host that sits on the same LAN—PC1 in this case. (Refer to Table 2 where you took notes on addresses, or to the completed Table 4, for the list of IP addresses.) Did the ping work?

_____

Step 10. Repeat Steps 4 through 9 for routers R2, R3, and R4. By the end of this step, each router should be able to ping the PC that sits on the same subnet.

Part 3: Configure the Router WAN Interfaces

In Part 2, you provided the necessary Layer 3 addresses for the LAN interfaces and enabled these router interfaces. In Part 3, you examine the preconfigured WAN interfaces and then add IP addresses to the configuration.

Step 11. Connect to router R1 from the simulator user interface and move into enable mode.

Step 12. Use the **show ip interface brief** command to display all current interfaces and their status. Other than Fa0/0, what interfaces are listed in an "up/up" state?

\
\

Step 13. Use the **show running-config** command to display information about the mapping of DLCIs to different subinterfaces. Compare that information to Figure 1 and the information gathered in the previous step. Which subinterface is configured to support the subnet connected to router R2? Which subinterface supports the subnet connected to both R3 and R4?

\
\

Step 14. Use the **show running-config** command to display information about the current configuration. Look at interface S0/0/0 and the subinterfaces that follow. Do any of these have IP addresses assigned?

\
\

R1 uses subinterface S0/0/0.102 for its PVC connected to R2 and subinterface S0/0/0.34 for its PVC connected to both R3 and R4. However, neither subinterface has an IP address assigned.

Step 15. Move into configuration mode and add the IP addresses to the two subinterfaces of S0/0/0, using the addresses in Table 2 or Table 4. Record the configuration commands you use, and exit configuration mode when finished.

\
\
\

Step 16. Examine the routing table to determine if the routes for the two new connected networks are listed in the routing table. Do the subnet numbers match those you calculated and recorded in Table 1?

_____

The other three routers (R2, R3, and R4) each have a single serial subinterface, as noted in Tables 1, 2, 3, and 4. The rest of this part completes the configuration process on the WAN interfaces.

Step 17. From the simulator user interface, connect to R2, R3, and R4 in turn, and configure each router's single WAN subinterface with the IP address and mask listed in Table 2. Record the commands you used in each case.

_____

_____

_____

_____

_____

Step 18. Now that the Layer 3 addresses have been assigned to the WAN interfaces, you should verify that the routers can ping the IP addresses on the other end of the WAN links. To do so, first move back to router R1 from the simulator user interface.

Step 19. Referring to Table 2's IP addresses, ping the WAN IP address on R2, R3, and R4. Which pings were successful? Which were not?

_____

_____

_____

Step 20. Move to R2 from the simulator user interface and ping the WAN IP addresses of R1, R3, and R4. Which pings were successful? Which were not? Why?

_____

_____

_____

Step 21. Move to R3 from the simulator user interface and ping the WAN IP addresses of R1, R2, and R4. Which pings were successful? Which were not? Why?

_____

_____

_____

Step 22. Move to R4 from the simulator user interface and ping the WAN IP addresses of R1, R2, and R3. Which pings were successful? Which were not? Why?

_____

_____

_____

Part 4: Configure Routing Protocols and Verify the Network Works

In Part 3, you established the WAN connection between routers and ensured that the routers can ping each other—at least in cases where two routers connect to the same subnet. However, the routing tables are not fully populated with all the routes in the internetwork. In Part 4, you will add a routing protocol to the routers. For this internetwork, you will use EIGRP 1.

Step 23. On routers R1, R2, R3, and R4, configure the commands **router eigrp 1** and **network 10.0.0.0**. These commands enable EIGRP with the same ASN on all four routers, enabling EIGRP on all interfaces in Class A network 10.0.0.0.

Step 24. Move to router R1 from the simulator user interface and display its IP routing table. How many routes are displayed? How many are connected routes? How many are EIGRP-learned routes, as evidenced with a "D" on the left side of the line for that route?

_____

_____

_____

Step 25. Continuing to look at that same output, how many different subnet masks are used by the subnets listed in R1's routing table?

_____

_____

_____

Step 26. Using Table 2 to remind yourself of the IP addresses, ping the four PCs from R1. Which of the pings worked?

_____

Step 27. Move to router R2 from the simulator user interface and display its IP routing table. How many routes are displayed? How many are connected routes? How many are EIGRP-learned routes, as evidenced with a "D" on the left side of the line for that route? Why does R2 have more EIGRP-learned routes than did R1?

_____

_____

_____

Step 28. Using Table 2 to remind yourself of the IP addresses, ping the four PCs from R2. Which of the pings worked?

_____

Hints and Answers

Table 3 lists a completed version of Table 1, listing the subnet information for the internetwork. Table 4 is a completed form of Table 2, listing addressing information for the devices. Table 5 provides hints and tips for any lab steps that do not supply complete details and provides answers for any lab steps that ask questions.

Table 3   IP Subnet Address Planning

Subnet Number	Number of Network	Subnet Host Addresses	Number	Mask	Lowest Address	Highest Address
1	R1 LAN	200	10.0.0.0/24	255.255.255.0	10.0.0.1	10.0.0.254
2	R3 LAN	70	10.0.1.0/25	255.255.255.128	10.0.1.1	10.0.1.126
3	R2 LAN	25	10.0.1.128/27	255.255.255.224	10.0.1.129	10.0.1.158
4	R4 LAN	12	10.0.1.160/28	255.255.255.240	10.0.1.161	10.0.1.174
5	R1-R3-R4 WAN	3	10.0.1.176/29	255.255.255.248	10.0.1.177	10.0.1.182
6	R1-R2 WAN	2	10.0.1.184/30	255.255.255.252	10.0.1.185	10.0.1.186

Table 4   IP Addressing Reference

Device	Interface	IP Address	Mask	Default Gateway
R1	S0/0/0.2	10.0.1.186	255.255.255.252	
	S0/0/0.34	10.0.1.182	255.255.255.248	
	Fa0/0	10.0.0.254	255.255.255.0	
R2	S0/0/0.1	10.0.1.185	255.255.255.252	
	Fa0/0	10.0.1.158	255.255.255.224	

Device	Interface	IP Address	Mask	Default Gateway
R3	S0/0/0.14	10.0.1.181	255.255.255.248	
	Fa0/0	10.0.1.126	255.255.255.128	
R4	S0/0/0.13	10.0.1.180	255.255.255.248	
	Fa0/0	10.0.1.174	255.255.255.240	
PC1		10.0.0.1	255.255.255.0	10.0.0.254
PC2		10.0.1.129	255.255.255.224	10.0.1.158
PC3		10.0.1.1	255.255.255.128	10.0.1.126
PC4		10.0.1.161	255.255.255.240	10.0.1.174

Table 5   Hints and Answers

Step	Hint or Answer
1, 2	The solution to the IP subnet address planning information can be found in Table 3.
3	The solution to the device IP address planning information can be found in Table 4.
4	Use the **enable** command to move to privileged mode.
5	Use Table 1 as the reference for the addresses. Use the following commands: **configure terminal** **interface fastethernet0/0** **ip address 10.0.0.254 255.255.255.0** **end**
6	Use the **show ip route** command on R1 to view the routing table. R1 did not add a connected route for this subnet because the Fa0/0 is not up.
7	Use the following commands: **configure terminal** **interface fastethernet0/0** **no shutdown** **end**
8	Use the **show ip route** command to look for the connected network of 10.0.0.0/24.
9	The **ping 10.0.0.1** command should work.

continues

Table 5   **Hints and Answers**   *continued*

Step	Hint or Answer

10	On R2:
	
	interface fastethernet0/0
	  ip address 10.0.1.158 255.255.255.224
	  no shutdown
	
	The **show ip route** command on R2 should show a connected network of 10.0.1.128/27.
	On R3:
	
	interface fastethernet0/0
	  ip address 10.0.1.126 255.255.255.128
	  no shutdown
	
	The **show ip route** command on R3 should show a connected network of 10.0.1.0/25.
	On R4:
	
	interface fastethernet0/0
	  ip address 10.0.1.174 255.255.255.240
	  no shutdown
	
	The **show ip route** command on R4 should show a connected network of 10.0.1.160/28.

11	Use the **enable** command to move to privileged mode.
12	The output lists S0/0/0.2 and S0/0/0.34.
13	The mapping shows DLCI 102 with S0/0/0.2; according to Figure 1, this DLCI is part of subnet 6, which connects to router R2. DLCIs 103 and 104 are associated with subinterface S0/0/0.34; according to Figure 1, these two DLCIs are part of subnet 5, which connects to routers R3 and R4.
14	The configuration shows the Frame Relay interface configuration, but without any IP addresses on the physical interface or the subinterfaces.

15	**configure terminal**
	interface S0/0/0.2
	  ip address 10.0.1.186 255.255.255.252
	interface S0/0/0.34
	  ip address 10.0.1.182 255.255.255.248
	  end

16	The subnets are S0/0/0.2: 10.0.1.184/30 S0/0/0.34: 10.0.1.176/29

Step	Hint or Answer
17	On R2: **configure terminal** **interface s0/0/0.1** **ip address 10.0.1.185 255.255.255.252** **end** On R3: **configure terminal** **interface s0/0/0.14** **ip address 10.0.1.181 255.255.255.248** **end** On R4: **configure terminal** **interface s0/0/0.13** **ip address 10.0.1.180 255.255.255.248** **end**
19	The pings should work. The commands are **ping 10.0.1.185** (R2) **ping 10.0.1.181** (R3) **ping 10.0.1.180** (R4)
20	The ping to R1's IP address (**ping 10.0.1.186**) should work. The other two pings do not work. The reason is that R3's and R4's WAN interfaces are in the same subnet as R2's WAN subinterface, and R2 does not have a routing protocol with which to learn routes yet.
21	The pings to both R1's and R4's WAN IP addresses work. The ping to R2's WAN interface (**ping 10.0.1.185**) fails. The reason is that R3's WAN interface is not in the same subnet as R2's WAN subinterface, and R3 does not have a routing protocol with which to learn routes yet.
22	The pings to both R1's and R3's WAN IP addresses work. The ping to R2's WAN interface (**ping 10.0.1.185**) fails. The reason is that R4's WAN interface is not in the same subnet as R2's WAN subinterface, and R4 does not have a routing protocol with which to learn routes yet.
24	R1 has six routes: three connected routes and three EIGRP-learned routes.
25	All six subnets use a different subnet mask. The masks, in prefix notation, are /24, /25, /27, /28, /29, and /30.
26	The pings should work at this point.
27	R2 has six routes: two connected routes and four EIGRP-learned routes. R2 is directly connected to only two subnets, so R2 must learn about the other four subnets using EIGRP.
28	The pings should work at this point.

Configuration

Example 1 shows the configuration commands added to the routers during this lab.

Author's note: This lab begins with all serial subinterfaces having been preconfigured. As a result, the interface command can be used either with or without the multipoint keyword, or with or without the point-to-point keyword. The Simulator's grading function requires that you omit these keywords. The keywords, however, are included in Example 1 for the purpose of reminding you of the complete syntax.

Example 1   Configuration on the Routers During This Lab

```
! The following was configured on R1:


interface FastEthernet0/0
 ip address 10.0.0.254 255.255.255.0
 no shutdown


interface serial 0/0/0.34 multipoint
 ip address 10.0.1.182 255.255.255.248


interface serial 0/0/0.2 point-to-point
 ip address 10.0.1.186 255.255.255.252

Router eigrp 1
 Network 10.0.0.0


! The following was configured on R2:


interface FastEthernet0/0
 ip address 10.0.1.158 255.255.255.224
 no shutdown


interface serial 0/0/0.1 point-to-point
 ip address 10.0.1.185 255.255.255.252
!
Router eigrp 1
 Network 10.0.0.0


! The following was configured on R3:


interface FastEthernet0/0
```

continues

```
  ip address 10.0.1.126 255.255.255.128
  no shutdown


interface serial 0/0/0.14 multipoint
  ip address 10.0.1.181 255.255.255.248


Router eigrp 1
  Network 10.0.0.0


! The following was configured on R4:
interface fastEthernet0/0
  ip address 10.0.1.174 255.255.255.240
  no shutdown


interface serial 0/0/0.13 multipoint
  ip address 10.0.1.180 255.255.255.248


!
Router eigrp 1
  Network 10.0.0.0
```

ICND2 Skill Builders

Part 3: IP Routing Protocols

Lab 19: OSPF Serial Configuration I

Overview

This lab begins with a working internetwork with valid IP addresses on all routers and PCs and with OSPF fully configured on R1. This lab guides you through the manual configuration of R2's OSPF configuration and then shows the resulting exchange of routing information.

Topology

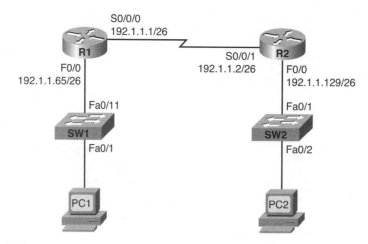

Figure 1   Network Topology for This Lab

Detailed Lab Steps

Step 1.   Connect to R2 from the simulator user interface using the password **ciscopress**.

Step 2.   Show the current IP-enabled interfaces by issuing the **show ip interface brief** command. Write down the configured interfaces and IP addresses.

_____

_____

Step 3.   Enter privileged exec mode using the **enable** command and password **ciscopress**.

Step 4.   Move to global configuration mode using the **configure terminal** command.

Step 5.   Configure OSPF with a process ID of 10 by entering the router configuration mode for OSPF and entering the **router ospf 10** command.

Step 6.   Configure the OSPF network 192.1.1.0 in area 0 by entering the **network 192.1.1.0 0.0.0.255 area 0** command. On what interfaces will R2 enable OSPF as a result? Does this command enable OSPF on all interfaces noted in Step 2?

_____

_____

_____

Step 7.   Exit back into enable mode by entering the **end** command.

Step 8. View the IP routing table by entering the **show ip route** command. What routes are in R2's routing table?

_____

_____

_____

Step 9. Connect to R1 from the simulator user interface using the password **ciscopress**.

Step 10. View the IP routing table by entering the **show ip route** command. What routes are in R1's routing table?

_____

_____

_____

Hints and Answers

Table 1 provides hints and tips for any lab steps that do not supply complete details and provides answers for any lab steps that ask questions.

Table 1   Hints and Answers

Step	Hint or Answer
2	S0/0/1 – 192.1.1.2/26
	Fa0/0 – 192.1.1.129/26
6	Interfaces:
	Fa0/0
	S0/0/1
8	R2's connected routes:
	192.1.1.128/26
	192.1.1.0/26
	R2's routes learned from R1:
	192.1.1.64/26
10	R1's connected routes:
	192.1.1.0/26
	192.1.1.64/26
	R1's routes learned from R2:
	192.1.1.128/26

Configuration Steps

Example 1 shows a sample of the lab exercise being completed from R2's CLI.

Example 1 Example of Performing This Lab

```
R2#configure terminal
R2(config)#router ospf 10
R2(config-router)#network 192.1.1.0 0.0.0.255 area 0
R2(config-router)#end
```

ICND2 Skill Builders

Part 3: IP Routing Protocols

Lab 25: OSPF Router ID I

Overview

This lab begins with a working internetwork with valid IP addresses on all routers and PCs and with OSPF fully configured on all routers. This lab shows the use of the OSPF router ID and how it can be controlled through the use of a loopback interface.

Topology

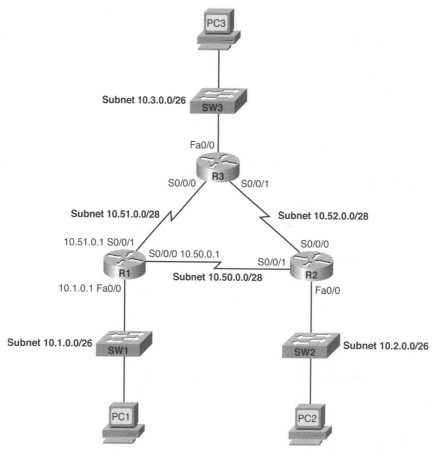

Figure 1   Network Topology for This Lab

Detailed Lab Steps

Step 1. Connect to R1 from the simulator user interface using the password **ciscopress**.

Step 2. Show the current IP-enabled interfaces by issuing the **show ip interface brief** command. Write down the configured interfaces and IP addresses.

_____

_____

Step 3. Based on the IP addresses gathered in the previous step, what OSPF router ID do you think R1 will use? Why?

_____

_____

_____

Step 4. Show the OSPF router ID by issuing the **show ip ospf** command. Write down the current router ID.

_____

_____

Step 5. Move to global configuration mode first issuing the **enable** command (with password **ciscopress**) and then using the **configure terminal** command.

Step 6. Create a loopback interface by issuing the **interface loopback 0** command.

Step 7. Assign the loopback 0 interface an IP address of 1.1.1.1 by issuing the **ip address 1.1.1.1 255.255.255.255** command.

Step 8. Exit back into enable mode by entering the **end** command.

Step 9. Save the running-configuration file to starting configuration file by issuing the **copy run start** command.

Step 10. Restart R1 by entering the **reload** command.

Step 11. After R1 has reloaded, login again and show the current IP enabled interfaces by issuing the **show ip interface brief** command. Note the IP address of all interfaces that are in an "up/up" state.

_____

_____

Step 12. Of the IP addresses found at the previous step, which is the highest number? Based on the previous step, what OSPF Router ID do you think R1 will use? Why?

_____

_____

_____

Step 13. Show the OSPF router ID again by entering the **show ip ospf** command. Write down the current router ID and notice that it has changed to the IP address of the loopback interface.

_____

_____

Hints and Answers

Table 1 provides hints and tips for any lab steps that do not supply complete details and provides answers for any lab steps that ask questions.

Table 1   Hints and Answers

Step	Hint or Answer
2	S0/0/0 – 10.50.0.1 /28
	S0/0/1 – 10.51.0.1 /28
	Fa0/0 – 10.1.0.1 /26
3	Of R1's IP addresses, 10.51.0.1 is the highest number, so R1 will use 10.51.0.1.
4	R1's router ID:
	10.51.0.1
11	The same three interface IP addresses found in Step 2 are listed here, as well as the 1.1.1.1 IP address on the loopback interface.
12	Although 10.51.0.1 is still R1's highest-value IP address, R1 should choose the highest IP address on a loopback interface if available, so R1 should choose 1.1.1.1.
13	The output confirms that R1 now uses 1.1.1.1 as its router ID.

Configuration Steps

Example 1 shows a sample of the lab exercise being completed from R1's CLI.

Example 1 Example of Performing This Lab

```
R1#configure terminal
R1(config)#interface loopback 0
R1(config-if)#ip address 1.1.1.1 255.255.255.255
R1(config-if)#end
R1#
```

ICND2 Skill Builders
Part 3: IP Routing Protocols

Lab 32: OSPF Metric Tuning I

Overview

This lab begins with a working internetwork with valid IP addresses on all routers and PCs and OSPF configured on all routers. This lab shows the modification of the default OSPF interface cost and its effect on OSPF metrics and the resulting entries in the IP routing table.

Topology

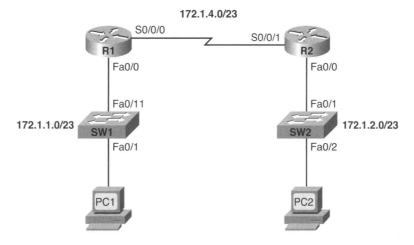

Figure 1   Network Topology for This Lab

Detailed Lab Steps

Step 1.   Connect to R1 from the simulator user interface using the password **ciscopress**.

Step 2.   Show R1's route to reach the subnet off R2's Fa0/0 interface by issuing the **show ip route 172.1.2.0** command. Write down the metric for this route.

_____

_____

Step 3. Show the OSPF cost associated with R1's S0/0/0 interface using the **show ip ospf interface S0/0/0** command. Write down the OSPF cost associated with this interface.

Step 4. Enter privileged exec mode using the password **ciscopress** and then move to global configuration mode using the **configure terminal** command.

Step 5. Enter interface configuration mode for the S0/0/0 interface by issuing the **interface s0/0/0** command.

Step 6. Change the cost of this interface by issuing the **ip ospf cost 14** command.

Step 7. Exit out of configuration mode and again display the OSPF cost of R1's S0/0/0 interface (using the **show ip ospf interface s0/0/0** command). What is the new cost value?

Step 8. Again show R1's route to reach the subnet off R2's Fa0/0 interface by issuing the **show ip route 172.1.2.0** command. What is the metric? Is the metric 50 less than it was in Step 2?

Hints and Answers

Table 1 provides hints and tips for any lab steps that do not supply complete details and provides answers for any lab steps that ask questions.

Table 1   Hints and Answers

Step	Hint or Answer
2	65 (R1's Serial 0/0/0 = 64, R2's Fa0/0 = 1)
3	The cost is 64.
7	The cost is now 14.
8	The metric for this route is now 15, based on R1's S0/0/0 cost of 14 plus R2's Fa0/0 cost of 1. As a result, the cost for this route is 15, instead of the cost of 65 as calculated earlier, making the new cost 50 less than the old cost.

Configuration Steps

Example 1 shows a sample of the lab exercise being completed from R1's CLI.

Example 1   Example of Performing This Lab

```
R1#configure terminal
R1(config)#interface s0/0/0
R1(config-if)#ip ospf cost 14
R1(config-if)#end
```

ICND2 Skill Builders

Part 3: IP Routing Protocols

Lab 35: OSPF Neighbors I

Overview

This lab begins with a working internetwork with valid IP addresses on all routers and PCs and OSPF configured on all routers. This lab shows the modification of the default OSPF Hello timer from the default and its effect on the neighbor table.

Topology

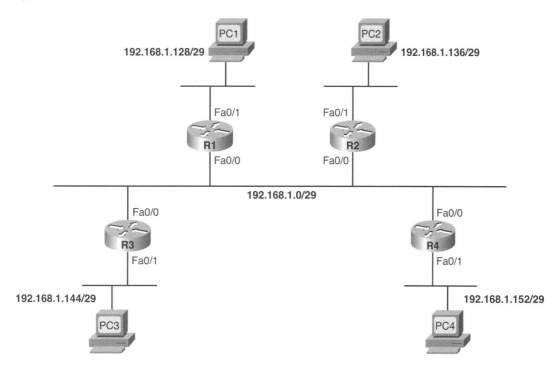

Figure 1   Network Topology for This Lab

Detailed Lab Steps

Step 1.   Connect to R1 from the simulator user interface using the password **ciscopress**.

Step 2.   Show R1's OSPF neighbors by issuing the **show ip ospf neighbor** command. Write down the router ID and interface IP address for each of R1's neighbors.

_____

_____

Step 3. Display and record R1's current OSPF Hello and Dead timer settings using the **show ip ospf interface fa0/0** command.

_____

_____

Step 4. Consider the facts gathered in the last two steps and write any predictions you can make about the OSPF Hello and Dead timer settings on the Fa0/0 interface on R2, R3, and R4, respectively.

_____

_____

Step 5. Enter privileged exec mode using the **enable** command with password **ciscopress**.

Step 6. Move to global configuration mode using the **configure terminal** command.

Step 7. Enter interface configuration mode for interface Fa0/0 by issuing the **interface fa0/0** command.

Step 8. Shut down the Fa0/0 interface by issuing the **shutdown** command.

Step 9. Change the OSPF Hello timer to 20 seconds by issuing the **ip ospf hello-interval 20** command.

Step 10. Re-enable the Fa0/0 interface by issuing the **no shutdown** command.

Step 11. Exit back into enable mode by entering the **end** command.

Step 12. Show R1's OSPF neighbors again by issuing the **show ip ospf neighbor** command. How many neighbors does R1 have now? Record their OSPF router IDs.

_____

_____

Hints and Answers

Table 1 provides hints and tips for any lab steps that do not supply complete details and provides answers for any lab steps that ask questions.

Table 1   Hints and Answers

Step	Hint or Answer
2	R1 has three neighbors:
	R2: RID 2.2.2.2, interface address 192.168.1.2
	R3: RID 3.3.3.3, interface address 192.168.1.3
	R4: RID 4.4.4.4, interface address 192.168.1.4
3	The Hello interval is 10 seconds, and the Dead interval is 40 seconds.

Step	Hint or Answer
4	Because both the Hello and Dead intervals must match in order for routers to become OSPF neighbors, you can surmise that R2's, R3's, and R4's Fa0/0 interfaces also have a Hello timer of 10 and a Dead timer of 40.
12	Notice that none of the neighbor relationships have formed as a result of R1's mismatched Hello timer compared to the other three routers.

Configuration Steps

Example 1 shows a sample of the lab exercise being completed on R1's CLI.

Example 1   Example of Performing This Lab

```
R1#configure terminal
R1(config)#interface fa0/0
R1(config-if)#shutdown
R1(config-if)#ip ospf hello-interval 20
R1(config-if)#no shutdown
```

ICND2 Troubleshooting Scenarios

Lab 10: Routing Analysis III

Overview

This lab begins with an internetwork of four routers that have been configured for IPv4 and with the OSPF routing protocol. The design calls for OSPF to be used on all the router interfaces shown in Figure 1 with all links in area 0. Although the PCs' IP addresses, masks, and default gateway settings are all configured correctly, unfortunately the engineer made three mistakes when configuring the routers in the internetwork. Your job is to find and document the errors and then reconfigure the routers to overcome the problems.

Topology

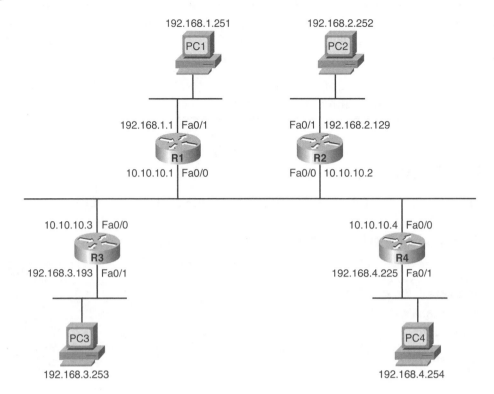

Figure 1   Network Topology for This Lab

General Lab Instructions

For this lab, you have two choices for how to proceed. One option is to follow the process in the "Detailed Lab Steps" section of this lab. These steps guide you through the troubleshooting process. The alternative is to follow the general instructions in this section.

Begin by doing two sets of **ping** commands from each PC. From each PC, ping each PC's default gateway, confirming that all pings work. Then, from each PC, ping each other PC, confirming which combinations do not work. Use Tables 1 and 2 to record the results for reference.

Then, without using enable mode on any of the routers, discover the three configuration problems. Using only user mode, and avoiding enable mode, forces you to use the same kind of thinking and analysis required by Simlet questions on the exam. List your ideas about each configuration problem in Table 3.

After you have identified the problems, reconfigure the routers to solve the problems, documenting the commands you configured in Table 4.

Finally, repeat the pings from each PC to each other PC, confirming that all PCs can now ping each other.

Reference Tables

Tables 1 provides a convenient place to record each PC's default gateway IP address and the results of each PC's attempt to ping their default gateway in the beginning of the lab.

Table 1   Ping Results When Pinging Default Gateways

PC	Default Gateway IP Address	Ping Worked?
PC1		
PC2		
PC3		
PC4		

Note that in Table 2, TS stands for "troubleshooting." Table 2 allows you to record failure and success depending on whether you do the **ping** commands before you do troubleshooting or after you do troubleshooting.

Table 2   Ping Results When Pinging Other PCs

Ping Commands	PC1		PC2		PC3		PC4	
Run On...	Pre-TS	Post TS	Pre-TS	Post TS	Pre-TS	Post TS	Pre-TS	Post TS
PC1								
PC2								
PC3								
PC4								

Table 3   Problems Found in This Lab

Problem Router	Description

Table 4   **Configuration Commands Used to Solve Each Problem**

Router	Configuration

Detailed Lab Steps

Part 1: Verify Ability to Ping from PCs

This part suggests steps for verifying IP addresses and determining which IP addresses can be pinged from each device.

Step 1.   Connect to each PC's user interface, in succession. On each PC, discover the IP address, mask, and default gateway settings, and record that information in Table 5.

Table 5   **IP Address, Mask, and Default Gateway on Each PC**

PC	IP Address	Mask	Default Gateway	Did Ping Work?
PC1				
PC2				
PC3				
PC4				

Step 2.   Again on each PC, ping the IP address of each PC's respective default gateway. Record whether the ping worked or not in Table 5.

Step 3.   From each PC, ping the IP address of the other three PCs. Record the results of each ping in Table 6 with a check mark for a successful ping and an X for a failed ping.

Table 6   Ping Results When Pinging Other PCs

Ping Commands Run On...	PC1	PC2	PC3	PC4
PC1				
PC2				
PC3				
PC4				

Part 2: Verify Ability to Ping Between Routers

Step 4.   Log in to each of the four routers, using **ciscopress** as the console password. Find the IP address and mask used on the two LAN interfaces on each router, and record each IP address in Table 7.

Table 7   IP Address/Mask Reference for the Routers

Router	Fa0/0 IP Address	Fa0/0 Mask	Fa0/1 IP Address	Fa0/1 Mask
R1				
R2				
R3				
R4				

Step 5.   From each router's user mode command prompt, ping the IP addresses of each other router. Make notes about which IP addresses can be pinged from each router.

_____

_____

_____

_____

_____

_____

_____

_____

Step 6. Use the **show ip route** and **show ip route ospf** commands to examine each router's routing tables. Do any of the four routers know any routes other than connected routes? Do any of the routers know any OSPF-learned routes?

_____

_____

_____

_____

Step 7. From each router, use the **show ip ospf neighbor** command to discover with which other routers each router has formed a neighbor relationship. List the router pairs that have formed any kind of neighbor relationship on the lines below.

_____

_____

_____

_____

Step 8. From each router, use the **show ip ospf interface** command to list the interfaces on which OSPF has been enabled. Does it appear that OSPF has been enabled on both interfaces on each of the four routers? List any routers and interfaces on which OSPF should be enabled but is not.

_____

_____

_____

_____

Part 3: Find Two of the Problems Using **show ip ospf interface**

At this point, you have seen that none of the routers have learned any OSPF routes. You should also see that OSPF has been configured on both interfaces on each of the routers, but none of the routers have formed a neighbor relationship. This part of the lab helps you find two of the problems that are currently preventing the routers from becoming neighbors.

Step 9. On the lines below, make a list from memory of everything that can prevent OSPF routers from becoming neighbors.

_____

_____

_____

_____

_____

_____

_____

Step 10. From each router, use the **show ip ospf interface** command. From this command, find the IP address, mask, router ID, Hello timer, Dead Interval, and area ID. Record those details in Table 8.

Table 8   Information from the **show ip ospf interface** Command

Router / interface	IP Address	Prefix Length	Hello Timer	Dead Interval	Area ID
R1 Fa0/0					
R1 Fa0/1					
R2 Fa0/0					
R2 Fa0/1					
R3 Fa0/0					
R3 Fa0/1					
R4 Fa0/0					
R4 Fa0/1					

Step 11. Examine the details collected in Table 8. Which values need to match in order to allow the routers to become neighbors? On which interfaces? Do you see any problems?

_____

_____

_____

_____

_____

Step 12. Routers attached to the same LAN must be in the same subnet with the same subnet mask before they can become OSPF neighbors. Which of the four routers' Fa0/0 interfaces, which connect to the same LAN, has a different mask?

_____

_____

Step 13. Routers attached to the same LAN must use the same OSPF Hello timer and Dead Interval. Which of the four routers' Fa0/0 interfaces differs for one of these settings? What is the setting on that one router, and what is the setting on the other three routers?

_____

_____

_____

Step 14. Record the details of these two problems either in Table 4 (at the beginning of this lab) or on a separate piece of paper.

Note: R2's Hello timer of 9 on its Fa0/1 interface does not cause any problems, because the Hello timer must match for all routers on a single subnet, and the subnet off R2's Fa0/1 interface does not contain any other routers.

Part 4: Find the Third Problem

Step 15. Determine the router ID used by OSPF on each of the four routers. To do so, connect to each router's console in succession, and use the **show ip ospf** command on each router. Record the router IDs below. Are the values unique?

_____

_____

_____

_____

Step 16. Either look back at your notes in Table 8 or repeat the **show ip ospf interface** command on each router. In either case, look for the area number associated with each router's Fa0/0 interface, which connects to the common subnet between the four routers. Are they all configured with the same area? If not, which router has a different area listed?

_____

_____

_____

Step 17. From each router, use the **show ip ospf interface fa0/0** command and look toward the end of the output. The output mentioned the authentication type used in each case. Do all the routers claim to be using the same authentication type on their Fa0/0 interfaces? If not, which routers use which types?

_____

_____

_____

Part 5: Solution

Part 5 summarizes the three problems found in this lab.

OSPF routers that share the same subnet must meet the following requirements in order to become neighbors:

1. The IP subnet number and mask must match.

2. The Hello and Dead Timers must match.

3. The interfaces must be in the same area.

4. The router IDs must be unique.

5. The routers must pass the OSPF authentication process (if any).

This lab shows three different examples of problems like these, as summarized in Table 9.

Table 9 The Three Problems in This Lab

Problem Router	Description
R1	R1 was configured with a Hello timer of 9 on its Fa0/0 interface, which makes R1's Hello timer different from the default setting of 10 seconds on the other three routers' Fa0/0 interfaces.
R3	R3's Fa0/0 interface has a mask of 255.255.255.240 (/28), instead of the 255.255.255.248 (/29) mask used on the other three routers.
R4	R4 has been configured to use plain-text authentication, while the other three routers have been configured to use a message digest.

Part 6: Reconfigure the Routers to Solve the Problems

Step 18. Connect to R1's console and enter configuration mode.

Step 19. Reconfigure R1's Fa0/0 Hello timer to 10 seconds using the **interface fastethernet0/0** and **ip ospf hello 10** commands.

Step 20. Connect to R3's console and enter configuration mode.

Step 21. Reconfigure R3's Fa0/0 mask using the **interface fastethernet0/0** and **ip address 10.10.10.3 255.255.255.248** commands.

Step 22. Exit configuration mode and issue the **show running-config** command. Look for interface Fa0/0 and write down the two interface subcommands related to OSPF authentication.

_____

_____

Step 23. Connect to R4's console and enter configuration mode.

Step 24. Configure R4's Fa0/0 OSPF authentication with the same two commands you just saw in the output of **show running-config** on router R3.

Step 25. At this point, you should have solved all the problems. Use the **show ip ospf neighbor**, **show ip ospf interface**, **show ip route**, **show ip route ospf**, and **ping** commands to confirm that the routers are working correctly, that each router has routes to each subnet, and that the PCs can all ping each other.

Hints and Answers

Table 10 provides hints and tips for any lab steps that do not supply complete details and provides answers for any lab steps that ask questions.

Table 10   Hints and Answers

Step	Hint or Answer
1	Use the **ipconfig /all** command to display the IP settings for the PC.
2	Due to the initial state and configuration of the lab, each PC should be able to ping its respective default gateway.
3	None of the four PCs should be able to ping any of the other three PCs at this point in the lab.
5	The pings should reveal that each router successfully pings the other three routers' IP addresses on the common LAN subnet, but all pings fail from a router to each other router's Fa0/1 IP address.
6	None of the four routers have any OSPF-learned routes at this point; this is one underlying reason why the PCs cannot ping each other, and the routers cannot ping the other routers' Fa0/1 interfaces.
7	None of the routers have OSPF neighbor relationships with any of the other routers at this point.
8	OSPF has been enabled on both LAN interfaces on each router.
9	OSPF neighbors must be in the same subnet, must pass authentication checks, must match the Hello and Dead timers, must be in the same area, and the router IDs must be unique. (See the _ICND2 Exam Certification Guide_, Chapter 11, for additional details.)
11	An inspection of the information in Table 8 should show two problems: 1) R1's Hello timer is 9 (other routers use a default of 10). 2) R3 uses a /28 mask, not /29, making it use a different subnet.

Step	Hint or Answer
12	R3 uses a /28 mask (255.255.255.240), while the other routers use /29 (255.255.255.248).
13	R1 is set to use a Hello timer of 9, while the other routers are set to use the default of 10.
15	All RIDs are unique in this case.
16	All four routers are in area 0.
17	R4 has been configured to use plain-text authentication, while the other three routers have been configured to use a message digest.
22	The two subcommands are:
	ip ospf authentication message-digest
	ip ospf message-digest-key 1 md5 weekiwoo

Configuration Steps

Example 1 show the configuration added to routers R1, R3, and R4 to solve the three problems that existed in this lab.

Example 1   R1 Configuration in This Lab

```
! Configuration on R1
R1#configure terminal
R1(config)#interface fastethernet0/0
R1(config-if)#ip ospf hello 10
R1(config-if)#end



! Configuration on R3
R3#configure terminal
R3(config)#interface fastethernet0/0
R3(config-if)#ip address 10.10.10.3 255.255.255.248
R3(config-if)#end
R3#



! Configuration on R4
R4#configure terminal
R4(config)#interface fastethernet0/0
R4(config-if)#ip ospf authentication message-digest
R4(config-if)#ip ospf message-digest-key 1 md5 weekiwoo
R4(config-if)#end
R4#
```

ICND2 Troubleshooting Scenarios

Lab 13: IP Routing II

Overview

In this lab, you have four routers that are configured with IP addresses and RIP 2. All routers and host PCs should be able to ping all other routers and PCs, but there are some cases where the PCs in the network cannot ping each other. Your job is to find and document the error(s) and make whatever configuration changes are necessary to provide full connectivity between the routers and the PCs.

Note: Use a password of **ciscopress** for all routers in this lab.

Topology

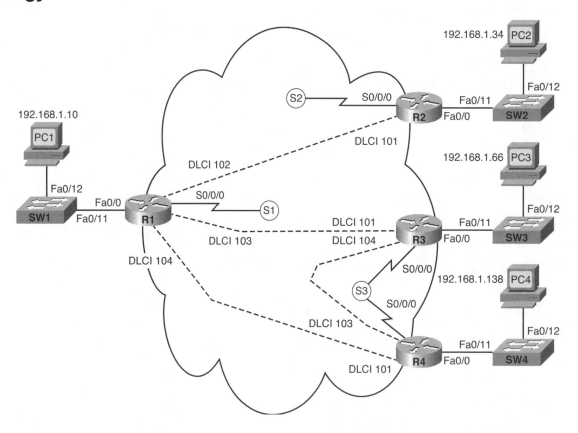

Figure 1   Network Topology for This Lab

General Lab Instructions

For this lab, you have two choices for how to proceed. One option is to follow the steps in this lab. These steps guide you through the troubleshooting process as described in both the ICND1 and ICND2 Exam Certification Guides from Cisco Press. (You do not need a copy of those books to do the lab, though.)

Alternately, you may follow any troubleshooting steps you like until you find the two root causes of IP routing problems in this lab. Then, check your answers against the reference tables at the end of the lab, which list the two root causes and the expected solution for this lab. For the lab to grade as correct, you must solve the two problems in the same way as suggested by this lab.

Note: As with many of the troubleshooting labs, the problems in this lab are introduced by configuration errors. However, the lab is more meaningful if you resist the urge to simply browse the configuration.

Generally, you should start by pinging each PC from each other PC, and when you find pairs of PCs that cannot ping each other, troubleshoot to find why the ping fails.

Reference Tables

Tables 1 through 5 are handy places to record information as you work through the lab. Note that the detailed lab steps may not ask you to complete all parts of the tables.

Table 1   IP Address Reference

Device	Interface	IP Address	Subnet Mask
R1	FastEthernet 0/0		
	Serial 0/0/0.1		
	Serial 0/0/0.2		
	Serial 0/0/0.3		
R2	FastEthernet 0/0		
	Serial 0/0/0		
R3	FastEthernet 0/0		
	Serial 0/0/0.1		
	Serial 0/0/0.2		
R4	FastEthernet 0/0		
	Serial 0/0/0.1		
	Serial 0/0/0.2		
PC1			
PC2			
PC3			
PC4			

Table 2   Ping Results at the Beginning of the Lab

Did ping work?	PC1	PC2	PC3	PC4
PC1				
PC2				
PC3				
PC4				

Table 3   IP Subnet Reference

Device	Subnet Number	First IP Address	Last IP Address
PC1			
PC2			
PC3			
PC4			

Table 4   Problems Found in This Lab

Problem Router	Description

Table 5   Configuration Commands Used to Solve Problem

Router	Configuration

Detailed Lab Steps

Part 1: Discover Which PCs Cannot Ping Each Other

This part suggests steps for discovering IP addresses and confirming whether each device can ping PC1 and PC3.

Step 1. Connect to each PC's user interface in succession. On each PC, use the **ipconfig /all** command to find its own IP address, mask, and default gateway, and record that information in Table 6.

Table 6   **IP Address, Mask, and Gateway on Each PC**

	IP Address	Mask	Default Gateway
PC1			
PC2			
PC3			
PC4			

Step 2. Calculate the subnet number and range of addresses for each subnet. Record the information in Table 3.

Step 3. From each PC, ping each other PC and record in Table 2 which pings work and which do not work—or if you prefer, list the results on the following lines.

_____

_____

_____

Step 4. The first step in troubleshooting host connectivity problems is to ping the host's default gateway from that host. For each PC, ping its configured default gateway and list which pings did not work.

_____

_____

_____

Part 2: Test the Forward Route from PC1 to PC4

The pings in Part 1 should reveal that PC1 cannot ping PC4, and that PC2 cannot ping any of the other PCs. However, the ping of each PC's default gateway has confirmed that the PCs should each be able to forward packets to their respective default gateways (routers). This part of the lab focuses on routing by the routers, beginning with the PC1-PC4 ping failure, and analyzes the forward route toward PC4.

Step 5. Connect to PC1 and trace the route from PC1 to PC4's IP address. What IP addresses are listed? What is the last IP address listed?

_____

_____

_____

Step 6. Connect to router R1 and move into user mode.

Step 7. Use a **show** command to list all IP addresses on R1, and record the interface type/number for the interface IP address discovered in Step 5. According to the network diagram, does this appear to be the correct interface and IP address?

_____

_____

_____

Step 8. Use the **show ip route 192.168.1.138** command to find the route R1 will use when forwarding packets to PC4 (192.168.1.138). Write down the subnet number, next-hop IP address, and outgoing interface.

_____

_____

_____

Step 9. Ping the next-hop address from the previous step. Does the ping work?

_____

Part 3: Test the Reverse Route from R4 to PC1

So far, Parts 1 and 2 have shown that when PC1 sends packets to PC4, PC1 should be able to send the packet to its default gateway, and R1 should be able to forward the packet to the next router—the router with address 192.168.1.162 (which is R4). So, it looks like the forward route from PC1 to R1 and then to R4 looks good. This part examines the reverse route—in other words, the route that should be on R4, back toward R1, when forwarding packets back to PC1.

Step 10. Connect to R4 from the simulator user interface and move into user mode.

Step 11. Issue the **show ip route 192.168.1.10** command to find the route on R4 that R4 should use to forward packets to PC1. Write down the subnet number, next-hop IP address, and outgoing interface. Does the forwarding information (outgoing interface and next-hop address) look correct?

_____

_____

_____

Step 12. Issue the **show ip route** command. Find all connected routes that refer to interface Fa0/0, and list them on the lines below. How could there be two connected routes on the same interface?

_____

_____

_____

Step 13. Move to enable mode and then examine the current configuration on R4 for the Fa0/0 interface. Write down the command that causes R4 to have a connected route for subnet 192.168.1.0/28.

_____

_____

_____

This secondary IP address and its associated connected subnet means that when R4 tries to send a packet to the real PC1, R4 finds the connected route for 192.168.1.0/28 instead and tries to find PC1 off its Fa0/0 interface.

Step 14. To solve the problem, move into configuration mode for interface Fa0/0.

Step 15. Use the **no** version of the command recorded in Step 13 to remove the secondary IP address.

Step 16. Move back to PC1 and retest the ping from PC1 to PC4. Does the ping work?

Step 17. Repeat the **tracert 192.168.1.138** command from PC1. Does it complete? List the three IP addresses listed in the output.

_____

_____

_____

Step 18. At your option, complete the descriptions in Tables 4 and 5 for the root cause of the problem and the solution.

Part 4: Test the Forward Route from PC1 to PC2

The second major class of problem with the ping tests is that PC2 cannot ping any of the other three PCs, and PC1, PC3, and PC4 cannot ping PC2. This part suggests a troubleshooting process by examining PC1's ping of PC2.

Step 19. Connect to PC1 from the user interface and ping PC2's IP address. Confirm that the result is a failure to receive any responses.

_____

Step 20. Trace the route from PC1 to PC2's IP address. What IP addresses are listed? What is the last IP address listed? Does the command finish before you press Ctrl-C?

_____

_____

_____

Step 21. Connect to R1 from the simulator user interface and move into user mode.

Step 22. List all of R1's interface IP addresses, and note which interface is associated with which IP addresses found in Step 20's **tracert** command.

_____

_____

_____

Step 23. Use the **show cdp neighbor detail** command to try to find the other IP address (the address that is not one of R1's IP addresses) found in Step 20's **tracert** command output. What router hostname is listed?

_____

_____

_____

Step 24. Telnet to this other IP address (192.168.1.22) and log in using the password **ciscopress**.

Step 25. List all IP addresses on router R3, and confirm that the IP address listed in PC1's **tracert** command in Step 20 is indeed an IP address on R3.

_____

_____

_____

Part 5: Find the Root Cause of the Ping to/from PC2 Problem

At this point, you have shown that PC1's **tracert 192.168.1.34** command, tracing the route to PC2, is showing that the packets are forwarded first to R1 (192.168.1.9), and then to R3 (192.168.1.22). Clearly, R1 should not forward these packets to R3, but instead forward them to R2. The final part of this lab finds the root cause of the problem.

Step 26. Disconnect from the Telnet connection to R3, suspending back to router R1.

Step 27. Issue the **show ip route 192.168.1.34** command to find the route on R1 that R1 currently uses to forward packets to PC2. Write down the subnet number, next-hop IP address, and outgoing interface. What next-hop router is referenced?

Step 28. Issue the **show ip route** command. Find the same route found in the previous step. What code is listed on the far-left side of the output? Why did R1 add this route to its routing table?

Step 29. Move to enable mode and then examine the current configuration on R1 and find the static route command that causes this problem. Record that command on the lines below.

Step 30. Configure R1 and remove this static route using the **no** version of the command recorded in Step 29.

Step 31. Move back to PC1 and retest the ping from PC1 to PC2. Does the ping work?

Step 32. Move back to PC2 and retest the pings to PC1, PC3, and PC4. Do the pings work?

Step 33. At your option, complete the descriptions in Tables 4 and 5 for the root cause of the problem and the solution.

Hints and Answers

This section lists several useful tables, including

- Table 7: A completed version of Table 1, listing all interface IP addresses
- Table 8: A completed version of Table 3, listing the subnet numbers and address ranges as calculated based on the various PCs' IP addresses and masks
- Table 9: A completed version of Table 4, describing the two problems in this lab
- Table 10: A completed version of Table 5, showing the configuration commands that solve each problem

Additionally, Table 11 provides hints and tips for any lab steps that do not supply complete details and provides answers for any lab steps that ask questions.

Table 7   IP Address Reference

Device	Interface	IP Address	Subnet Mask
R1	FastEthernet 0/0	192.168.1.9	255.255.255.240
	Serial 0/0/0.1	192.168.1.97	255.255.255.240
	Serial 0/0/0.2	192.168.1.21	255.255.255.240
	Serial 0/0/0.3	192.168.1.161	255.255.255.240
R2	FastEthernet 0/0	192.168.1.33	255.255.255.240
	Serial 0/0/0.1	192.168.1.98	255.255.255.240
R3	FastEthernet 0/0	192.168.1.65	255.255.255.240
	Serial 0/0/0.1	192.168.1.22	255.255.255.240
	Serial 0/0/0.2	192.168.1.	255.255.255.240
R4	FastEthernet 0/0	192.168.1.137	255.255.255.240
	Serial 0/0/0.1	192.168.1.162	255.255.255.240
	Serial 0/0/0.2	192.168.1.	255.255.255.240
PC1		192.168.1.10	255.255.255.240
PC2		192.168.1.34	255.255.255.240
PC3		192.168.1.66	255.255.255.240
PC4		192.168.1.138	255.255.255.240

Table 8   IP Subnet Reference

Device	Subnet Number	First IP Address	Last IP Address
PC1	192.168.1.0	192.168.1.1	192.168.1.14
PC2	192.168.1.32	192.168.1.33	192.168.1.46
PC3	192.168.1.64	192.168.1.65	192.168.1.78
PC4	192.168.1.128	192.168.1.129	192.168.1.142

Table 9   Root Causes of the Two Problems in This Lab

Problem Router	Description
R1	R1 had an **ip route 192.168.1.32 255.255.255.240 192.168.1.22** command configured, which causes packets destined to subnet 192.168.1.32/28—which includes PC2's IP address—to be incorrectly routed to R3 instead of R2.
R4	R4 had an **ip address 192.168.1.11 255.255.255.240 secondary** command configured, which caused R4 to create a connected route for subnet 192.168.1.0/28. This route overlapped with the legitimate 192.168.1.0/28 subnet located on R1's Fa0/0 interface. R4's route prevented R4 from forwarding packets for subnet 192.168.1.0/28 back to R1.

Table 10   Configuration Commands Used to Solve Problems

Router	Configuration
R1	Configure the **no ip route 192.168.1.32 255.255.255.240 192.168.1.22** global configuration command.
R4	Use the **no ip address 192.168.1.11 255.255.255.248 secondary** interface subcommand for R4's Fa0/0 interface.

Table 11   Hints and Answers

Step	Hint or Answer
2	Refer to Table 8 for a completed version of Table 3.
3	The ping from PC1 to PC4 fails, and the pings from PC2 to each of the other PCs fail as well.
4	All the pings of the respective default gateways should work.
5	Use the **tracert 192.168.1.138** command. The only and last IP address listed is 192.168.1.9, which is R1's Fa0/0 IP address.
7	R1's Fa0/0 interface is listed with IP address 192.168.1.9, which is the same IP address PC1 has configured as its default gateway. The diagram also shows R1's Fa0/0 interface as being connected to PC1's LAN switch. You can use the **show interfaces** or **show ip interface brief** command to find the IP addresses and interfaces.

continues

Table 11　　Hints and Answers　*continued*

Step	Hint or Answer
8	Look for the line that begins "Routing entry…" for the subnet number. Look at the second-to-last line for the next-hop address (192.168.1.162 in this case) and outgoing interface (S0/0/0.3).
9	The **ping 192.168.1.162** command should work at this point.
11	Look for the line that begins "Routing entry…" for the subnet number. Look at the second-to-last line for the fact that the forwarding information lists this route as a connected route of R4's Fa0/0 interface. The information is incorrect because the 192.168.1.0/28 subnet is actually located off router R1's LAN interface.
12	The output lists 192.168.1.128/28 and 192.168.1.0/28 as being connected routes on Fa0/0.
13	The **ip address 192.168.1.11 255.255.255.240 secondary** command adds a secondary address on router R4's Fa0/0 interface, causing R4 to add a connected route.
14	Use the **enable**, **configure terminal**, and **interface fastethernet 0/0** commands in succession.
15	Use the **no ip address 192.168.1.11 255.255.255.240 secondary** command.
16	The **ping 192.168.1.138** command on PC1 should now work.
17	The **tracert** command lists 192.168.1.9, which is R1's Fa0/0 IP address; 192.168.1.162, which is R4's Frame Relay interface IP address; and 192.168.1.138, which is PC4's IP address.
20	Use the **tracert 192.168.1.34** command. The output lists 192.168.1.9 and 192.168.1.22, but never lists the 192.168.1.34 IP address.
22	R1's IP addresses include 192.168.1.9, its Fa0/0 address; 192.168.1.97, its S0/0/0.1 IP address; 192.168.1.21, its S0/0/0.2 IP address; and 192.168.1.161, its S0/0/0.3 IP address.
23	The output should list address 192.168.1.22 as on router R3.
24	Use the **telnet 192.168.1.22** command.
25	The **show ip interface brief** command will confirm that 192.168.1.22 is R3's S0/0/0.1 IP address. It also lists R3's Fa0/0 as 192.168.1.65 and S0/0/0.2 as 192.168.1.177.
26	Use the **Ctrl-Shift-6, x** key sequence.
27	The output lists subnet 192.168.1.32/28, but with R3's 192.168.1.22 IP address as the next hop.
28	The output of the **show ip route** command lists a route for 192.168.1.32/28, but it is a static route with R3's 192.168.1.22 as the next-hop IP address.
29	The command is i**p route 192.168.1.32 255.255.255.240 192.168.1.22**.
30	Use the **no ip route 192.168.1.32 255.255.255.240 192.168.1.22** command.
31	The **ping 192.168.1.34** command on PC1 should now work.
32	All the pings should now work.
33	Refer to Tables 9 and 10 for completed versions of Tables 4 and 5, respectively.

Configuration

Example 1 shows the configuration commands added to R1 and R4 during this lab.

Example 1 Configuration on R1 and R4 During This Lab

```
R1
no ip route 192.168.1.32 255.255.255.240 192.168.1.22


R4
interface Fa0/0
 no ip address 192.168.1.11 255.255.255.240 secondary
```

ICND2 Subnetting Exercises
Part 1: VLSM Overlap

Lab 1: VLSM Overlap I

Overview

When an engineer configures the **ip address** interface subcommand on an interface that is in a working state, the router performs several verification checks before accepting the command. Those checks include a check of the subnet implied by the newly configured IP address compared to existing subnets connected to working local interfaces. If an overlap exists—that is, if the new subnet's range of addresses overlaps with the range of addresses on an existing connected subnet—the local router rejects the just-entered **ip address** command.

In this exercise, you determine the current IP address/mask pair configured on two interfaces on Router R1. Then you consider two potential new IP address/mask pairs to be configured on another router interface. Your job: Do the necessary calculations to determine whether either or both of these proposed new address/mask pairs would cause an overlap. Then you configure each IP address/mask pair to determine whether an overlap exists.

The IP addresses to consider for this lab are as follows in Table 1.

Table 1 IP Address/Mask Reference

Address	Mask	Prediction: Overlap? If so, with the subnet on interface . . .
10.4.130.1	255.255.224.0	
10.4.230.1	255.255.192.0	

Topology

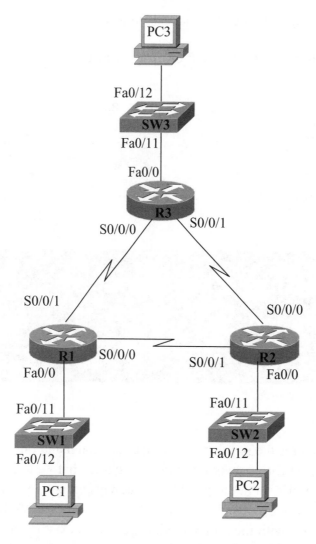

Figure 1 **Topology for IP Address Configuration**

Detailed Lab Steps

Step 1.   Connect to R1 from the simulator user interface. All passwords are **cs**.

Step 2.   Enter privileged exec ("enable") mode by issuing the **enable** command, again using password **cs**.

Step 3.   Use the **show interfaces** command to confirm the two status words for interfaces FastEthernet0/0, Serial0/0/0, and Serial0/0/1. Note whether all are up/up, and if not, which ones are not up.

Step 4. Use the **show interfaces** command to record the IP address and mask already configured on interfaces Serial0/0/0 and Serial0/0/1. Also confirm that interface FastEthernet0/0 does not currently have an IP address configured.

_____

_____

Step 5. For any IP addresses found in the previous step, calculate the subnet ID and range of addresses in the subnet for each subnet.

_____

_____

Step 6. Refer to the table near the beginning of this lab, and calculate the subnet ID and range of addresses for the two IP address/mask pairs listed in the table. Then make a prediction: Will either or both of these IP address/mask pairs, when configured with the **ip address** command on interface FastEthernet0/0, be rejected?

_____

_____

Next, you test your prediction in the previous step by determining whether the router rejects the commands.

Step 7. Enter global configuration mode using the **configure terminal** command.

Step 8. Configure the FastEthernet0/0 interface by issuing the **interface fa0/0** command.

Step 9. Use the **ip address** command to test the IP address and mask for the first entry in the table at the beginning of this lab. Is the command rejected? If so, what does the error message tell you about the reason? With what interface does an overlap occur?

_____

_____

Step 10. Use the **ip address** command to test the IP address and mask for the second entry in the table at the beginning of this lab. Is the command rejected? If so, what does the error message tell you about the reason? With what interface does an overlap occur?

_____

_____

Hints and Answers

Table 2 lists hints and tips for any lab steps that do not supply all the details in the lab step, and for lab steps that ask questions about the lab.

Table 2   Hints

Step	Hint
3	All three interfaces should be up/up, as noted in the first line of output for each interface. For example: `FastEthernet0/0 is up, line protocol is up`
4	The IP address and prefix mask will be in the third line of output in each section. For example: `Internet address is 10.4.130.1/19`
5	The subnet ID and subnet broadcast address are the low and high ends of the range of numbers in a subnet. For the two interfaces in this lab: S0/0/0: 10.4.150.0–10.4.150.255 S0/0/1: 10.4.160.0–10.4.191.255
6	Rather than spoil the answer here, at this step continue with the next steps.
9	Use the **ip address 10.4.130.1 255.255.224.0** interface subcommand. In this case, the router rejects the command because this new subnet has a range from 10.4.128.0 to 10.4.159.255, which overlaps with the subnet on interface S0/0/0. (The error message lists the subnet ID and the interface with which the overlap occurs.)
10	Use the **ip address 10.4.230.1 255.255.192.0** interface subcommand. In this case, no overlap occurs and the router accepts the command.

Configuration Steps

Example 1 shows a sample of the lab exercise being completed from R1's CLI.

Example 1   Example of Performing This Lab

```
(Press enter)
Password: cs
R1> enable
Password: cs
R1#
R1# configure terminal
R1(config)# interface Fastethernet0/0
R1(config-if)# ip address 10.4.130.1 255.255.224.0
% 10.4.128.0 overlaps with Serial0/0/0
R1(config-if)# ip address 10.4.230.1 255.255.192.0
R1(config-if)#
```

ICND2 Subnetting Exercises
Part 1: VLSM Overlap

Lab 2: VLSM Overlap II

Overview

When an engineer configures the **ip address** interface subcommand on an interface that is in a working state, the router performs several verification checks before accepting the command. Those checks include a check of the subnet implied by the newly configured IP address compared to existing subnets connected to working local interfaces. If an overlap exists—that is, if the new subnet's range of addresses overlaps with the range of addresses on an existing connected subnet—the local router rejects the just-entered **ip address** command.

In this exercise, you determine the current IP address/mask pair configured on two interfaces on Router R1. Then you consider two potential new IP address/mask pairs to be configured on another router interface. Your job: Do the necessary calculations to determine whether either or both of these proposed new address/mask pairs would cause an overlap. Then you configure each IP address/mask pair to determine whether an overlap exists.

The IP addresses to consider for this lab are as follows in Table 1.

Table 1 IP Address/Mask Reference

Address	Mask	Prediction: Overlap? If so, with the subnet on interface . . .
10.9.155.22	255.255.255.0	
10.9.165.22	255.255.254.0	

Topology

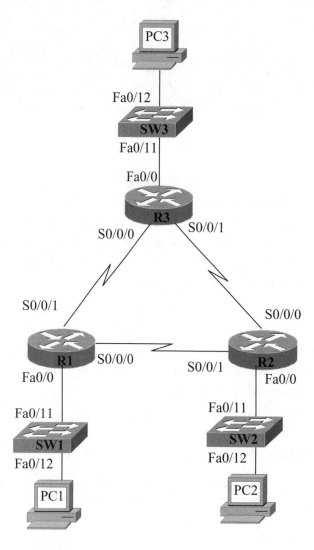

Figure 1   Topology for IP Address Configuration

Detailed Lab Steps

Step 1.   Connect to R1 from the simulator user interface. All passwords are **cs**.

Step 2.   Enter privileged exec ("enable") mode by issuing the **enable** command, again using password **cs**.

Step 3.   Use the **show interfaces** command to confirm the two status words for interfaces FastEthernet0/0, Serial0/0/0, and Serial0/0/1. Note whether all are up/up, and if not, which ones are not up.

_____

_____

Step 4. Use the **show interfaces** command to record the IP address and mask already configured on interfaces Serial0/0/0 and Serial0/0/1. Also confirm that interface FastEthernet0/0 does not currently have an IP address configured.

_____

_____

Step 5. For any IP addresses found in the previous step, calculate the subnet ID and range of addresses in the subnet for each subnet.

_____

_____

Step 6. Refer to the table near the beginning of this lab, and calculate the subnet ID and range of addresses for the two IP address/mask pairs listed in the table. Then make a prediction: Will either or both of these IP address/mask pairs, when configured with the **ip address** command on interface FastEthernet0/0, be rejected?

_____

_____

Next, you test your prediction in the previous step by determining whether the router rejects the commands.

Step 7. Enter global configuration mode using the **configure terminal** command.

Step 8. Configure the FastEthernet0/0 interface by issuing the **interface fa0/0** command.

Step 9. Use the **ip address** command to test the IP address and mask for the first entry in the table at the beginning of this lab. Is the command rejected? If so, what does the error message tell you about the reason? With what interface does an overlap occur?

_____

_____

Step 10. Use the **ip address** command to test the IP address and mask for the second entry in the table at the beginning of this lab. Is the command rejected? If so, what does the error message tell you about the reason? With what interface does an overlap occur?

_____

_____

Hints and Answers

Table 2 lists hints and tips for any lab steps that do not supply all the details in the lab step, and for lab steps that ask questions about the lab.

Table 2   Hints

Step	Hint
3	All three interfaces should be up/up, as noted in the first line of output for each interface. For example: `FastEthernet0/0 is up, line protocol is up`
4	The IP address and prefix mask will be in the third line of output in each section. For example: `Internet address is 10.4.130.1/19`
5	The subnet ID and subnet broadcast address are the low and high ends of the range of numbers in a subnet. For the two interfaces in this lab: S0/0/0: 10.9.160.0–10.9.163.255 S0/0/1: 10.9.152.0–10.9.159.255
6	Rather than spoil the answer here, at this step continue with the next steps.
9	Use the **ip address 10.9.155.22 255.255.255.0** interface subcommand. In this case, the router rejects the command because this new subnet has a range from 10.9.155.0 to 10.9.155.255, which overlaps with the subnet on interface S0/0/1. (The error message lists the subnet ID and the interface with which the overlap occurs.)
10	Use the **ip address 10.9.165.22 255.255.254.0** interface subcommand. In this case, no overlap occurs and the router accepts the command.

Configuration Steps

Example 1 shows a sample of the lab exercise being completed from R1's CLI.

Example 1   Example of Performing This Lab

```
(Press enter)
Password: cs
R1> enable
Password: cs
R1#
R1# configure terminal
R1(config)# interface Fastethernet0/0
R1(config-if)#ip address 10.9.155.22 255.255.255.0
% 10.9.155.0 overlaps with Serial0/0/1
R1(config-if)#ip address 10.9.165.22 255.255.254.0

R1(config-if)#
```

ICND2 Subnetting Exercises

Part 1: VLSM Overlap

Lab 3: VLSM Overlap III

Overview

When an engineer configures the **ip address** interface subcommand on an interface that is in a working state, the router performs several verification checks before accepting the command. Those checks include a check of the subnet implied by the newly configured IP address compared to existing subnets connected to working local interfaces. If an overlap exists—that is, if the new subnet's range of addresses overlaps with the range of addresses on an existing connected subnet—the local router rejects the just-entered **ip address** command.

In this exercise, you determine the current IP address/mask pair configured on two interfaces on Router R1. Then you consider two potential new IP address/mask pairs to be configured on another router interface. Your job: Do the necessary calculations to determine whether either or both of these proposed new address/mask pairs would cause an overlap. Then you configure each IP address/mask pair to determine whether an overlap exists.

The IP addresses to consider for this lab are as follows in Table 1.

Table 1   IP Address/Mask Reference

Address	Mask	Prediction: Overlap? If so, with the subnet on interface . . .
172.16.0.1	255.255.255.240	
172.16.0.254	255.255.255.240	

Topology

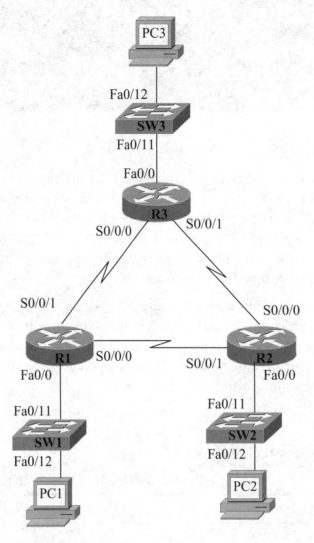

Figure 1   Topology for IP Address Configuration

Detailed Lab Steps

Step 1.   Connect to R1 from the simulator user interface. All passwords are **cs**.

Step 2.   Enter privileged exec ("enable") mode by issuing the **enable** command, again using password **cs**.

Step 3.   Use the **show interfaces** command to confirm the two status words for interfaces FastEthernet0/0, Serial0/0/0, and Serial0/0/1. Note whether all are up/up, and if not, which ones are not up.

_____

_____

Step 4. Use the **show interfaces** command to record the IP address and mask already configured on interfaces Serial0/0/0 and Serial0/0/1. Also confirm that interface FastEthernet0/0 does not currently have an IP address configured.

_____

_____

Step 5. For any IP addresses found in the previous step, calculate the subnet ID and range of addresses in the subnet for each subnet.

_____

_____

Step 6. Refer to the table near the beginning of this lab, and calculate the subnet ID and range of addresses for the two IP address/mask pairs listed in the table. Then make a prediction: Will either or both of these IP address/mask pairs, when configured with the **ip address** command on interface FastEthernet0/0, be rejected?

_____

_____

Next, you test your prediction in the previous step by determining whether the router rejects the commands.

Step 7. Enter global configuration mode using the **configure terminal** command.

Step 8. Configure the FastEthernet0/0 interface by issuing the **interface fa0/0** command.

Step 9. Use the **ip address** command to test the IP address and mask for the first entry in the table at the beginning of this lab. Is the command rejected? If so, what does the error message tell you about the reason? With what interface does an overlap occur?

_____

_____

Step 10. Use the **ip address** command to test the IP address and mask for the second entry in the table at the beginning of this lab. Is the command rejected? If so, what does the error message tell you about the reason? With what interface does an overlap occur?

_____

_____

Hints and Answers

Table 2 lists hints and tips for any lab steps that do not supply all the details in the lab step, and for lab steps that ask questions about the lab.

Table 2　Hints

Step	Hint
3	All three interfaces should be up/up, as noted in the first line of output for each interface. For example: `FastEthernet0/0 is up, line protocol is up`
4	The IP address and prefix mask will be in the third line of output in each section. For example: `Internet address is 10.4.130.1/19`
5	The subnet ID and subnet broadcast address are the low and high ends of the range of numbers in a subnet. For the two interfaces in this lab: S0/0/0: 172.16.0.64–172.16.0.127 S0/0/1: 172.16.0.128–172.16.0.255
6	Rather than spoil the answer here, at this step continue with the next steps.
9	Use the **ip address 172.16.0.1 255.255.255.240** interface subcommand. In this case, no overlap occurs and the router accepts the command.
10	Use the **ip address 172.16.0.254 255.255.255.240** interface subcommand. In this case, the router rejects the command because this new subnet has a range from 172.16.0.240 to 172.16.0.255, which overlaps with the subnet on interface S0/0/1. (The error message lists the subnet ID and the interface with which the overlap occurs.)

Configuration Steps

Example 1 shows a sample of the lab exercise being completed from R1's CLI.

Example 1　Example of Performing This Lab

```
(Press enter)
Password: cs
R1> enable
Password: cs
R1#
R1# configure terminal
R1(config)# interface Fastethernet0/0
R1(config-if)#ip address 172.16.0.1 255.255.255.240
R1(config-if)#ip address 172.16.0.254 255.255.255.240
% 172.16.0.240 overlaps with Serial0/0/1


R1(config-if)#
```

ICND2 Subnetting Exercises

Part 1: VLSM Overlap

Lab 4: VLSM Overlap IV

Overview

When an engineer configures the **ip address** interface subcommand on an interface that is in a working state, the router performs several verification checks before accepting the command. Those checks include a check of the subnet implied by the newly configured IP address compared to existing subnets connected to working local interfaces. If an overlap exists—that is, if the new subnet's range of addresses overlaps with the range of addresses on an existing connected subnet—the local router rejects the just-entered **ip address** command.

In this exercise, you determine the current IP address/mask pair configured on two interfaces on Router R1. Then you consider two potential new IP address/mask pairs to be configured on another router interface. Your job: Do the necessary calculations to determine whether either or both of these proposed new address/mask pairs would cause an overlap. Then you configure each IP address/mask pair to determine whether an overlap exists.

The IP addresses to consider for this lab are as follows in Table 1.

Table 1   IP Address/Mask Reference

Address	Mask	Prediction: Overlap? If so, with the subnet on interface . . .
192.168.8.141	255.255.255.252	
192.168.8.161	255.255.255.252	

Topology

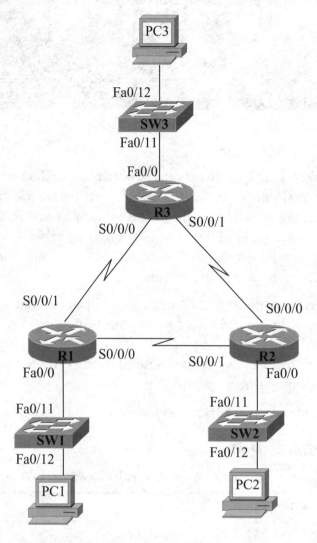

Figure 1   Topology for IP Address Configuration

Detailed Lab Steps

Step 1.   Connect to R1 from the simulator user interface. All passwords are **cs**.

Step 2.   Enter privileged exec ("enable") mode by issuing the **enable** command, again using password **cs**.

Step 3.   Use the **show interfaces** command to confirm the two status words for interfaces FastEthernet0/0, Serial0/0/0, and Serial0/0/1. Note whether all are up/up, and if not, which ones are not up.

Step 4. Use the **show interfaces** command to record the IP address and mask already configured on interfaces Serial0/0/0 and Serial0/0/1. Also confirm that interface FastEthernet0/0 does not currently have an IP address configured.

_____

_____

Step 5. For any IP addresses found in the previous step, calculate the subnet ID and range of addresses in the subnet for each subnet.

_____

_____

Step 6. Refer to the table near the beginning of this lab, and calculate the subnet ID and range of addresses for the two IP address/mask pairs listed in the table. Then make a prediction: Will either or both of these IP address/mask pairs, when configured with the **ip address** command on interface FastEthernet0/0, be rejected?

_____

_____

Next, you test your prediction in the previous step by determining whether the router rejects the commands.

Step 7. Enter global configuration mode using the **configure terminal** command.

Step 8. Configure the FastEthernet0/0 interface by issuing the **interface fa0/0** command.

Step 9. Use the **ip address** command to test the IP address and mask for the first entry in the table at the beginning of this lab. Is the command rejected? If so, what does the error message tell you about the reason? With what interface does an overlap occur?

_____

_____

Step 10. Use the **ip address** command to test the IP address and mask for the second entry in the table at the beginning of this lab. Is the command rejected? If so, what does the error message tell you about the reason? With what interface does an overlap occur?

_____

_____

Hints and Answers

Table 2 lists hints and tips for any lab steps that do not supply all the details in the lab step, and for lab steps that ask questions about the lab.

Table 2   Hints

Step	Hint
3	All three interfaces should be up/up, as noted in the first line of output for each interface. For example: `FastEthernet0/0 is up, line protocol is up`
4	The IP address and prefix mask will be in the third line of output in each section. For example: `Internet address is 10.4.130.1/19`
5	The subnet ID and subnet broadcast address are the low and high ends of the range of numbers in a subnet. For the two interfaces in this lab: S0/0/0: 192.168.8.144–192.168.8.151 S0/0/1: 192.168.8.160–192.168.8.191
6	Rather than spoil the answer here, at this step continue with the next steps.
9	Use the **ip address 192.168.8.141 255.255.255.252** interface subcommand. In this case, no overlap occurs and the router accepts the command.
10	Use the **ip address 192.168.8.161 255.255.255.252** interface subcommand. In this case, the router rejects the command because this new subnet has a range from 192.168.8.160 to 192.168.8.163, which overlaps with the subnet on interface S0/0/1. (The error message lists the subnet ID and the interface with which the overlap occurs.)

Configuration Steps

Example 1 shows a sample of the lab exercise being completed from R1's CLI.

Example 1   Example of Performing This Lab

```
(Press enter)
Password: cs
R1> enable
Password: cs
R1#
R1# configure terminal
R1(config)# interface Fastethernet0/0
R1(config-if)#ip address 192.168.8.141 255.255.255.252
R1(config-if)#ip address 192.168.8.161 255.255.255.252
% 192.168.8.160 overlaps with Serial0/0/1

R1(config-if)#
```

ICND2 Subnetting Exercises

Part 1: VLSM Overlap

Lab 5: VLSM Overlap V

Overview

When an engineer configures the **ip address** interface subcommand on an interface that is in a working state, the router performs several verification checks before accepting the command. Those checks include a check of the subnet implied by the newly configured IP address compared to existing subnets connected to working local interfaces. If an overlap exists—that is, if the new subnet's range of addresses overlaps with the range of addresses on an existing connected subnet—the local router rejects the just-entered **ip address** command.

In this exercise, you determine the current IP address/mask pair configured on two interfaces on Router R1. Then you consider two potential new IP address/mask pairs to be configured on another router interface. Your job: Do the necessary calculations to determine whether either or both of these proposed new address/mask pairs would cause an overlap. Then you configure each IP address/mask pair to determine whether an overlap exists.

The IP addresses to consider for this lab are as follows in Table 1.

Table 1   IP Address/Mask Reference

Address	Mask	Prediction: Overlap? If so, with the subnet on interface . . .
192.168.9.126	255.255.255.240	
192.168.9.129	255.255.255.224	

Topology

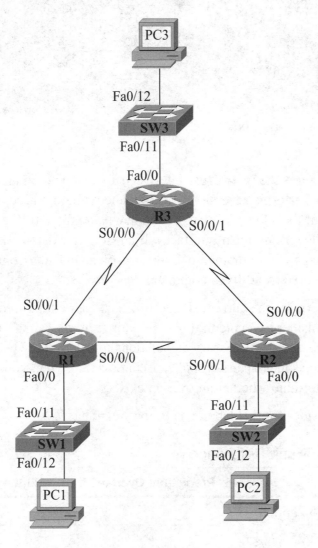

Figure 1 **Topology for IP Address Configuration**

Detailed Lab Steps

Step 1. Connect to R1 from the simulator user interface. All passwords are **cs**.

Step 2. Enter privileged exec ("enable") mode by issuing the **enable** command, again using password **cs**.

Step 3. Use the **show interfaces** command to confirm the two status words for interfaces FastEthernet0/0, Serial0/0/0, and Serial0/0/1. Note whether all are up/up, and if not, which ones are not up.

_____

_____

Step 4. Use the **show interfaces** command to record the IP address and mask already configured on interfaces Serial0/0/0 and Serial0/0/1. Also confirm that interface FastEthernet0/0 does not currently have an IP address configured.

_____

_____

Step 5. For any IP addresses found in the previous step, calculate the subnet ID and range of addresses in the subnet for each subnet.

_____

_____

Step 6. Refer to the table near the beginning of this lab, and calculate the subnet ID and range of addresses for the two IP address/mask pairs listed in the table. Then make a prediction: Will either or both of these IP address/mask pairs, when configured with the **ip address** command on interface FastEthernet0/0, be rejected?

_____

_____

Next, you test your prediction in the previous step by determining whether the router rejects the commands.

Step 7. Enter global configuration mode using the **configure terminal** command.

Step 8. Configure the FastEthernet0/0 interface by issuing the **interface fa0/0** command.

Step 9. Use the **ip address** command to test the IP address and mask for the first entry in the table at the beginning of this lab. Is the command rejected? If so, what does the error message tell you about the reason? With what interface does an overlap occur?

_____

_____

Step 10. Use the **ip address** command to test the IP address and mask for the second entry in the table at the beginning of this lab. Is the command rejected? If so, what does the error message tell you about the reason? With what interface does an overlap occur?

_____

_____

Hints and Answers

Table 2 lists hints and tips for any lab steps that do not supply all the details in the lab step, and for lab steps that ask questions about the lab.

Table 2 Hints

Step	Hint
3	All three interfaces should be up/up, as noted in the first line of output for each interface. For example: `FastEthernet0/0 is up, line protocol is up`
4	The IP address and prefix mask will be in the third line of output in each section. For example: `Internet address is 10.4.130.1/19`
5	The subnet ID and subnet broadcast address are the low and high ends of the range of numbers in a subnet. For the two interfaces in this lab: S0/0/0: 192.168.9.0–192.168.9.127 S0/0/1: 192.168.9.128–192.168.9.255
6	Rather than spoil the answer here, at this step continue with the next steps.
9	Use the **ip address 192.168.9.126 255.255.255.240** interface subcommand. In this case, the router rejects the command because this new subnet has a range from 192.168.9.112 to 192.168.9.127, which overlaps with the subnet on interface S0/0/0. (The error message lists the subnet ID and the interface with which the overlap occurs.)
10	Use the **ip address 192.168.9.129 255.255.255.224** interface subcommand. In this case, the router rejects the command because this new subnet has a range from 192.168.9.128 to 192.168.9.159, which overlaps with the subnet on interface S0/0/1. (The error message lists the subnet ID and the interface with which the overlap occurs.)

Configuration Steps

Example 1 shows a sample of the lab exercise being completed from R1's CLI.

Example 1   Example of Performing This Lab

```
(Press enter)
Password: cs
R1> enable
Password: cs
R1#
R1# configure terminal
R1(config)# interface Fastethernet0/0
R1(config-if)#ip address 192.168.9.126 255.255.255.240
% 192.168.9.112 overlaps with Serial0/0/0
R1(config-if)#ip address 192.168.9.129 255.255.255.224
% 192.168.9.128 overlaps with Serial0/0/1


R1(config-if)#
```

ICND2 Subnetting Exercises

Part 1: VLSM Overlap

Lab 6: VLSM Overlap VI

Overview

When an engineer configures the **ip address** interface subcommand on an interface that is in a working state, the router performs several verification checks before accepting the command. Those checks include a check of the subnet implied by the newly configured IP address compared to existing subnets connected to working local interfaces. If an overlap exists—that is, if the new subnet's range of addresses overlaps with the range of addresses on an existing connected subnet—the local router rejects the just-entered **ip address** command.

In this exercise, you determine the current IP address/mask pair configured on two interfaces on Router R1. Then you consider two potential new IP address/mask pairs to be configured on another router interface. Your job: Do the necessary calculations to determine whether either or both of these proposed new address/mask pairs would cause an overlap. Then you configure each IP address/mask pair to determine whether an overlap exists.

The IP addresses to consider for this lab are as follows in Table 1.

Table 1   IP Address/Mask Reference

Address	Mask	Prediction: Overlap? If so, with the subnet on interface . . .
10.1.204.161	255.255.255.240	
10.1.210.113	255.255.255.248	

Topology

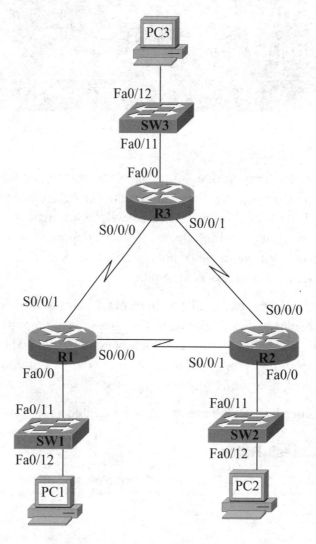

Figure 1   Topology for IP Address Configuration

Detailed Lab Steps

Step 1.   Connect to R1 from the simulator user interface. All passwords are **cs**.

Step 2.   Enter privileged exec ("enable") mode by issuing the **enable** command, again using password **cs**.

Step 3.   Use the **show interfaces** command to confirm the two status words for interfaces FastEthernet0/0, Serial0/0/0, and Serial0/0/1. Note whether all are up/up, and if not, which ones are not up.

_____

_____

Step 4. Use the **show interfaces** command to record the IP address and mask already configured on interfaces Serial0/0/0 and Serial0/0/1. Also confirm that interface FastEthernet0/0 does not currently have an IP address configured.

_____

_____

Step 5. For any IP addresses found in the previous step, calculate the subnet ID and range of addresses in the subnet for each subnet.

_____

_____

Step 6. Refer to the table near the beginning of this lab, and calculate the subnet ID and range of addresses for the two IP address/mask pairs listed in the table. Then make a prediction: Will either or both of these IP address/mask pairs, when configured with the **ip address** command on interface FastEthernet0/0, be rejected?

_____

_____

Next, you test your prediction in the previous step by determining whether the router rejects the commands.

Step 7. Enter global configuration mode using the **configure terminal** command.

Step 8. Configure the FastEthernet0/0 interface by issuing the **interface fa0/0** command.

Step 9. Use the **ip address** command to test the IP address and mask for the first entry in the table at the beginning of this lab. Is the command rejected? If so, what does the error message tell you about the reason? With what interface does an overlap occur?

_____

_____

Step 10. Use the **ip address** command to test the IP address and mask for the second entry in the table at the beginning of this lab. Is the command rejected? If so, what does the error message tell you about the reason? With what interface does an overlap occur?

_____

_____

Hints and Answers

Table 2 lists hints and tips for any lab steps that do not supply all the details in the lab step, and for lab steps that ask questions about the lab.

Table 2   Hints

Step	Hint
3	All three interfaces should be up/up, as noted in the first line of output for each interface. For example: `FastEthernet0/0 is up, line protocol is up`
4	The IP address and prefix mask will be in the third line of output in each section. For example: `Internet address is 10.4.130.1/19`
5	The subnet ID and subnet broadcast address are the low and high ends of the range of numbers in a subnet. For the two interfaces in this lab: S0/0/0: 10.1.192.0–10.1.207.255 S0/0/1: 10.1.212.0–10.1.215.255
6	Rather than spoil the answer here, at this step continue with the next steps.
9	Use the **ip address 10.1.204.161 255.255.255.240** interface subcommand. In this case, the router rejects the command because this new subnet has a range from 10.1.204.160 to 10.1.204.175, which overlaps with the subnet on interface S0/0/0. (The error message lists the subnet ID and the interface with which the overlap occurs.)
10	Use the **ip address 10.1.210.113 255.255.255.248** interface subcommand. In this case, no overlap occurs and the router accepts the command.

Configuration Steps

Example 1 shows a sample of the lab exercise being completed from R1's CLI.

Example 1   Example of Performing This Lab

```
(Press enter)
Password: cs
R1> enable
Password: cs
R1#
R1# configure terminal
R1(config)# interface Fastethernet0/0
R1(config-if)# ip address 10.1.204.161 255.255.255.240
% 10.1.204.160 overlaps with Serial0/0/0
R1(config-if)# ip address 10.1.210.113 255.255.255.248
R1(config-if)#
```

ICND2 Subnetting Exercises
Part 1: VLSM Overlap

Lab 7: VLSM Overlap VII

Overview

When an engineer configures the **ip address** interface subcommand on an interface that is in a working state, the router performs several verification checks before accepting the command. Those checks include a check of the subnet implied by the newly configured IP address compared to existing subnets connected to working local interfaces. If an overlap exists—that is, if the new subnet's range of addresses overlaps with the range of addresses on an existing connected subnet—the local router rejects the just-entered **ip address** command.

In this exercise, you determine the current IP address/mask pair configured on two interfaces on Router R1. Then you consider two potential new IP address/mask pairs to be configured on another router interface. Your job: Do the necessary calculations to determine whether either or both of these proposed new address/mask pairs would cause an overlap. Then you configure each IP address/mask pair to determine whether an overlap exists.

The IP addresses to consider for this lab are as follows in Table 1.

Table 1   IP Address/Mask Reference

Address	Mask	Prediction: Overlap? If so, with the subnet on interface . . .
10.2.70.1	255.255.224.0	
10.2.90.1	255.255.248.0	

Topology

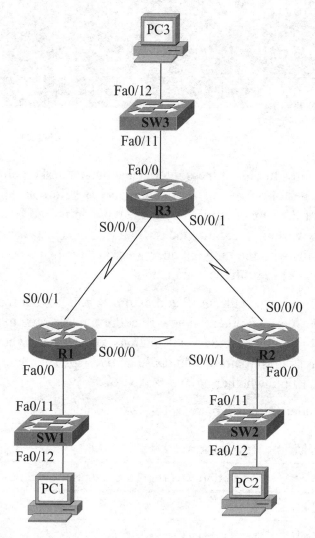

Figure 1   Topology for IP Address Configuration

Detailed Lab Steps

Step 1. Connect to R1 from the simulator user interface. All passwords are **cs**.

Step 2. Enter privileged exec ("enable") mode by issuing the **enable** command, again using password **cs**.

Step 3. Use the **show interfaces** command to confirm the two status words for interfaces FastEthernet0/0, Serial0/0/0, and Serial0/0/1. Note whether all are up/up, and if not, which ones are not up.

Step 4. Use the **show interfaces** command to record the IP address and mask already configured on interfaces Serial0/0/0 and Serial0/0/1. Also confirm that interface FastEthernet0/0 does not currently have an IP address configured.

_____

_____

Step 5. For any IP addresses found in the previous step, calculate the subnet ID and range of addresses in the subnet for each subnet.

_____

_____

Step 6. Refer to the table near the beginning of this lab, and calculate the subnet ID and range of addresses for the two IP address/mask pairs listed in the table. Then make a prediction: Will either or both of these IP address/mask pairs, when configured with the **ip address** command on interface FastEthernet0/0, be rejected?

_____

_____

Next, you test your prediction in the previous step by determining whether the router rejects the commands.

Step 7. Enter global configuration mode using the **configure terminal** command.

Step 8. Configure the FastEthernet0/0 interface by issuing the **interface fa0/0** command.

Step 9. Use the **ip address** command to test the IP address and mask for the first entry in the table at the beginning of this lab. Is the command rejected? If so, what does the error message tell you about the reason? With what interface does an overlap occur?

_____

_____

Step 10. Use the **ip address** command to test the IP address and mask for the second entry in the table at the beginning of this lab. Is the command rejected? If so, what does the error message tell you about the reason? With what interface does an overlap occur?

_____

_____

Hints and Answers

Table 2 lists hints and tips for any lab steps that do not supply all the details in the lab step, and for lab steps that ask questions about the lab.

Table 2   Hints

Step	Hint
3	All three interfaces should be up/up, as noted in the first line of output for each interface. For example: `FastEthernet0/0 is up, line protocol is up`
4	The IP address and prefix mask will be in the third line of output in each section. For example: `Internet address is 10.4.130.1/19`
5	The subnet ID and subnet broadcast address are the low and high ends of the range of numbers in a subnet. For the two interfaces in this lab: S0/0/0: 10.2.80.80–10.2.80.83 S0/0/1: 10.2.97.48–10.2.97.63
6	Rather than spoil the answer here, at this step continue with the next steps.
9	Use the **ip address 10.2.70.1 255.255.224.0** interface subcommand. In this case, the router rejects the command because this new subnet has a range from 10.2.64.0 to 10.2.95.255, which overlaps with the subnet on interface S0/0/0. (The error message lists the subnet ID and the interface with which the overlap occurs.)
10	Use the **ip address 10.2.90.1 255.255.248.0** interface subcommand. In this case, no overlap occurs and the router accepts the command.

Configuration Steps

Example 1 shows a sample of the lab exercise being completed from R1's CLI.

Example 1   Example of Performing This Lab

```
(Press enter)
Password: cs
R1> enable
Password: cs
R1#
R1# configure terminal
R1(config)# interface Fastethernet0/0
R1(config-if)# ip address 10.2.70.1 255.255.224.0
% 10.2.64.0 overlaps with Serial0/0/0
R1(config-if)# ip address 10.2.90.1 255.255.248.0
R1(config-if)#
```

ICND2 Subnetting Exercises

Part 1: VLSM Overlap

Lab 8: VLSM Overlap VIII

Overview

When an engineer configures the **ip address** interface subcommand on an interface that is in a working state, the router performs several verification checks before accepting the command. Those checks include a check of the subnet implied by the newly configured IP address compared to existing subnets connected to working local interfaces. If an overlap exists—that is, if the new subnet's range of addresses overlaps with the range of addresses on an existing connected subnet—the local router rejects the just-entered **ip address** command.

In this exercise, you determine the current IP address/mask pair configured on two interfaces on Router R1. Then you consider two potential new IP address/mask pairs to be configured on another router interface. Your job: Do the necessary calculations to determine whether either or both of these proposed new address/mask pairs would cause an overlap. Then you configure each IP address/mask pair to determine whether an overlap exists.

The IP addresses to consider for this lab are as follows in Table 1.

Table 1   IP Address/Mask Reference

Address	Mask	Prediction: Overlap? If so, with the subnet on interface . . .
172.27.207.129	255.255.255.252	
172.27.213.129	255.255.255.252	

Topology

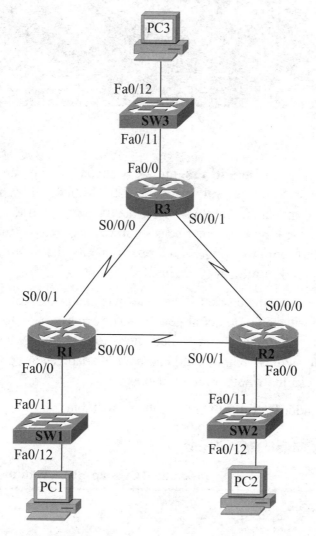

Figure 1   Topology for IP Address Configuration

Detailed Lab Steps

Step 1.   Connect to R1 from the simulator user interface. All passwords are **cs**.

Step 2.   Enter privileged exec ("enable") mode by issuing the **enable** command, again using password **cs**.

Step 3.   Use the **show interfaces** command to confirm the two status words for interfaces FastEthernet0/0, Serial0/0/0, and Serial0/0/1. Note whether all are up/up, and if not, which ones are not up.

_____

_____

Step 4. Use the **show interfaces** command to record the IP address and mask already configured on interfaces Serial0/0/0 and Serial0/0/1. Also confirm that interface FastEthernet0/0 does not currently have an IP address configured.

_____

_____

Step 5. For any IP addresses found in the previous step, calculate the subnet ID and range of addresses in the subnet for each subnet.

_____

_____

Step 6. Refer to the table near the beginning of this lab, and calculate the subnet ID and range of addresses for the two IP address/mask pairs listed in the table. Then make a prediction: Will either or both of these IP address/mask pairs, when configured with the **ip address** command on interface FastEthernet0/0, be rejected?

_____

_____

Next, you test your prediction in the previous step by determining whether the router rejects the commands.

Step 7. Enter global configuration mode using the **configure terminal** command.

Step 8. Configure the FastEthernet0/0 interface by issuing the **interface fa0/0** command.

Step 9. Use the **ip address** command to test the IP address and mask for the first entry in the table at the beginning of this lab. Is the command rejected? If so, what does the error message tell you about the reason? With what interface does an overlap occur?

_____

_____

Step 10. Use the **ip address** command to test the IP address and mask for the second entry in the table at the beginning of this lab. Is the command rejected? If so, what does the error message tell you about the reason? With what interface does an overlap occur?

_____

_____

Hints and Answers

Table 2 lists hints and tips for any lab steps that do not supply all the details in the lab step, and for lab steps that ask questions about the lab.

Table 2   Hints

Step	Hint
3	All three interfaces should be up/up, as noted in the first line of output for each interface. For example: `FastEthernet0/0 is up, line protocol is up`
4	The IP address and prefix mask will be in the third line of output in each section. For example: `Internet address is 10.4.130.1/19`
5	The subnet ID and subnet broadcast address are the low and high ends of the range of numbers in a subnet. For the two interfaces in this lab: S0/0/0: 172.27.210.0–172.27.211.255 S0/0/1: 172.27.200.0–172.27.207.255
6	Rather than spoil the answer here, at this step continue with the next steps.
9	Use the **ip address 172.27.207.129 255.255.255.252** interface subcommand. In this case, the router rejects the command because this new subnet has a range from 172.27.207.128 to 172.27.207.131, which overlaps with the subnet on interface S0/0/1. (The error message lists the subnet ID and the interface with which the overlap occurs.)
10	Use the **ip address 172.27.213.129 255.255.255.252** interface subcommand. In this case, no overlap occurs and the router accepts the command.

Configuration Steps

Example 1 shows a sample of the lab exercise being completed from R1's CLI.

Example 1   Example of Performing This Lab

```
(Press enter)
Password: cs
R1> enable
Password: cs
R1#
R1# configure terminal
R1(config)# interface Fastethernet0/0
R1(config-if)# ip address 172.27.207.129 255.255.255.252
% 172.27.207.128 overlaps with Serial0/0/1
R1(config-if)# ip address 172.27.213.129 255.255.255.252
R1(config-if)#
```

ICND2 Subnetting Exercises

Part 1: VLSM Overlap

Lab 9: VLSM Overlap IX

Overview

When an engineer configures the **ip address** interface subcommand on an interface that is in a working state, the router performs several verification checks before accepting the command. Those checks include a check of the subnet implied by the newly configured IP address compared to existing subnets connected to working local interfaces. If an overlap exists—that is, if the new subnet's range of addresses overlaps with the range of addresses on an existing connected subnet—the local router rejects the just-entered **ip address** command.

In this exercise, you determine the current IP address/mask pair configured on two interfaces on Router R1. Then you consider two potential new IP address/mask pairs to be configured on another router interface. Your job: Do the necessary calculations to determine whether either or both of these proposed new address/mask pairs would cause an overlap. Then you configure each IP address/mask pair to determine whether an overlap exists.

The IP addresses to consider for this lab are as follows in Table 1.

Table 1   IP Address/Mask Reference

Address	Mask	Prediction: Overlap? If so, with the subnet on interface . . .
172.28.111.101	255.255.255.128	
172.28.111.201	255.255.255.192	

Topology

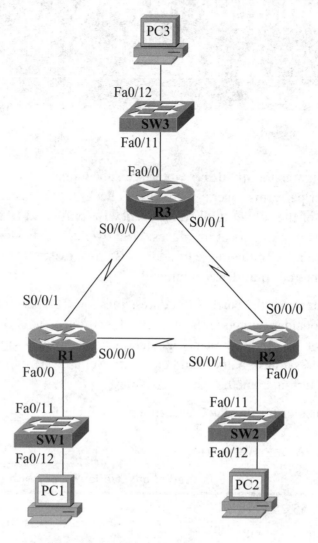

Figure 1   Topology for IP Address Configuration

Detailed Lab Steps

Step 1.   Connect to R1 from the simulator user interface. All passwords are **cs**.

Step 2.   Enter privileged exec ("enable") mode by issuing the **enable** command, again using password **cs**.

Step 3.   Use the **show interfaces** command to confirm the two status words for interfaces FastEthernet0/0, Serial0/0/0, and Serial0/0/1. Note whether all are up/up, and if not, which ones are not up.

_____

_____

Step 4. Use the **show interfaces** command to record the IP address and mask already configured on interfaces Serial0/0/0 and Serial0/0/1. Also confirm that interface FastEthernet0/0 does not currently have an IP address configured.

_____

_____

Step 5. For any IP addresses found in the previous step, calculate the subnet ID and range of addresses in the subnet for each subnet.

_____

_____

Step 6. Refer to the table near the beginning of this lab, and calculate the subnet ID and range of addresses for the two IP address/mask pairs listed in the table. Then make a prediction: Will either or both of these IP address/mask pairs, when configured with the **ip address** command on interface FastEthernet0/0, be rejected?

_____

_____

Next, you test your prediction in the previous step by determining whether the router rejects the commands.

Step 7. Enter global configuration mode using the **configure terminal** command.

Step 8. Configure the FastEthernet0/0 interface by issuing the **interface fa0/0** command.

Step 9. Use the **ip address** command to test the IP address and mask for the first entry in the table at the beginning of this lab. Is the command rejected? If so, what does the error message tell you about the reason? With what interface does an overlap occur?

_____

_____

Step 10. Use the **ip address** command to test the IP address and mask for the second entry in the table at the beginning of this lab. Is the command rejected? If so, what does the error message tell you about the reason? With what interface does an overlap occur?

_____

_____

Hints and Answers

Table 2 lists hints and tips for any lab steps that do not supply all the details in the lab step, and for lab steps that ask questions about the lab.

Table 2   **Hints**

Step	Hint
3	All three interfaces should be up/up, as noted in the first line of output for each interface. For example: `FastEthernet0/0 is up, line protocol is up`
4	The IP address and prefix mask will be in the third line of output in each section. For example: `Internet address is 10.4.130.1/19`
5	The subnet ID and subnet broadcast address are the low and high ends of the range of numbers in a subnet. For the two interfaces in this lab: S0/0/0: 172.28.111.0–172.28.111.3 S0/0/1: 172.28.111.140–172.28.111.143
6	Rather than spoil the answer here, at this step continue with the next steps.
9	Use the **ip address 172.28.111.101 255.255.255.128** interface subcommand. In this case, the router rejects the command because this new subnet has a range from 172.28.111.0 to 172.28.111.127, which overlaps with the subnet on interface S0/0/0. (The error message lists the subnet ID and the interface with which the overlap occurs.)
10	Use the **ip address 172.28.111.201 255.255.255.192** interface subcommand. In this case, no overlap occurs and the router accepts the command.

Configuration Steps

Example 1 shows a sample of the lab exercise being completed from R1's CLI.

Example 1   Example of Performing This Lab

```
(Press enter)
Password: cs
R1> enable
Password: cs
R1#
R1# configure terminal
R1(config)# interface Fastethernet0/0
R1(config-if)# ip address 172.28.111.101 255.255.255.128
% 172.28.111.0 overlaps with Serial0/0/0
R1(config-if)# ip address 172.28.111.201 255.255.255.192
R1(config-if)#
```

ICND2 Subnetting Exercises

Part 1: VLSM Overlap

Lab 10: VLSM Overlap X

Overview

When an engineer configures the **ip address** interface subcommand on an interface that is in a working state, the router performs several verification checks before accepting the command. Those checks include a check of the subnet implied by the newly configured IP address compared to existing subnets connected to working local interfaces. If an overlap exists—that is, if the new subnet's range of addresses overlaps with the range of addresses on an existing connected subnet—the local router rejects the just-entered **ip address** command.

In this exercise, you determine the current IP address/mask pair configured on two interfaces on Router R1. Then you consider two potential new IP address/mask pairs to be configured on another router interface. Your job: Do the necessary calculations to determine whether either or both of these proposed new address/mask pairs would cause an overlap. Then you configure each IP address/mask pair to determine whether an overlap exists.

The IP addresses to consider for this lab are as follows in Table 1.

Table 1   IP Address/Mask Reference

Address	Mask	Prediction: Overlap? If so, with the subnet on interface . . .
192.168.7.130	255.255.255.248	
192.168.7.102	255.255.255.252	

Topology

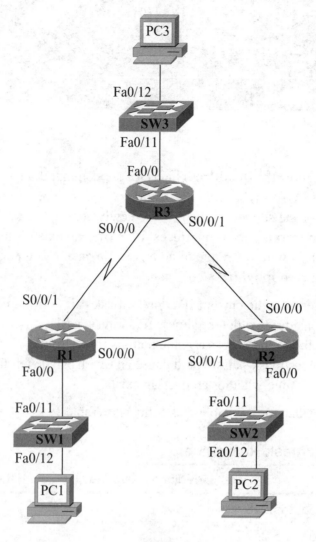

Figure 1   Topology for IP Address Configuration

Detailed Lab Steps

Step 1.   Connect to R1 from the simulator user interface. All passwords are **cs**.

Step 2.   Enter privileged exec ("enable") mode by issuing the **enable** command, again using password **cs**.

Step 3.   Use the **show interfaces** command to confirm the two status words for interfaces FastEthernet0/0, Serial0/0/0, and Serial0/0/1. Note whether all are up/up, and if not, which ones are not up.

_____

_____

Step 4. Use the **show interfaces** command to record the IP address and mask already configured on interfaces Serial0/0/0 and Serial0/0/1. Also confirm that interface FastEthernet0/0 does not currently have an IP address configured.

_____

_____

Step 5. For any IP addresses found in the previous step, calculate the subnet ID and range of addresses in the subnet for each subnet.

_____

_____

Step 6. Refer to the table near the beginning of this lab, and calculate the subnet ID and range of addresses for the two IP address/mask pairs listed in the table. Then make a prediction: Will either or both of these IP address/mask pairs, when configured with the **ip address** command on interface FastEthernet0/0, be rejected?

_____

_____

Next, you test your prediction in the previous step by determining whether the router rejects the commands.

Step 7. Enter global configuration mode using the **configure terminal** command.

Step 8. Configure the FastEthernet0/0 interface by issuing the **interface fa0/0** command.

Step 9. Use the **ip address** command to test the IP address and mask for the first entry in the table at the beginning of this lab. Is the command rejected? If so, what does the error message tell you about the reason? With what interface does an overlap occur?

_____

_____

Step 10. Use the **ip address** command to test the IP address and mask for the second entry in the table at the beginning of this lab. Is the command rejected? If so, what does the error message tell you about the reason? With what interface does an overlap occur?

_____

_____

Hints and Answers

Table 2 lists hints and tips for any lab steps that do not supply all the details in the lab step, and for lab steps that ask questions about the lab.

Table 2   Hints

Step	Hint
3	All three interfaces should be up/up, as noted in the first line of output for each interface. For example: `FastEthernet0/0 is up, line protocol is up`
4	The IP address and prefix mask will be in the third line of output in each section. For example: `Internet address is 10.4.130.1/19`
5	The subnet ID and subnet broadcast address are the low and high ends of the range of numbers in a subnet. For the two interfaces in this lab: S0/0/0: 192.168.7.96–192.168.7.127 S0/0/1: 192.168.7.64–192.168.7.79
6	Rather than spoil the answer here, at this step continue with the next steps.
9	Use the **ip address 192.168.7.130 255.255.255.248** interface subcommand. In this case, no overlap occurs and the router accepts the command.
10	Use the **ip address 192.168.7.102 255.255.255.252** interface subcommand. In this case, the router rejects the command because this new subnet has a range from 192.168.7.100 to 192.168.7.103, which overlaps with the subnet on interface S0/0/0. (The error message lists the subnet ID and the interface with which the overlap occurs.)

Configuration Steps

Example 1 shows a sample of the lab exercise being completed from R1's CLI.

Example 1   Example of Performing This Lab

```
(Press enter)
Password: cs
R1> enable
Password: cs
R1#
R1# configure terminal
R1(config)# interface Fastethernet0/0
R1(config-if)# ip address 192.168.7.130 255.255.255.248
R1(config-if)# ip address 192.168.7.102 255.255.255.252
% 192.168.7.100 overlaps with Serial0/0/0
R1(config-if)#
```

ICND2 Subnetting Exercises

Part 1: VLSM Overlap

Lab 11: VLSM Overlap XI

Overview

When an engineer configures the **ip address** interface subcommand on an interface that is in a working state, the router performs several verification checks before accepting the command. Those checks include a check of the subnet implied by the newly configured IP address compared to existing subnets connected to working local interfaces. If an overlap exists—that is, if the new subnet's range of addresses overlaps with the range of addresses on an existing connected subnet—the local router rejects the just-entered **ip address** command.

In this exercise, you determine the current IP address/mask pair configured on two interfaces on Router R1. Then you consider two potential new IP address/mask pairs to be configured on another router interface. Your job: Do the necessary calculations to determine whether either or both of these proposed new address/mask pairs would cause an overlap. Then you configure each IP address/mask pair to determine whether an overlap exists.

The IP addresses to consider for this lab are as follows in Table 1.

Table 1   IP Address/Mask Reference

Address	Mask	Prediction: Overlap? If so, with the subnet on interface . . .
192.168.8.120	255.255.255.128	
192.168.8.130	255.255.255.192	

Topology

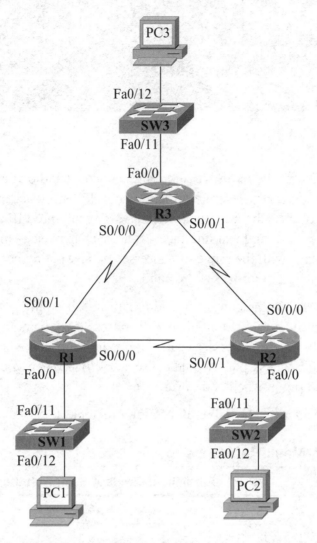

Figure 1   Topology for IP Address Configuration

Detailed Lab Steps

Step 1.   Connect to R1 from the simulator user interface. All passwords are **cs**.

Step 2.   Enter privileged exec ("enable") mode by issuing the **enable** command, again using password **cs**.

Step 3.   Use the **show interfaces** command to confirm the two status words for interfaces FastEthernet0/0, Serial0/0/0, and Serial0/0/1. Note whether all are up/up, and if not, which ones are not up.

_____

_____

Step 4. Use the **show interfaces** command to record the IP address and mask already configured on interfaces Serial0/0/0 and Serial0/0/1. Also confirm that interface FastEthernet0/0 does not currently have an IP address configured.

_____

_____

Step 5. For any IP addresses found in the previous step, calculate the subnet ID and range of addresses in the subnet for each subnet.

_____

_____

Step 6. Refer to the table near the beginning of this lab, and calculate the subnet ID and range of addresses for the two IP address/mask pairs listed in the table. Then make a prediction: Will either or both of these IP address/mask pairs, when configured with the **ip address** command on interface FastEthernet0/0, be rejected?

_____

_____

Next, you test your prediction in the previous step by determining whether the router rejects the commands.

Step 7. Enter global configuration mode using the **configure terminal** command.

Step 8. Configure the FastEthernet0/0 interface by issuing the **interface fa0/0** command.

Step 9. Use the **ip address** command to test the IP address and mask for the first entry in the table at the beginning of this lab. Is the command rejected? If so, what does the error message tell you about the reason? With what interface does an overlap occur?

_____

_____

Step 10. Use the **ip address** command to test the IP address and mask for the second entry in the table at the beginning of this lab. Is the command rejected? If so, what does the error message tell you about the reason? With what interface does an overlap occur?

_____

_____

Hints and Answers

Table 2 lists hints and tips for any lab steps that do not supply all the details in the lab step, and for lab steps that ask questions about the lab.

Table 2   Hints

Step	Hint
3	All three interfaces should be up/up, as noted in the first line of output for each interface. For example: `FastEthernet0/0 is up, line protocol is up`
4	The IP address and prefix mask will be in the third line of output in each section. For example: `Internet address is 10.4.130.1/19`
5	The subnet ID and subnet broadcast address are the low and high ends of the range of numbers in a subnet. For the two interfaces in this lab: S0/0/0: 192.168.8.208–192.168.8.211 S0/0/1: 192.168.8.176–192.168.8.179
6	Rather than spoil the answer here, at this step continue with the next steps.
9	Use the **ip address 192.168.8.120 255.255.255.128** interface subcommand. In this case, no overlap occurs and the router accepts the command.
10	Use the **ip address 192.168.8.130 255.255.255.192** interface subcommand. In this case, the router rejects the command because this new subnet has a range from 192.168.8.128 to 192.168.8.191, which overlaps with the subnet on interface S0/0/1. (The error message lists the subnet ID and the interface with which the overlap occurs.)

Configuration Steps

Example 1 shows a sample of the lab exercise being completed from R1's CLI.

Example 1   Example of Performing This Lab

```
(Press enter)
Password: cs
R1> enable
Password: cs
R1#
R1# configure terminal
R1(config)# interface Fastethernet0/0
R1(config-if)# ip address 192.168.8.120 255.255.255.128
R1(config-if)# ip address 192.168.8.130 255.255.255.192
% 192.168.8.128 overlaps with Serial0/0/1
R1(config-if)#
```

ICND2 Subnetting Exercises
Part 2: VLSM Route Selection

Lab 1: IP VLSM Route Selection 1

Overview

In this exercise, you focus on the routes known by Router R1. This lab essentially guides you to ask and then answer a question about three different IP addresses. The question: If three packets arrived at R1, each destined for one of the IP addresses listed in this lab, which of R1's routes, if any, would R1 use when forwarding each packet?

During this lab, you compare the IP addresses to R1's routing table and make your predictions. You then use commands to confirm which route R1 would use. The IP addresses to consider for this lab are as follows in Table 1.

Table 1   Destinations and Matching Route Info (to Be Completed)

Destination Address	Matching Route's Subnet/Mask	Matching Route's Outgoing Interface
10.99.90.2		
10.99.100.2		
10.99.110.2		

Topology

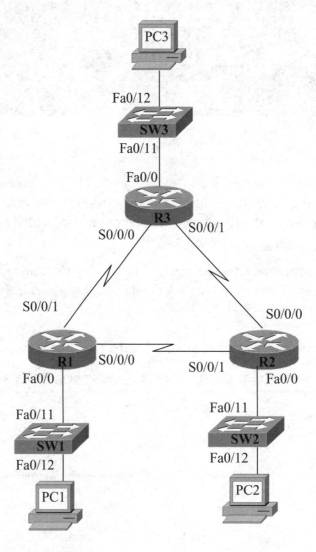

Figure 1   Topology for IP Address Configuration

Detailed Lab Steps

Step 1.   Connect to R1 from the simulator user interface. All passwords are **cs**.

Step 2.   Enter privileged exec ("enable") mode by issuing the **enable** command.

Step 3.   Use the output from the **show cdp neighbors detail** command, along with the diagram in this lab, to discover key facts about R1's outgoing interfaces for its routes. What local interfaces does R1 have? What other routers are neighbors of R1? Per the command output, what IP address does R2 use on the other end of the serial link? R3? Record your answers on the following lines.

_____

_____

_____

Step 4. Display R1's IP routing table using the **show ip route** exec command. How many routes does R1 know in network 10.0.0.0? How many different masks per the heading line for network 10.0.0.0?

_____

_____

Step 5. Examine the first of the three IP addresses in the table at the beginning of this lab, and imagine that a packet arrives at R1 with that IP address as the destination. Compare that destination IP address to R1's IP routing table displayed in the previous step. Decide whether any routes match the packet. If so, complete the table's last two columns for that IP address.

_____

_____

In the previous step, you predicted which route R1 would match. Next, you use a command to answer that same question.

The command **show ip route** *address*, where *address* is some IP address, lists details about a route. Which route? The route that this router would use to forward a packet sent to that address.

For example, the **show ip route 1.1.1.1** command lists information about the route used to forward packets destined for 1.1.1.1. If the router does not match any routes, the output lists either nothing or an error message.

Step 6. Issue the **show ip route** *address* command, where *address* is the first IP address listed in the table. Does this command list several lines of output for a route, or give no response or an error message? Does the output list the same route that you predicted and recorded in the table per Step 5?

_____

_____

Step 7. Issue the **traceroute** *address* command, where *address* is the first IP address listed in the table. Does the command show either R2's IP address or R3's IP address? Does it show a series of asterisks, signifying that no route existed?

_____

_____

Step 8. Similar to Step 5, examine the second IP address in the table at the beginning of this lab, and make predictions about which of R1's routes this packet will match. Complete the appropriate row of the table at the beginning of this lab.

_____

_____

Step 9. Similar to Step 6, confirm whether you made the correct prediction using the **show ip route** *address* command, where *address* is the second IP address listed in the table. Does the output list the same subnet ID, and same outgoing interface, that you predicted and recorded in the table per the previous step?

_____

_____

Step 10. Issue the **traceroute** *address* command, where *address* is the second IP address listed in the table. Does the command show a first entry with either R2's IP address or R3's IP address?

_____

_____

Step 11. Similar to Step 5, examine the third IP address in the table at the beginning of this lab, and make predictions about which of R1's routes this packet will match. Complete the appropriate row of the table at the beginning of this lab.

_____

_____

Step 12. Similar to Step 6, confirm whether you made the correct prediction using the **show ip route** *address* command, where *address* is the third IP address listed in the table. Does the output list the same subnet ID, and same outgoing interface, that you predicted and recorded in the table per the previous step?

_____

_____

Step 13. Issue the **traceroute** *address* command, where *address* is the IP address listed in the table. Does the command show a first entry with either R2's IP address or R3's IP address?

_____

_____

Hints and Answers

Table 2 lists hints and tips for any lab steps that do not supply all the details in the lab step, and for lab steps that ask questions about the lab.

Table 2   Hints

Step	Hint
3	The **show cdp neighbors detail** command lists a group of messages per neighbor. For each neighbor, the output lists the local router interface, the neighbor's host name, and the neighbor's IP address. In this case, from R1's perspective, R1's S0/0/0 interface connects to R2, whose IP address is 10.1.12.2. Also, R1's S0/0/1 interface connects to R3, whose IP address is 10.1.3.2.
4	The output lists a heading line as follows: `10.0.0.0/8 is variably subnetted, 8 subnets, 6 masks` Per this line, eight subnets exist with six different subnet masks. With more than one mask used, VLSM is in use in network 10.0.0.0.
5	The method used to determine the matching route is to look at each subnet in the routing table and mentally calculate the range of addresses in the subnet. Then choose the route whose subnet range includes the IP address in question. If more than one route's subnet range matches the IP address, choose the route with the more specific match; that is, the longer prefix mask.
6	The output of the **show ip route 10.99.90.2** command should list subnet 10.99.88.0/21 (/21 is equal to 255.255.248.0). It also should list R2's IP address 10.1.12.2 as the next-hop, with R1's outgoing interface of S0/0/0.
7	It lists a single line, 10.1.12.2, which is R2's IP address. So the **traceroute 10.99.90.2** command confirms that the next-hop router in the route is R2.
9	The output of the **show ip route 10.99.100.2** command should list subnet 10.99.100.0/22 (/22 is equal to 255.255.252.0). It also should list R2's IP address 10.1.12.2 as the next-hop, with R1's outgoing interface of S0/0/0.
10	It lists a single line, 10.1.12.2, which is R2's IP address. So the **traceroute 10.99.100.2** command confirms that the next-hop router in the route is R2.
12	The output of the **show ip route 10.99.110.2** command should list subnet 10.99.110.0/24 (/24 is equal to 255.255.255.0). It also should list R3's IP address 10.1.3.2 as the next-hop, with R1's outgoing interface of S0/0/1.
13	It lists a single line, 10.1.3.2, which is R3's IP address. So the **traceroute 10.99.110.2** command confirms that the next-hop router in the route is R3.

Configuration Steps

This lab requires no configuration.

ICND2 Subnetting Exercises
Part 2: VLSM Route Selection

Lab 2: IP VLSM Route Selection II

Overview

In this exercise, you focus on the routes known by Router R1. This lab essentially guides you to ask and then answer a question about three different IP addresses. The question: If three packets arrived at R1, each destined for one of the IP addresses listed in this lab, which of R1's routes, if any, would R1 use when forwarding each packet?

During this lab, you compare the IP addresses to R1's routing table and make your predictions. You then use commands to confirm which route R1 would use. The IP addresses to consider for this lab are as follows in Table 1.

Table 1   Destinations and Matching Route Info (to Be Completed)

Destination Address	Matching Route's Subnet/Mask	Matching Route's Outgoing Interface
10.2.80.2		
10.2.100.2		
10.2.150.2		

Topology

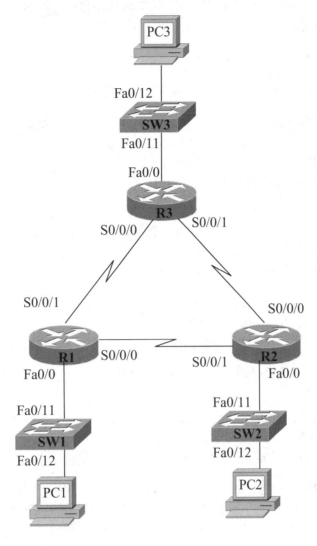

Figure 1   Topology for IP Address Configuration

Detailed Lab Steps

Step 1.   Connect to R1 from the simulator user interface. All passwords are **cs**.

Step 2.   Enter privileged exec ("enable") mode by issuing the **enable** command.

Step 3.   Use the output from the **show cdp neighbors detail** command, along with the diagram in this lab, to discover key facts about R1's outgoing interfaces for its routes. What local interfaces does R1 have? What other routers are neighbors of R1? Per the command output, what IP address does R2 use on the other end of the serial link? R3? Record your answers on the following lines.

_____

_____

_____

Step 4. Display R1's IP routing table using the **show ip route** exec command. How many routes does R1 know in network 10.0.0.0? How many different masks per the heading line for network 10.0.0.0?

_____

_____

Step 5. Examine the first of the three IP addresses in the table at the beginning of this lab, and imagine that a packet arrives at R1 with that IP address as the destination. Compare that destination IP address to R1's IP routing table displayed in the previous step. Decide whether any routes match the packet. If so, complete the table's last two columns for that IP address.

_____

_____

In the previous step, you predicted which route R1 would match. Next, you use a command to answer that same question.

The command **show ip route** *address*, where *address* is some IP address, lists details about a route. Which route? The route that this router would use to forward a packet sent to that address.

For example, the **show ip route 1.1.1.1** command lists information about the route used to forward packets destined for 1.1.1.1. If the router does not match any routes, the output lists either nothing or an error message.

Step 6. Issue the **show ip route** *address* command, where *address* is the first IP address listed in the table. Does this command list several lines of output for a route, or give no response or an error message? Does the output list the same route that you predicted and recorded in the table per Step 5?

_____

_____

Step 7. Issue the **traceroute** *address* command, where *address* is the first IP address listed in the table. Does the command show either R2's IP address or R3's IP address? Does it show a series of asterisks, signifying that no route existed?

_____

_____

Step 8. Similar to Step 5, examine the second IP address in the table at the beginning of this lab, and make predictions about which of R1's routes this packet will match. Complete the appropriate row of the table at the beginning of this lab.

_____

_____

Step 9. Similar to Step 6, confirm whether you made the correct prediction using the **show ip route** *address* command, where *address* is the second IP address listed in the table. Does the output list the same subnet ID, and same outgoing interface, that you predicted and recorded in the table per the previous step?

Step 10. Issue the **traceroute** *address* command, where *address* is the second IP address listed in the table. Does the command show a first entry with either R2's IP address or R3's IP address?

Step 11. Similar to Step 5, examine the third IP address in the table at the beginning of this lab, and make predictions about which of R1's routes this packet will match. Complete the appropriate row of the table at the beginning of this lab.

Step 12. Similar to Step 6, confirm whether you made the correct prediction using the **show ip route** *address* command, where *address* is the third IP address listed in the table. Does the output list the same subnet ID, and same outgoing interface, that you predicted and recorded in the table per the previous step?

Step 13. Issue the **traceroute** *address* command, where *address* is the IP address listed in the table. Does the command show a first entry with either R2's IP address or R3's IP address?

Hints and Answers

Table 2 lists hints and tips for any lab steps that do not supply all the details in the lab step, and for lab steps that ask questions about the lab.

Table 2   Hints

Step	Hint
3	The **show cdp neighbors detail** command lists a group of messages per neighbor. For each neighbor, the output lists the local router interface, the neighbor's host name, and the neighbor's IP address. In this case, from R1's perspective, R1's S0/0/0 interface connects to R2, whose IP address is 10.1.12.2. Also, R1's S0/0/1 interface connects to R3, whose IP address is 10.1.3.2.
4	The output lists a heading line as follows: `10.0.0.0/8 is variably subnetted, 8 subnets, 3 masks` Per this line, eight subnets exist with three different subnet masks. With more than one mask used, VLSM is in use in network 10.0.0.0.
5	The method used to determine the matching route is to look at each subnet in the routing table and mentally calculate the range of addresses in the subnet. Then choose the route whose subnet range includes the IP address in question. If more than one route's subnet range matches the IP address, choose the route with the more specific match; that is, the longer prefix mask.
6	The output of the **show ip route 10.2.80.2** command lists a message which means that R1 matches no routes.
7	It lists three lines of three asterisks, which in the simulator means that the command would not complete and did not even get a response from the next router. In this case, the **traceroute 10.2.80.2** command confirms that R1 has no matching route for 10.2.80.2.
9	The output of the **show ip route 10.2.100.2** command should list subnet 10.2.96.0/19 (/19 is equal to 255.255.224.0). It also should list R3's IP address 10.1.3.2 as the next-hop, with R1's outgoing interface of S0/0/1.
10	It lists a single line, 10.1.3.2, which is R3's IP address. So the **traceroute 10.2.100.2** command confirms that the next-hop router in the route is R3.
12	The output of the **show ip route 10.2.150.2** command should list subnet 10.2.128.0/18 (/18 is equal to 255.255.192.0). It also should list R2's IP address 10.1.12.2 as the next-hop, with R1's outgoing interface of S0/0/0.
13	It lists a single line, 10.1.12.2, which is R2's IP address. So the **traceroute 10.2.150.2** command confirms that the next-hop router in the route is R2.

Configuration Steps

This lab requires no configuration.

ICND2 Subnetting Exercises
Part 2: VLSM Route Selection

Lab 3: IP VLSM Route Selection III

Overview

In this exercise, you focus on the routes known by Router R1. This lab essentially guides you to ask and then answer a question about three different IP addresses. The question: If three packets arrived at R1, each destined for one of the IP addresses listed in this lab, which of R1's routes, if any, would R1 use when forwarding each packet?

During this lab, you compare the IP addresses to R1's routing table and make your predictions. You then use commands to confirm which route R1 would use. The IP addresses to consider for this lab are as follows in Table 1.

Table 1   Destinations and Matching Route Info (to Be Completed)

Destination Address	Matching Route's Subnet/Mask	Matching Route's Outgoing Interface
10.4.4.65		
10.4.4.75		
10.4.4.85		

Topology

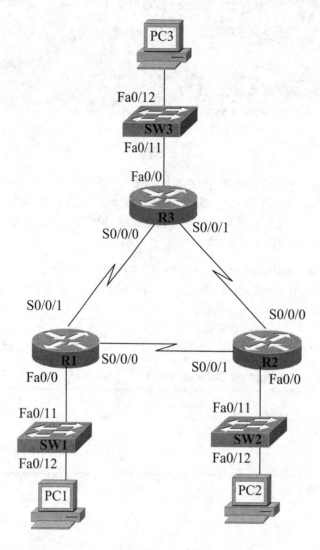

Figure 1   Topology for IP Address Configuration

Detailed Lab Steps

Step 1.   Connect to R1 from the simulator user interface. All passwords are **cs**.

Step 2.   Enter privileged exec ("enable") mode by issuing the **enable** command.

Step 3.   Use the output from the **show cdp neighbors detail** command, along with the diagram in this lab, to discover key facts about R1's outgoing interfaces for its routes. What local interfaces does R1 have? What other routers are neighbors of R1? Per the command output, what IP address does R2 use on the other end of the serial link? R3? Record your answers on the following lines.

_____

_____

_____

Step 4.   Display R1's IP routing table using the **show ip route** exec command. How many routes does R1 know in network 10.0.0.0? How many different masks per the heading line for network 10.0.0.0?

_____

_____

Step 5.   Examine the first of the three IP addresses in the table at the beginning of this lab, and imagine that a packet arrives at R1 with that IP address as the destination. Compare that destination IP address to R1's IP routing table displayed in the previous step. Decide whether any routes match the packet. If so, complete the table's last two columns for that IP address.

_____

_____

In the previous step, you predicted which route R1 would match. Next, you use a command to answer that same question.

The command **show ip route** _address_, where _address_ is some IP address, lists details about a route. Which route? The route that this router would use to forward a packet sent to that address.

For example, the **show ip route 1.1.1.1** command lists information about the route used to forward packets destined for 1.1.1.1. If the router does not match any routes, the output lists either nothing or an error message.

Step 6.   Issue the **show ip route** _address_ command, where _address_ is the first IP address listed in the table. Does this command list several lines of output for a route, or give no response or an error message? Does the output list the same route that you predicted and recorded in the table per Step 5?

_____

_____

Step 7.   Issue the **traceroute** _address_ command, where _address_ is the first IP address listed in the table. Does the command show either R2's IP address or R3's IP address? Does it show a series of asterisks, signifying that no route existed?

_____

_____

Step 8.   Similar to Step 5, examine the second IP address in the table at the beginning of this lab, and make predictions about which of R1's routes this packet will match. Complete the appropriate row of the table at the beginning of this lab.

_____

_____

Step 9. Similar to Step 6, confirm whether you made the correct prediction using the **show ip route** *address* command, where *address* is the second IP address listed in the table. Does the output list the same subnet ID, and same outgoing interface, that you predicted and recorded in the table per the previous step?

_____

_____

Step 10. Issue the **traceroute** *address* command, where *address* is the second IP address listed in the table. Does the command show a first entry with either R2's IP address or R3's IP address?

_____

_____

Step 11. Similar to Step 5, examine the third IP address in the table at the beginning of this lab, and make predictions about which of R1's routes this packet will match. Complete the appropriate row of the table at the beginning of this lab.

_____

_____

Step 12. Similar to Step 6, confirm whether you made the correct prediction using the **show ip route** *address* command, where *address* is the third IP address listed in the table. Does the output list the same subnet ID, and same outgoing interface, that you predicted and recorded in the table per the previous step?

_____

_____

Step 13. Issue the **traceroute** *address* command, where *address* is the IP address listed in the table. Does the command show a first entry with either R2's IP address or R3's IP address?

_____

_____

Hints and Answers

Table 2 lists hints and tips for any lab steps that do not supply all the details in the lab step, and for lab steps that ask questions about the lab.

Table 2   Hints

Step	Hint
3	The **show cdp neighbors detail** command lists a group of messages per neighbor. For each neighbor, the output lists the local router interface, the neighbor's host name, and the neighbor's IP address. In this case, from R1's perspective, R1's S0/0/0 interface connects to R2, whose IP address is 10.1.12.2. Also, R1's S0/0/1 interface connects to R3, whose IP address is 10.1.3.2.
4	The output lists a heading line as follows: `10.0.0.0/8 is variably subnetted, 8 subnets, 6 masks` Per this line, eight subnets exist with six different subnet masks. With more than one mask used, VLSM is in use in network 10.0.0.0.
5	The method used to determine the matching route is to look at each subnet in the routing table and mentally calculate the range of addresses in the subnet. Then choose the route whose subnet range includes the IP address in question. If more than one route's subnet range matches the IP address, choose the route with the more specific match; that is, the longer prefix mask.
6	The output of the **show ip route 10.4.4.65** command should list subnet 10.4.4.64/30 (/30 is equal to 255.255.255.252). It also should list R2's IP address 10.1.12.2 as the next-hop, with R1's outgoing interface of S0/0/0.
7	It lists a single line, 10.1.12.2, which is R2's IP address. So the **traceroute 10.4.4.65** command confirms that the next-hop router in the route is R2.
9	The output of the **show ip route 10.4.4.75** command lists a message which means that R1 matches no routes.
10	It lists three lines of three asterisks, which in the simulator means that the command would not complete and did not even get a response from the next router. In this case, the **traceroute 10.4.4.75** command confirms that R1 has no matching route for 10.4.4.75.
12	The output of the **show ip route 10.4.4.85** command should list subnet 10.4.4.80/28 (/28 is equal to 255.255.255.240). It also should list R3's IP address 10.1.3.2 as the next-hop, with R1's outgoing interface of S0/0/1.
13	It lists a single line, 10.1.3.2, which is R3's IP address. So the **traceroute 10.4.4.85** command confirms that the next-hop router in the route is R3.

Configuration Steps

This lab requires no configuration.

ICND2 Subnetting Exercises
Part 2: VLSM Route Selection

Lab 4: IP VLSM Route Selection IV

Overview

In this exercise, you focus on the routes known by Router R1. This lab essentially guides you to ask and then answer a question about three different IP addresses. The question: If three packets arrived at R1, each destined for one of the IP addresses listed in this lab, which of R1's routes, if any, would R1 use when forwarding each packet?

During this lab, you compare the IP addresses to R1's routing table and make your predictions. You then use commands to confirm which route R1 would use. The IP addresses to consider for this lab are as follows in Table 1.

Table 1   **Destinations and Matching Route Info (to Be Completed)**

Destination Address	Matching Route's Subnet/Mask	Matching Route's Outgoing Interface
172.30.130.1		
172.30.120.1		
172.30.150.1		

Topology

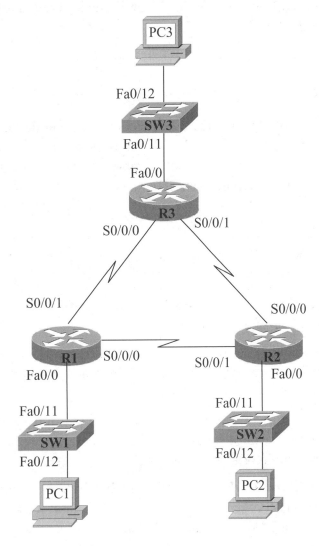

Figure 1   Topology for IP Address Configuration

Detailed Lab Steps

Step 1.   Connect to R1 from the simulator user interface. All passwords are **cs**.

Step 2.   Enter privileged exec ("enable") mode by issuing the **enable** command.

Step 3.   Use the output from the **show cdp neighbors detail** command, along with the diagram in this lab, to discover key facts about R1's outgoing interfaces for its routes. What local interfaces does R1 have? What other routers are neighbors of R1? Per the command output, what IP address does R2 use on the other end of the serial link? R3? Record your answers on the following lines.

_____

_____

_____

Step 4. Display R1's IP routing table using the **show ip route** exec command. How many routes does R1 know in network 172.30.0.0? How many different masks per the heading line for network 172.30.0.0?

_____

_____

Step 5. Examine the first of the three IP addresses in the table at the beginning of this lab, and imagine that a packet arrives at R1 with that IP address as the destination. Compare that destination IP address to R1's IP routing table displayed in the previous step. Decide whether any routes match the packet. If so, complete the table's last two columns for that IP address.

_____

_____

In the previous step, you predicted which route R1 would match. Next, you use a command to answer that same question.

The command **show ip route** *address*, where *address* is some IP address, lists details about a route. Which route? The route that this router would use to forward a packet sent to that address.

For example, the **show ip route 1.1.1.1** command lists information about the route used to forward packets destined for 1.1.1.1. If the router does not match any routes, the output lists either nothing or an error message.

Step 6. Issue the **show ip route** *address* command, where *address* is the first IP address listed in the table. Does this command list several lines of output for a route, or give no response or an error message? Does the output list the same route that you predicted and recorded in the table per Step 5?

_____

_____

Step 7. Issue the **traceroute** *address* command, where *address* is the first IP address listed in the table. Does the command show either R2's IP address or R3's IP address? Does it show a series of asterisks, signifying that no route existed?

_____

_____

Step 8. Similar to Step 5, examine the second IP address in the table at the beginning of this lab, and make predictions about which of R1's routes this packet will match. Complete the appropriate row of the table at the beginning of this lab.

_____

_____

Step 9. Similar to Step 6, confirm whether you made the correct prediction using the **show ip route** *address* command, where *address* is the second IP address listed in the table. Does the output list the same subnet ID, and same outgoing interface, that you predicted and recorded in the table per the previous step?

_____

_____

Step 10. Issue the **traceroute** *address* command, where *address* is the second IP address listed in the table. Does the command show a first entry with either R2's IP address or R3's IP address?

_____

_____

Step 11. Similar to Step 5, examine the third IP address in the table at the beginning of this lab, and make predictions about which of R1's routes this packet will match. Complete the appropriate row of the table at the beginning of this lab.

_____

_____

Step 12. Similar to Step 6, confirm whether you made the correct prediction using the **show ip route** *address* command, where *address* is the third IP address listed in the table. Does the output list the same subnet ID, and same outgoing interface, that you predicted and recorded in the table per the previous step?

_____

_____

Step 13. Issue the **traceroute** *address* command, where *address* is the IP address listed in the table. Does the command show a first entry with either R2's IP address or R3's IP address?

_____

_____

Hints and Answers

Table 2 lists hints and tips for any lab steps that do not supply all the details in the lab step, and for lab steps that ask questions about the lab.

Table 2   Hints

Step	Hint
3	The **show cdp neighbors detail** command lists a group of messages per neighbor. For each neighbor, the output lists the local router interface, the neighbor's host name, and the neighbor's IP address. In this case, from R1's perspective, R1's S0/0/0 interface connects to R2, whose IP address is 172.30.1.2. Also, R1's S0/0/1 interface connects to R3, whose IP address is 172.30.3.3.
4	The output lists a heading line as follows: `172.30.0.0/16 is variably subnetted, 8 subnets, 6 masks` Per this line, eight subnets exist with four different subnet masks. With more than one mask used, VLSM is in use in network 172.30.0.0.
5	The method used to determine the matching route is to look at each subnet in the routing table and mentally calculate the range of addresses in the subnet. Then choose the route whose subnet range includes the IP address in question. If more than one route's subnet range matches the IP address, choose the route with the more specific match; that is, the longer prefix mask.
6	The output of the **show ip route 172.30.130.1** command lists a message which means that R1 matches no routes.
7	It lists three lines of three asterisks, which in the simulator means that the command would not complete and did not even get a response from the next router. In this case, the **traceroute 172.30.130.1** command confirms that R1 has no matching route for 172.30.130.1.
9	The output of the **show ip route 172.30.120.1** command should list subnet 172.30.112.0/20 (/20 is equal to 255.255.240.0). It also should list R2's IP address 172.30.1.2 as the next-hop, with R1's outgoing interface of S0/0/0.
10	It lists a single line, 172.30.1.2, which is R2's IP address. So the **traceroute 172.30.120.1** command confirms that the next-hop router in the route is R2.
12	The output of the **show ip route 172.30.150.1** command should list subnet 172.30.144.0/20 (/20 is equal to 255.255.240.0). It also should list R3's IP address 172.30.3.3 as the next-hop, with R1's outgoing interface of S0/0/1.
13	It lists a single line, 172.30.3.3, which is R3's IP address. So the **traceroute 172.30.150.1** command confirms that the next-hop router in the route is R3.

Configuration Steps

This lab requires no configuration.

ICND2 Subnetting Exercises

Part 2: VLSM Route Selection

Lab 5: IP VLSM Route Selection V

Overview

In this exercise, you focus on the routes known by Router R1. This lab essentially guides you to ask and then answer a question about three different IP addresses. The question: If three packets arrived at R1, each destined for one of the IP addresses listed in this lab, which of R1's routes, if any, would R1 use when forwarding each packet?

During this lab, you compare the IP addresses to R1's routing table and make your predictions. You then use commands to confirm which route R1 would use. The IP addresses to consider for this lab are as follows in Table 1.

Table 1   **Destinations and Matching Route Info (to Be Completed)**

Destination Address	Matching Route's Subnet/Mask	Matching Route's Outgoing Interface
172.30.202.150		
172.30.206.150		
172.30.209.150		

Topology

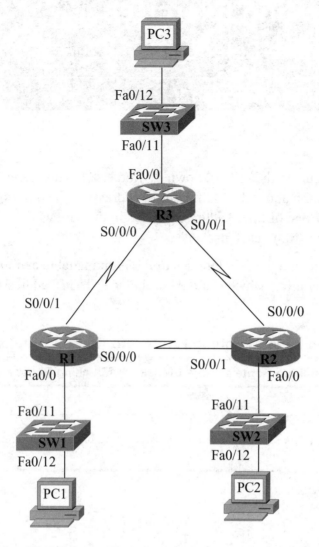

Figure 1   **Topology for IP Address Configuration**

Detailed Lab Steps

Step 1.   Connect to R1 from the simulator user interface. All passwords are **cs**.

Step 2.   Enter privileged exec ("enable") mode by issuing the **enable** command.

Step 3.   Use the output from the **show cdp neighbors detail** command, along with the diagram in this lab, to discover key facts about R1's outgoing interfaces for its routes. What local interfaces does R1 have? What other routers are neighbors of R1? Per the command output, what IP address does R2 use on the other end of the serial link? R3? Record your answers on the following lines.

_____

_____

_____

Step 4. Display R1's IP routing table using the **show ip route** exec command. How many routes does R1 know in network 172.30.0.0? How many different masks per the heading line for network 172.30.0.0?

_____

_____

Step 5. Examine the first of the three IP addresses in the table at the beginning of this lab, and imagine that a packet arrives at R1 with that IP address as the destination. Compare that destination IP address to R1's IP routing table displayed in the previous step. Decide whether any routes match the packet. If so, complete the table's last two columns for that IP address.

_____

_____

In the previous step, you predicted which route R1 would match. Next, you use a command to answer that same question.

The command **show ip route** _address_, where _address_ is some IP address, lists details about a route. Which route? The route that this router would use to forward a packet sent to that address.

For example, the **show ip route 1.1.1.1** command lists information about the route used to forward packets destined for 1.1.1.1. If the router does not match any routes, the output lists either nothing or an error message.

Step 6. Issue the **show ip route** _address_ command, where _address_ is the first IP address listed in the table. Does this command list several lines of output for a route, or give no response or an error message? Does the output list the same route that you predicted and recorded in the table per Step 5?

_____

_____

Step 7. Issue the **traceroute** _address_ command, where _address_ is the first IP address listed in the table. Does the command show either R2's IP address or R3's IP address? Does it show a series of asterisks, signifying that no route existed?

_____

_____

Step 8. Similar to Step 5, examine the second IP address in the table at the beginning of this lab, and make predictions about which of R1's routes this packet will match. Complete the appropriate row of the table at the beginning of this lab.

_____

_____

Step 9. Similar to Step 6, confirm whether you made the correct prediction using the **show ip route** *address* command, where *address* is the second IP address listed in the table. Does the output list the same subnet ID, and same outgoing interface, that you predicted and recorded in the table per the previous step?

_____

_____

Step 10. Issue the **traceroute** *address* command, where *address* is the second IP address listed in the table. Does the command show a first entry with either R2's IP address or R3's IP address?

_____

_____

Step 11. Similar to Step 5, examine the third IP address in the table at the beginning of this lab, and make predictions about which of R1's routes this packet will match. Complete the appropriate row of the table at the beginning of this lab.

_____

_____

Step 12. Similar to Step 6, confirm whether you made the correct prediction using the **show ip route** *address* command, where *address* is the third IP address listed in the table. Does the output list the same subnet ID, and same outgoing interface, that you predicted and recorded in the table per the previous step?

_____

_____

Step 13. Issue the **traceroute** *address* command, where *address* is the IP address listed in the table. Does the command show a first entry with either R2's IP address or R3's IP address?

_____

_____

Hints and Answers

Table 2 lists hints and tips for any lab steps that do not supply all the details in the lab step, and for lab steps that ask questions about the lab.

Table 2   Hints

Step	Hint
3	The **show cdp neighbors detail** command lists a group of messages per neighbor. For each neighbor, the output lists the local router interface, the neighbor's host name, and the neighbor's IP address. In this case, from R1's perspective, R1's S0/0/0 interface connects to R2, whose IP address is 172.30.1.2. Also, R1's S0/0/1 interface connects to R3, whose IP address is 172.30.3.3.
4	The output lists a heading line as follows: `172.30.0.0/16 is variably subnetted, 8 subnets, 6 masks` Per this line, eight subnets exist with six different subnet masks. With more than one mask used, VLSM is in use in network172.30.0.0.
5	The method used to determine the matching route is to look at each subnet in the routing table and mentally calculate the range of addresses in the subnet. Then choose the route whose subnet range includes the IP address in question. If more than one route's subnet range matches the IP address, choose the route with the more specific match; that is, the longer prefix mask.
6	The output of the **show ip route 172.30.202.150** command lists a message which means that R1 matches no routes.
7	It lists three lines of three asterisks, which in the simulator means that the command would not complete and did not even get a response from the next router. In this case, the **traceroute 172.30.202.150** command confirms that R1 has no matching route for 172.30.202.150.
9	The output of the **show ip route 172.30.206.150** command lists a message which means that R1 matches no routes.
10	It lists three lines of three asterisks, which in the simulator means that the command would not complete and did not even get a response from the next router. In this case, the **traceroute 172.30.206.150** command confirms that R1 has no matching route for 172.30.206.150.
12	The output of the **show ip route 172.30.209.150** command lists a message which means that R1 matches no routes.
13	It lists three lines of three asterisks, which in the simulator means that the command would not complete and did not even get a response from the next router. In this case, the **traceroute 172.30.209.150** command confirms that R1 has no matching route for 172.30.209.150.

Configuration Steps

This lab requires no configuration.

ICND2 Subnetting Exercises

Part 2: VLSM Route Selection

Lab 6: IP VLSM Route Selection VI

Overview

In this exercise, you focus on the routes known by Router R1. This lab essentially guides you to ask and then answer a question about three different IP addresses. The question: If three packets arrived at R1, each destined for one of the IP addresses listed in this lab, which of R1's routes, if any, would R1 use when forwarding each packet?

During this lab, you compare the IP addresses to R1's routing table and make your predictions. You then use commands to confirm which route R1 would use. The IP addresses to consider for this lab are as follows in Table 1.

Table 1   Destinations and Matching Route Info (to Be Completed)

Destination Address	Matching Route's Subnet/Mask	Matching Route's Outgoing Interface
192.168.1.220		
192.168.1.240		
192.168.1.200		

Topology

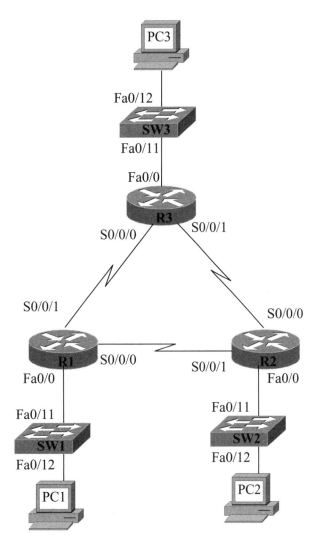

Figure 1   Topology for IP Address Configuration

Detailed Lab Steps

Step 1.   Connect to R1 from the simulator user interface. All passwords are **cs**.

Step 2.   Enter privileged exec ("enable") mode by issuing the **enable** command.

Step 3.   Use the output from the **show cdp neighbors detail** command, along with the diagram in this lab, to discover key facts about R1's outgoing interfaces for its routes. What local interfaces does R1 have? What other routers are neighbors of R1? Per the command output, what IP address does R2 use on the other end of the serial link? R3? Record your answers on the following lines.

Step 4. Display R1's IP routing table using the **show ip route** exec command. How many routes does R1 know in network 192.168.1.0? How many different masks per the heading line for network 192.168.1.0?

_____

_____

Step 5. Examine the first of the three IP addresses in the table at the beginning of this lab, and imagine that a packet arrives at R1 with that IP address as the destination. Compare that destination IP address to R1's IP routing table displayed in the previous step. Decide whether any routes match the packet. If so, complete the table's last two columns for that IP address.

_____

_____

In the previous step, you predicted which route R1 would match. Next, you use a command to answer that same question.

The command **show ip route** *address*, where *address* is some IP address, lists details about a route. Which route? The route that this router would use to forward a packet sent to that address.

For example, the **show ip route 1.1.1.1** command lists information about the route used to forward packets destined for 1.1.1.1. If the router does not match any routes, the output lists either nothing or an error message.

Step 6. Issue the **show ip route** *address* command, where *address* is the first IP address listed in the table. Does this command list several lines of output for a route, or give no response or an error message? Does the output list the same route that you predicted and recorded in the table per Step 5?

_____

_____

Step 7. Issue the **traceroute** *address* command, where *address* is the first IP address listed in the table. Does the command show either R2's IP address or R3's IP address? Does it show a series of asterisks, signifying that no route existed?

_____

_____

Step 8. Similar to Step 5, examine the second IP address in the table at the beginning of this lab, and make predictions about which of R1's routes this packet will match. Complete the appropriate row of the table at the beginning of this lab.

_____

_____

Step 9. Similar to Step 6, confirm whether you made the correct prediction using the **show ip route** *address* command, where *address* is the second IP address listed in the table. Does the output list the same subnet ID, and same outgoing interface, that you predicted and recorded in the table per the previous step?

_____

_____

Step 10. Issue the **traceroute** *address* command, where *address* is the second IP address listed in the table. Does the command show a first entry with either R2's IP address or R3's IP address?

_____

_____

Step 11. Similar to Step 5, examine the third IP address in the table at the beginning of this lab, and make predictions about which of R1's routes this packet will match. Complete the appropriate row of the table at the beginning of this lab.

_____

_____

Step 12. Similar to Step 6, confirm whether you made the correct prediction using the **show ip route** *address* command, where *address* is the third IP address listed in the table. Does the output list the same subnet ID, and same outgoing interface, that you predicted and recorded in the table per the previous step?

_____

_____

Step 13. Issue the **traceroute** *address* command, where *address* is the IP address listed in the table. Does the command show a first entry with either R2's IP address or R3's IP address?

_____

_____

Hints and Answers

Table 2 lists hints and tips for any lab steps that do not supply all the details in the lab step, and for lab steps that ask questions about the lab.

Table 2   Hints

Step	Hint
3	The **show cdp neighbors detail** command lists a group of messages per neighbor. For each neighbor, the output lists the local router interface, the neighbor's host name, and the neighbor's IP address. In this case, from R1's perspective, R1's S0/0/0 interface connects to R2, whose IP address is 192.168.1.2. Also, R1's S0/0/1 interface connects to R3, whose IP address is 192.168.1.6.
4	The output lists a heading line as follows: `192.168.1.0/24 is variably subnetted, 8 subnets, 4 masks` Per this line, eight subnets exist with four different subnet masks. With more than one mask used, VLSM is in use in network 192.168.1.0.
5	The method used to determine the matching route is to look at each subnet in the routing table and mentally calculate the range of addresses in the subnet. Then choose the route whose subnet range includes the IP address in question. If more than one route's subnet range matches the IP address, choose the route with the more specific match; that is, the longer prefix mask.
6	The output of the **show ip route 192.168.1.220** command should list subnet 192.168.1.208/28 (/28 is equal to 255.255.255.240). It also should list R2's IP address 192.168.1.2 as the next-hop, with R1's outgoing interface of S0/0/0.
7	It lists a single line, 192.168.1.2, which is R2's IP address. So the **traceroute 192.168.1.220** command confirms that the next-hop router in the route is R2.
9	The output of the **show ip route 192.168.1.240** command should list subnet 192.168.1.224/27 (/27 is equal to 255.255.255.224). It also should list R3's IP address 192.168.1.6 as the next-hop, with R1's outgoing interface of S0/0/1.
10	It lists a single line, 192.168.1.6, which is R3's IP address. So the **traceroute 192.168.1.240** command confirms that the next-hop router in the route is R3.
12	The output of the **show ip route 192.168.1.200** command lists a message which means that R1 matches no routes.
13	It lists three lines of three asterisks, which in the simulator means that the command would not complete and did not even get a response from the next router. In this case, the **traceroute 192.168.1.200** command confirms that R1 has no matching route for 192.168.1.200.

Configuration Steps

This lab requires no configuration.

ICND2 Subnetting Exercises

Part 2: VLSM Route Selection

Lab 7: IP VLSM Route Selection VII

Overview

In this exercise, you focus on the routes known by Router R1. This lab essentially guides you to ask and then answer a question about three different IP addresses. The question: If three packets arrived at R1, each destined for one of the IP addresses listed in this lab, which of R1's routes, if any, would R1 use when forwarding each packet?

During this lab, you compare the IP addresses to R1's routing table and make your predictions. You then use commands to confirm which route R1 would use. The IP addresses to consider for this lab are as follows in Table 1.

Table 1   Destinations and Matching Route Info (to Be Completed)

Destination Address	Matching Route's Subnet/Mask	Matching Route's Outgoing Interface
192.168.1.183		
192.168.1.193		
192.168.1.163		

Topology

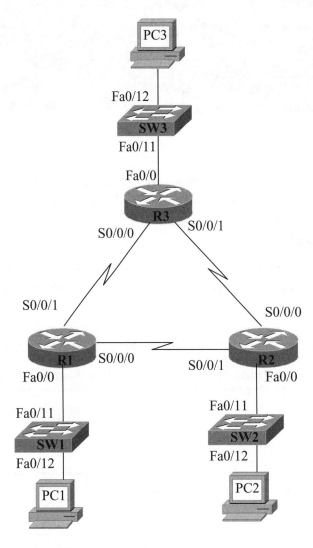

Figure 1   Topology for IP Address Configuration

Detailed Lab Steps

Step 1.   Connect to R1 from the simulator user interface. All passwords are **cs**.

Step 2.   Enter privileged exec ("enable") mode by issuing the **enable** command.

Step 3.   Use the output from the **show cdp neighbors detail** command, along with the diagram in this lab, to discover key facts about R1's outgoing interfaces for its routes. What local interfaces does R1 have? What other routers are neighbors of R1? Per the command output, what IP address does R2 use on the other end of the serial link? R3? Record your answers on the following lines.

_____

_____

_____

Step 4. Display R1's IP routing table using the **show ip route** exec command. How many routes does R1 know in network 192.168.1.0? How many different masks per the heading line for network 192.168.1.0?

_____

_____

Step 5. Examine the first of the three IP addresses in the table at the beginning of this lab, and imagine that a packet arrives at R1 with that IP address as the destination. Compare that destination IP address to R1's IP routing table displayed in the previous step. Decide whether any routes match the packet. If so, complete the table's last two columns for that IP address.

_____

_____

In the previous step, you predicted which route R1 would match. Next, you use a command to answer that same question.

The command **show ip route** _address_, where _address_ is some IP address, lists details about a route. Which route? The route that this router would use to forward a packet sent to that address.

For example, the **show ip route 1.1.1.1** command lists information about the route used to forward packets destined for 1.1.1.1. If the router does not match any routes, the output lists either nothing or an error message.

Step 6. Issue the **show ip route** _address_ command, where _address_ is the first IP address listed in the table. Does this command list several lines of output for a route, or give no response or an error message? Does the output list the same route that you predicted and recorded in the table per Step 5?

_____

_____

Step 7. Issue the **traceroute** _address_ command, where _address_ is the first IP address listed in the table. Does the command show either R2's IP address or R3's IP address? Does it show a series of asterisks, signifying that no route existed?

_____

_____

Step 8. Similar to Step 5, examine the second IP address in the table at the beginning of this lab, and make predictions about which of R1's routes this packet will match. Complete the appropriate row of the table at the beginning of this lab.

_____

_____

Step 9. Similar to Step 6, confirm whether you made the correct prediction using the **show ip route** *address* command, where *address* is the second IP address listed in the table. Does the output list the same subnet ID, and same outgoing interface, that you predicted and recorded in the table per the previous step?

_____

_____

Step 10. Issue the **traceroute** *address* command, where *address* is the second IP address listed in the table. Does the command show a first entry with either R2's IP address or R3's IP address?

_____

_____

Step 11. Similar to Step 5, examine the third IP address in the table at the beginning of this lab, and make predictions about which of R1's routes this packet will match. Complete the appropriate row of the table at the beginning of this lab.

_____

_____

Step 12. Similar to Step 6, confirm whether you made the correct prediction using the **show ip route** *address* command, where *address* is the third IP address listed in the table. Does the output list the same subnet ID, and same outgoing interface, that you predicted and recorded in the table per the previous step?

_____

_____

Step 13. Issue the **traceroute** *address* command, where *address* is the IP address listed in the table. Does the command show a first entry with either R2's IP address or R3's IP address?

_____

_____

Hints and Answers

Table 2 lists hints and tips for any lab steps that do not supply all the details in the lab step, and for lab steps that ask questions about the lab.

Table 2   Hints

Step	Hint
3	The **show cdp neighbors detail** command lists a group of messages per neighbor. For each neighbor, the output lists the local router interface, the neighbor's host name, and the neighbor's IP address. In this case, from R1's perspective, R1's S0/0/0 interface connects to R2, whose IP address is 192.168.1.2. Also, R1's S0/0/1 interface connects to R3, whose IP address is 192.168.1.6.
4	The output lists a heading line as follows: `192.168.1.0/24 is variably subnetted, 8 subnets, 2 masks` Per this line, eight subnets exist with two different subnet masks. With more than one mask used, VLSM is in use in network 192.168.1.0.
5	The method used to determine the matching route is to look at each subnet in the routing table and mentally calculate the range of addresses in the subnet. Then choose the route whose subnet range includes the IP address in question. If more than one route's subnet range matches the IP address, choose the route with the more specific match; that is, the longer prefix mask.
6	The output of the **show ip route 192.168.1.183** command lists a message which means that R1 matches no routes.
7	It lists three lines of three asterisks, which in the simulator means that the command would not complete and did not even get a response from the next router. In this case, the **traceroute 192.168.1.183** command confirms that R1 has no matching route for 192.168.1.183.
9	The output of the **show ip route 192.168.1.193** command should list subnet 192.168.1.192/29 (/29 is equal to 255.255.255.248). It also should list R2's IP address 192.168.1.2 as the next-hop, with R1's outgoing interface of S0/0/0.
10	It lists a single line, 192.168.1.2, which is R2's IP address. So the **traceroute 192.168.1.193** command confirms that the next-hop router in the route is R2.
12	The output of the **show ip route 192.168.1.163** command should list subnet 192.168.1.160/29 (/29 is equal to 255.255.255.248). It also should list R3's IP address 192.168.1.6 as the next-hop, with R1's outgoing interface of S0/0/1.
13	It lists a single line, 192.168.1.6, which is R3's IP address. So the **traceroute 192.168.1.163** command confirms that the next-hop router in the route is R3.

Configuration Steps

This lab requires no configuration.

Configuration Labs

Part 1: Router Configuration

Lab 4: Configuring OSPF Routing

Objective

The overall objective of this laboratory exercise is to gain experience with configuring Open Shortest Path First (OSPF) routing between two routers using the Cisco 640-802 Network Simulator. In this lab, you will gain an introductory understanding of the following:

- Configuring the computer's IP address

- Configuring the gateway address

- Configuring the IP addresses for the router interfaces

- Configuring OSPF routing

- Troubleshooting configuration problems

Topology

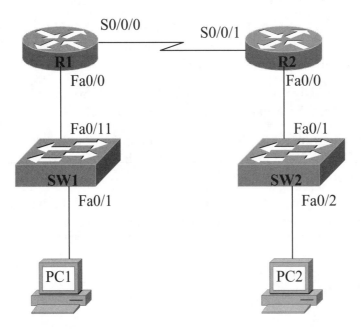

Figure 1   Network Topology for This Lab

Reference

The following simulator exercises provided with the CCNA 640-802 Network Simulator should be reviewed prior to starting this virtual laboratory exercise:

- OSPF Configuration I, II, and III

- OSPF Serial Configuration I–VI

- OSPF Router ID I, II

- OSPF Neighbors I–V

Key Concepts

The following concepts, terms, commands, and steps should have been mastered in this laboratory exercise:

- How to configure the IP address, subnet mask, and default gateway for the computers in your LAN.

- How the gateway address for your LAN router is configured.

- The steps for configuring the host name for your router.

- The steps for configuring the router interface's IP addresses and subnet masks.

- The commands for configuring OSPF routing from LAN-A to LAN-B.

- The two commands that can be used to verify that the routes are configured on the router.

- Using computers in your LAN to ping the computers in the adjacent LAN.

- Use the proper command to trace the route from a PC in LAN-A to the host in the connected LAN-B.

- Use the command to establish a Telnet connection to your router, and find out how to enable a Telnet connection to the router.

- The router command that displays the network routes stored in your router's routing table.

- The command used to save your router configuration to NVRAM.

- The command used to verify the routing protocol being used.

- The command that displays only the OSPF routes.

- The purpose of wildcard bits or inverse mask bits.

Reference Tables

Table 1 provides the IP addresses and masks of all necessary interfaces used to complete the lab.

Table 1   **Computer IP Addresses, Subnet Masks, and Gateway Addresses for Lab 4**

Computer/Interface - R1	IP Address	Subnet Mask	Gateway Address
PC1	172.20.15.8	255.255.255.224	172.20.15.1
R1-Fa0/0	172.20.15.1	255.255.255.224	—
R1-S0/0/0	10.10.1.1	255.255.255.252	—

Computer/Interface – R2	IP Address	Subnet Mask	Gateway Address
PC2	192.168.25.21	255.255.255.224	192.168.25.16
R2-Fa0/0	192.168.25.16	255.255.255.224	—
R2-S0/0/1	10.10.1.2	255.255.255.252	—

Detailed Lab Steps

Task 1

In this lab, you are configuring OSPF to the adjacent LAN for the network shown in Figure 1. You will be required to verify that computers in your LAN can ping the neighbor LAN. Note that a serial interface is being used to interconnect the LANs. You are configuring routing for both 172.20.15.0 and 192.168.25.0 networks. A subnet mask of 255.255.255.224 is being used. Use 56000 for the clock rate on the serial link (DCE interface). Use a subnet mask of 255.255.255.252 on the serial link connecting the two routers.

Step 1.   Configure the gateway address for FastEthernet 0/0 and the serial s0/0/0 interfaces on Router R1. You also need to configure the IP address and the gateway address for PC-1. Use the IP address and subnet mask specified in Table 1. You will need to enable each interface and set the clock rate on the serial interface to 56000. List the router prompts and commands used to configure the interfaces.

_____

_____

_____

Step 2.   Configure the gateway address for FastEthernet 0/0 and the serial s0/0/1 interfaces on Router R2. Use the IP addresses and subnet masks specified in Table 1. Enable each interface and list the router prompts and commands used to configure the interfaces.

_____

_____

_____

Step 3. Configure the host name for your routers. R1 should be renamed LAN-A, and R2 should be renamed LAN-B. List the router prompts and commands used to configure the router's host name.

_____

_____

_____

Step 4. List the proper commands to verify that the interfaces on the LAN-A and LAN-B routers have been properly configured. List the router prompts and commands used to configure the router's host name.

_____

_____

_____

Step 5. Configure OSPF routing between the LAN-A and LAN-B routers using a process ID of 100 and an area of 0. Use two commands to verify that the routes are configured. List the router prompts and commands used to configure the LAN-A and LAN-B routers.

_____

_____

_____

Step 6. Use the proper commands to display the routing table for both the LAN-A and LAN-B routers. Are all the possible network routes displayed? List the router prompts and commands used to display the routes.

_____

_____

_____

Step 7. Use the computers in each LAN to ping the computers in the adjacent LAN. List the commands used to ping the computer in the adjacent LAN.

_____

_____

_____

Step 8. Use the proper command to trace the route from the PC in LAN-A to the PC in LAN-B. Your trace should pass through two routers. List the command used and record the trace information. How may hops did you record?

_____

_____

_____

Step 9. Use the command to make a Telnet connection from the LAN-A router to the LAN-B router. Set the VTY password to **ciscopress** and enable remote login. Were you able to enter the privileged EXEC mode on the LAN-B router? Correct this problem if you can't enter the privileged EXEC mode on the LAN-B router. What did you have to do to correct the problem? List the commands used to establish the Telnet connection. What IP address did you use?

_____

_____

_____

Step 10. Use the command to save your router configuration to the startup configuration. What command did you use? Use the proper command to verify that the configuration has been saved to NVRAM. List the command prompts and the commands used.

_____

_____

_____

Step 11. What command is used to verify the routing protocol that is being used? List the command prompts and the commands used. Note that two commands can be used.

_____

_____

_____

Task 2

Answer the following questions regarding the Cisco IOS:

1. The command prompt changes on a Cisco router to reflect the current state the router is in. Define what each command prompt listed below represents:

   a. Router>

_____

b. Router#

c. Router(config)#

d. Router(config-if)#

e. Router(config-router)#

f. Router(config-line)#

2. Cisco IOS provides support for many editing functions in terms of "hot keys." A few of the functions are listed below. Briefly describe these functions.

   a. Delete

   b. Backspace

   c. Tab

   d. Ctrl-Z

Task 3: Configuration List

The following is a partial list of the items you might see when you issue the **show running-configuration [sh run]** command. Your task is to define each item and its purpose. You might need to go to the Cisco website (http://www.cisco.com) and look up what each of these commands means.

1. **ip cef**

2. no ip domain lookup

_____

_____

_____

3. log-adjacency-changes

_____

_____

_____

4. control-plane

_____

_____

_____

5. scheduler allocate 20000 1000

_____

_____

_____

6. description <—->

_____

_____

_____

Answer the following router questions:

1. What command is used to determine the version of the Cisco IOS?

_____

_____

_____

2. What version of IOS is running on the LAN-A router?

_____

_____

_____

3. What command is used to display the routing protocols configured on your router?

_____

_____

_____

4. What information is displayed when the **show start** command is entered?

_____

_____

_____

5. What router command is used to determine whether your serial interface is DTE or DCE?

_____

_____

_____

6. What is the command for setting the clock rate on a router's DCE serial interface to 56000?

_____

_____

_____

7. How long has it been since your router was last rebooted? Indicate how the system was restarted. Note: There is a Cisco command that provides this information. Cisco calls this the router uptime. The same command also specifies how the system was restarted.

_____

_____

_____

UNIT 8

Advanced IP Topics

Table 8-1 lists the labs for this unit. Check with your instructor or class syllabus to confirm what labs you should perform for class.

Table 8-1 Unit 8 Labs

Date	ICND1/ ICND2	Type	Part	Number	Name	Page
	ICND2	CS	2	1	IP Addressing and Configuration I	439
	ICND2	TS	1	9	OSPF Troubleshooting I	451
	ICND2	TS	1	7	Path Troubleshooting IV	463
	ICND2	SB	5	8	IPv6 Address Configuration I	476
	ICND2	SB	5	9	IPv6 Address Configuration II	479
	ICND2	SB	5	10	IPv6 Address Configuration III	481
	Ungraded	TL	1	1	Troubleshooting Lab I	484
	Ungraded	TL	1	2	Troubleshooting Lab II	486
	Ungraded	TL	1	9	Troubleshooting Lab IX	488
	Ungraded	CL	3	2	IPv6 Router Configuration	490

ICND2 Configuration Scenarios
Part 2: IP Addressing and Routing

Lab 1: IP Addressing and Configuration I

Overview

You are to plan and implement the multilocation internetwork based on some incomplete work from a fellow network engineer. First, you will choose the subnet numbers to use, and then the addresses to use for the devices shown in Figure 1. Following that, you will configure the router LAN interfaces, followed by the configuration of the router WAN interfaces. Finally, once all the configuration is complete, you need to establish a routing protocol between the routers to share the routes. Once the configuration is complete, you will need to perform network testing and correct any issues.

At the beginning of this lab, the PCs have been fully configured. The routers have their device names applied and passwords configured, and the console and vty lines are configured. The switches also do not require any further configuration and will essentially be ignored for the purposes of this lab.

Topology

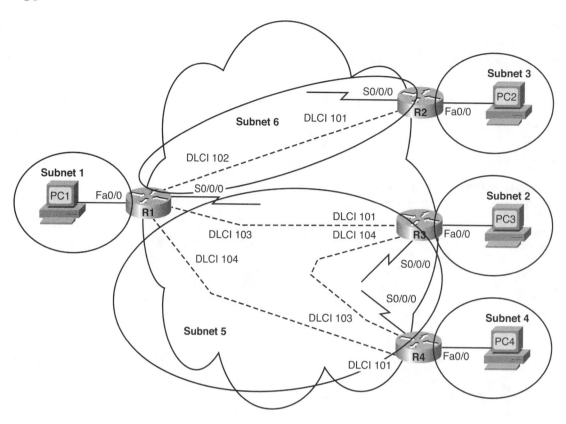

Figure 1   **Network Topology for This Lab**

Reference Tables

Table 1 provides a place to record the results of your subnet planning process, as requested by various steps in this lab. Table 2 is a place to record the IP address, mask, and default gateway information you choose during the lab.

Table 1   **IP Subnet Address Planning**

Generic Subnet Number	Network	Number of Host Addresses	Subnet Number	Mask	Lowest Address	Highest Address
1	R1 LAN	200				
2	R3 LAN	70				
3	R2 LAN	25				
4	R4 LAN	12				
5	R1-R3-R4 WAN	3				
6	R1-R2 WAN	2				

Table 2   IP Addressing Reference

Device	Interface	IP Address	Mask	Default Gateway
R1	S0/0/0.2			
	S0/0/0.34			
	Fa0/0			
R2	S0/0/0.1			
	Fa0/0			
R3	S0/0/0.14			
	Fa0/0			
R4	S0/0/0.13			
	Fa0/0			
PC1				
PC2				
PC3				
PC4				

Detailed Lab Steps

Part 1: Address Planning

In the first part of this lab, you will plan the subnet numbers you will configure during this lab, based on subnetting requirements and plans made by another engineer.

Note: Tables 3 and 4, in the "Hints and Answers" section of this lab, show the completed versions of Tables 1 and 2. To receive a passing score on this lab, you must use the addresses suggested in Tables 3 and 4.

Step 1.   Examine Figure 1, noting the six subnets planned for a small internetwork. For each subnet, Table 1 lists the generic subnet numbers to match the figure, along with the required number of hosts in each of the subnets. In this step, choose the mask to support each subnet so that the mask has the least number of host bits that supports the required number of hosts, and record those masks in Table 1.

Step 2.   Choose subnet numbers to use for each subnet. When making your choices, assign the lowest possible subnet numbers; the zero subnet is allowed to be used. Assign the subnets in the order listed in Table 1 (subnet 1 first, then subnet 2, and so forth).

Step 3.   Plan the specific addresses to be used by router interfaces and the PCs. By convention, assign the routers the highest IP address(es) in each subnet, and the hosts the lowest IP address. In the cases of more than one router interface in the same subnetwork, begin the addressing with the highest address applied to the interface of the lowest-numbered router. For example, R1 would get the highest address in the subnet, R2 would receive the next lower address in the subnet. Table 2 has been provided for planning this addressing scheme.

Part 2: Configure the Router LAN Interfaces

In Part 1, you created the addressing plan for the devices in the internetwork. In Part 2, you will begin the router configuration. With the routers preconfigured with the basic device information, you can concentrate on the configuration of the interface and the routing protocol.

Beginning with R1, you should add the address to the LAN interfaces. After all the LAN interfaces are operational, you will configure the Frame Relay subinterfaces for the WAN connections.

Step 4. From the simulator user interface, connect to R1 and move into enable mode.

Step 5. Add the IP address to the FastEthernet 0/0 interface of R1. What commands are used to add the address to Fa0/0 of R1? Exit configuration mode when finished.

_____

_____

Step 6. After adding the address to Fa0/0 of R1, examine the routing table to determine if the route of the network connected to this interface has been added to the routing table. Was the route added? Why or why not?

_____

_____

_____

Step 7. Move back into interface configuration mode to enable the Fa0/0 interface. Exit configuration mode when finished.

Step 8. Re-examine the routing table to verify that the connected route for Fa0/0 is present.

Step 9. To verify the operation of the Fa0/0 interface, ping the host that sits on the same LAN— PC1 in this case. (Refer to Table 2 where you took notes on addresses, or to the completed Table 4, for the list of IP addresses.) Did the ping work?

_____

Step 10. Repeat Steps 4 through 9 for routers R2, R3, and R4. By the end of this step, each router should be able to ping the PC that sits on the same subnet.

Part 3: Configure the Router WAN Interfaces

In Part 2, you provided the necessary Layer 3 addresses for the LAN interfaces and enabled these router interfaces. In Part 3, you examine the preconfigured WAN interfaces and then add IP addresses to the configuration.

Step 11. Connect to router R1 from the simulator user interface and move into enable mode.

Step 12. Use the **show ip interface brief** command to display all current interfaces and their status. Other than Fa0/0, what interfaces are listed in an "up/up" state?

_____

_____

Step 13. Use the **show running-config** command to display information about the mapping of DLCIs to different subinterfaces. Compare that information to Figure 1 and the information gathered in the previous step. Which subinterface is configured to support the subnet connected to router R2? Which subinterface supports the subnet connected to both R3 and R4?

_____

_____

Step 14. Use the **show running-config** command to display information about the current configuration. Look at interface S0/0/0 and the subinterfaces that follow. Do any of these have IP addresses assigned?

_____

_____

R1 uses subinterface S0/0/0.102 for its PVC connected to R2 and subinterface S0/0/0.34 for its PVC connected to both R3 and R4. However, neither subinterface has an IP address assigned.

Step 15. Move into configuration mode and add the IP addresses to the two subinterfaces of S0/0/0, using the addresses in Table 2 or Table 4. Record the configuration commands you use, and exit configuration mode when finished.

_____

_____

_____

Step 16. Examine the routing table to determine if the routes for the two new connected networks are listed in the routing table. Do the subnet numbers match those you calculated and recorded in Table 1?

_____

The other three routers (R2, R3, and R4) each have a single serial subinterface, as noted in Tables 1, 2, 3, and 4. The rest of this part completes the configuration process on the WAN interfaces.

Step 17. From the simulator user interface, connect to R2, R3, and R4 in turn, and configure each router's single WAN subinterface with the IP address and mask listed in Table 2. Record the commands you used in each case.

_____

_____

_____

_____

_____

Step 18. Now that the Layer 3 addresses have been assigned to the WAN interfaces, you should verify that the routers can ping the IP addresses on the other end of the WAN links. To do so, first move back to router R1 from the simulator user interface.

Step 19. Referring to Table 2's IP addresses, ping the WAN IP address on R2, R3, and R4. Which pings were successful? Which were not?

_____

_____

_____

Step 20. Move to R2 from the simulator user interface and ping the WAN IP addresses of R1, R3, and R4. Which pings were successful? Which were not? Why?

_____

_____

_____

Step 21. Move to R3 from the simulator user interface and ping the WAN IP addresses of R1, R2, and R4. Which pings were successful? Which were not? Why?

_____

_____

_____

Step 22. Move to R4 from the simulator user interface and ping the WAN IP addresses of R1, R2, and R3. Which pings were successful? Which were not? Why?

Part 4: Configure Routing Protocols and Verify the Network Works

In Part 3, you established the WAN connection between routers and ensured that the routers can ping each other—at least in cases where two routers connect to the same subnet. However, the routing tables are not fully populated with all the routes in the internetwork. In Part 4, you will add a routing protocol to the routers. For this internetwork, you will use EIGRP 1.

Step 23. On routers R1, R2, R3, and R4, configure the commands **router eigrp 1** and **network 10.0.0.0**. These commands enable EIGRP with the same ASN on all four routers, enabling EIGRP on all interfaces in Class A network 10.0.0.0.

Step 24. Move to router R1 from the simulator user interface and display its IP routing table. How many routes are displayed? How many are connected routes? How many are EIGRP-learned routes, as evidenced with a "D" on the left side of the line for that route?

Step 25. Continuing to look at that same output, how many different subnet masks are used by the subnets listed in R1's routing table?

Step 26. Using Table 2 to remind yourself of the IP addresses, ping the four PCs from R1. Which of the pings worked?

Step 27. Move to router R2 from the simulator user interface and display its IP routing table. How many routes are displayed? How many are connected routes? How many are EIGRP-learned routes, as evidenced with a "D" on the left side of the line for that route? Why does R2 have more EIGRP-learned routes than did R1?

_____

_____

_____

Step 28. Using Table 2 to remind yourself of the IP addresses, ping the four PCs from R2. Which of the pings worked?

_____

Hints and Answers

Table 3 lists a completed version of Table 1, listing the subnet information for the internetwork. Table 4 is a completed form of Table 2, listing addressing information for the devices. Table 5 provides hints and tips for any lab steps that do not supply complete details and provides answers for any lab steps that ask questions.

Table 3   IP Subnet Address Planning

Subnet Number	Number of Network	Subnet Host Addresses	Number	Mask	Lowest Address	Highest Address
1	R1 LAN	200	10.0.0.0/24	255.255.255.0	10.0.0.1	10.0.0.254
2	R3 LAN	70	10.0.1.0/25	255.255.255.128	10.0.1.1	10.0.1.126
3	R2 LAN	25	10.0.1.128/27	255.255.255.224	10.0.1.129	10.0.1.158
4	R4 LAN	12	10.0.1.160/28	255.255.255.240	10.0.1.161	10.0.1.174
5	R1-R3-R4 WAN	3	10.0.1.176/29	255.255.255.248	10.0.1.177	10.0.1.182
6	R1-R2 WAN	2	10.0.1.184/30	255.255.255.252	10.0.1.185	10.0.1.186

Table 4   IP Addressing Reference

Device	Interface	IP Address	Mask	Default Gateway
R1	S0/0/0.2	10.0.1.186	255.255.255.252	
	S0/0/0.34	10.0.1.182	255.255.255.248	
	Fa0/0	10.0.0.254	255.255.255.0	
R2	S0/0/0.1	10.0.1.185	255.255.255.252	
	Fa0/0	10.0.1.158	255.255.255.224	

Device	Interface	IP Address	Mask	Default Gateway
R3	S0/0/0.14	10.0.1.181	255.255.255.248	
	Fa0/0	10.0.1.126	255.255.255.128	
R4	S0/0/0.13	10.0.1.180	255.255.255.248	
	Fa0/0	10.0.1.174	255.255.255.240	
PC1		10.0.0.1	255.255.255.0	10.0.0.254
PC2		10.0.1.129	255.255.255.224	10.0.1.158
PC3		10.0.1.1	255.255.255.128	10.0.1.126
PC4		10.0.1.161	255.255.255.240	10.0.1.174

Table 5   Hints and Answers

Step	Hint or Answer
1, 2	The solution to the IP subnet address planning information can be found in Table 3.
3	The solution to the device IP address planning information can be found in Table 4.
4	Use the **enable** command to move to privileged mode.
5	Use Table 1 as the reference for the addresses. Use the following commands: **configure terminal** **interface fastethernet0/0** **ip address 10.0.0.254 255.255.255.0** **end**
6	Use the **show ip route** command on R1 to view the routing table. R1 did not add a connected route for this subnet because the Fa0/0 is not up.
7	Use the following commands: **configure terminal** **interface fastethernet0/0** **no shutdown** **end**
8	Use the **show ip route** command to look for the connected network of 10.0.0.0/24.
9	The **ping 10.0.0.1** command should work.

continues

Table 5   **Hints and Answers**   *continued*

Step	Hint or Answer
10	On R2:
	interface fastethernet0/0
	ip address 10.0.1.158 255.255.255.224
	no shutdown
	The **show ip route** command on R2 should show a connected network of 10.0.1.128/27.
	On R3:
	interface fastethernet0/0
	ip address 10.0.1.126 255.255.255.128
	no shutdown
	The **show ip route** command on R3 should show a connected network of 10.0.1.0/25.
	On R4:
	interface fastethernet0/0
	ip address 10.0.1.174 255.255.255.240
	no shutdown
	The **show ip route** command on R4 should show a connected network of 10.0.1.160/28.
11	Use the **enable** command to move to privileged mode.
12	The output lists S0/0/0.2 and S0/0/0.34.
13	The mapping shows DLCI 102 with S0/0/0.2; according to Figure 1, this DLCI is part of subnet 6, which connects to router R2. DLCIs 103 and 104 are associated with subinterface S0/0/0.34; according to Figure 1, these two DLCIs are part of subnet 5, which connects to routers R3 and R4.
14	The configuration shows the Frame Relay interface configuration, but without any IP addresses on the physical interface or the subinterfaces.
15	**configure terminal**
	interface S0/0/0.2
	ip address 10.0.1.186 255.255.255.252
	interface S0/0/0.34
	ip address 10.0.1.182 255.255.255.248
	end
16	The subnets are
	S0/0/0.2: 10.0.1.184/30
	S0/0/0.34: 10.0.1.176/29

Step	Hint or Answer
17	On R2: **configure terminal** **interface s0/0/0.1** **ip address 10.0.1.185 255.255.255.252** **end** On R3: **configure terminal** **interface s0/0/0.14** **ip address 10.0.1.181 255.255.255.248** **end** On R4: **configure terminal** **interface s0/0/0.13** **ip address 10.0.1.180 255.255.255.248** **end**
19	The pings should work. The commands are **ping 10.0.1.185** (R2) **ping 10.0.1.181** (R3) **ping 10.0.1.180** (R4)
20	The ping to R1's IP address (**ping 10.0.1.186**) should work. The other two pings do not work. The reason is that R3's and R4's WAN interfaces are in the same subnet as R2's WAN subinterface, and R2 does not have a routing protocol with which to learn routes yet.
21	The pings to both R1's and R4's WAN IP addresses work. The ping to R2's WAN interface (**ping 10.0.1.185**) fails. The reason is that R3's WAN interface is not in the same subnet as R2's WAN subinterface, and R3 does not have a routing protocol with which to learn routes yet.
22	The pings to both R1's and R3's WAN IP addresses work. The ping to R2's WAN interface (**ping 10.0.1.185**) fails. The reason is that R4's WAN interface is not in the same subnet as R2's WAN subinterface, and R4 does not have a routing protocol with which to learn routes yet.
24	R1 has six routes: three connected routes and three EIGRP-learned routes.
25	All six subnets use a different subnet mask. The masks, in prefix notation, are /24, /25, /27, /28, /29, and /30.
26	The pings should work at this point.
27	R2 has six routes: two connected routes and four EIGRP-learned routes. R2 is directly connected to only two subnets, so R2 must learn about the other four subnets using EIGRP.
28	The pings should work at this point.

Configuration

Example 1 shows the configuration commands added to the routers during this lab.

Author's note: This lab begins with all serial subinterfaces having been preconfigured. As a result, the interface command can be used either with or without the multipoint keyword, or with or without the point-to-point keyword. The Simulator's grading function requires that you omit these keywords. The keywords, however, are included in Example 1 for the purpose of reminding you of the complete syntax.

Example 1   Configuration on the Routers During This Lab

```
! The following was configured on R1:


interface FastEthernet0/0
 ip address 10.0.0.254 255.255.255.0
 no shutdown


interface serial 0/0/0.34 multipoint
 ip address 10.0.1.182 255.255.255.248


interface serial 0/0/0.2 point-to-point
 ip address 10.0.1.186 255.255.255.252


Router eigrp 1
 Network 10.0.0.0


! The following was configured on R2:


interface FastEthernet0/0
 ip address 10.0.1.158 255.255.255.224
 no shutdown


interface serial 0/0/0.1 point-to-point
 ip address 10.0.1.185 255.255.255.252
!
Router eigrp 1
 Network 10.0.0.0


! The following was configured on R3:


interface FastEthernet0/0
 ip address 10.0.1.126 255.255.255.128
```

continues

```
no shutdown

interface serial 0/0/0.14 multipoint
 ip address 10.0.1.181 255.255.255.248

Router eigrp 1
 Network 10.0.0.0

! The following was configured on R4:
interface fastEthernet0/0
 ip address 10.0.1.174 255.255.255.240
 no shutdown

interface serial 0/0/0.13 multipoint
 ip address 10.0.1.180 255.255.255.248

!
Router eigrp 1
 Network 10.0.0.0
```

ICND2 Troubleshooting Scenarios

Lab 9: OSPF Troubleshooting I

Overview

This lab begins with a small network with four routers connected to a total of five subnets/LANs. The internetwork uses OSPF with the entire network in area 0. The engineer has implemented the internetwork, but not all of the PCs can ping each other. As usual, your job is to find out which PCs cannot ping each other, find the underlying problems, and solve those problems.

Note: Use the password **ciscopress** for all routers in this lab.

Topology

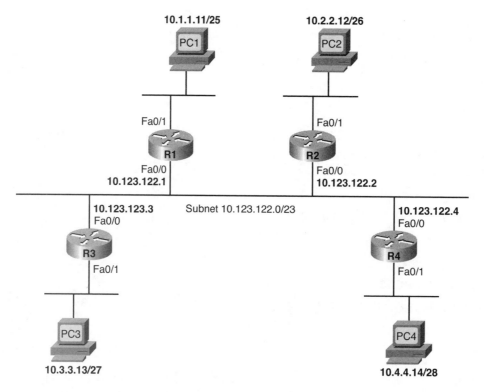

Figure 1   Network Topology for This Lab

General Lab Instructions

For this lab, you have two choices for how to proceed. One option is to follow the process in the "Detailed Lab Steps" section of this lab. The other option is to follow any troubleshooting steps you like until you find the two root causes of IP routing problems in this lab. If you use the second option, start by pinging each PC from each other PC. When you find pairs of PCs that cannot ping each other, troubleshoot to find why the ping fails, and continue to examine the ping results until all hosts can ping all other hosts.

Note: As with many of the troubleshooting labs, the problems in this lab are introduced by configuration errors. However, the lab is more meaningful if you resist the urge to simply browse the configuration.

Reference Tables

Table 1 lists the IP addresses, masks, and default gateway settings initially given to the four PCs in this lab.

Table 1   Host and Switch IP Address, Mask, and Gateway

Device	IP Address	Mask	Default Gateway
PC1	10.1.1.11	255.255.255.128	10.1.1.1
PC2	10.2.2.12	255.255.255.192	10.2.2.2

Device	IP Address	Mask	Default Gateway
PC3	10.3.3.13	255.255.255.224	10.3.3.3
PC4	10.4.4.14	255.255.255.240	10.4.4.4

Table 2 provides a convenient place to record the results of ping testing in Part 1 of the lab.

Table 2   Ping Testing Chart

	PC1	PC2	PC3	PC4	(Respective) Default Gateway
PC1					
PC2					
PC3					
PC4					

Table 3 provides a place to record your calculations about the subnets in which the hosts reside. Table 4 is a place to record your notes about the problems you find in these labs.

Table 3   IP Subnet Reference, According to the PC's View of the Subnet

Device	Subnet Number	First IP Address	Last IP Address
PC1			
PC2			
PC3			
PC4			

Table 4   Problems Found in This Lab and Their Proposed Solutions

Problem	Description and Suggested Configuration Changes
1	
2	

Detailed Lab Steps

Part 1: Test Pings to Each Default Gateway

The first part of this lab examines which pairs of PCs cannot ping each other, verifies IP addressing information, and confirms whether or not each PC can ping its default gateway.

Step 1. Connect to host PC1 and confirm that the IP address, mask, and default gateway information listed in Table 1 is correct. Is the information listed in Table 1 for PC1 correct?

_____

Step 2. From PC1, ping each of the other three hosts' IP addresses as listed in Table 1. Did any of the pings work? Which ones? Record the results in Table 2.

_____

_____

Step 3. Calculate the subnet number and range of IP addresses in PC1's subnet based on the information gathered in Step 1. Record this information in Table 3. Is PC1's default gateway in this range of IP addresses?

_____

Step 4. Ping PC1's default gateway IP address. Does the ping work?

_____

Step 5. Repeat Steps 1 through 4 for PC2, PC3, and PC4. Record the information in Tables 2 and 3.

Step 6. Make a general characterization about the four hosts, their IP addresses and default gateways, and the devices they can ping. Based on this information, which devices appear to be most likely to have a problem?

_____

_____

_____

_____

_____

_____

Part 2: Examine R3

In Part 1, you confirmed that both PC3 and PC4 cannot ping any other hosts, but that PC3 and PC4 can both ping their respective default gateways. As a result, the root cause of the pinging problem may be located at these two PCs' default gateway routers. Part 2 takes a closer look at the status of router R3.

Step 7. Connect to router R3 from the simulator user interface and move into user mode.

Step 8. Display all known IP routes on R3. What routes are listed? Which routes are OSPF-learned routes?

_____

_____

_____

Step 9. Use a **show** command to list R3's OSPF neighbors. What is the OSPF router ID of each neighbor? Which routers do you think use those IP addresses?

_____

_____

Step 10. Use the **show ip ospf interfaces brief** command to find out whether R3 has enabled OSPF on its two interfaces. On which interfaces is it enabled? For each interface, what is the OSPF process ID, OSPF area, and neighbor count?

_____

_____

_____

Step 11. Ping the IP addresses of the other three routers' Fa0/0 interfaces per the figure at the beginning of the lab. Do the pings work? Which ones do not?

_____

_____

At this point, it is clear that R3's Fa0/0 interface is enabled for OSPF and is in area 0. R3 can ping the IP addresses of the other routers with which it could form a neighbor relationship. However, none of those relationships have formed. The rest of Part 2 examines why R3 has failed to form those neighbor relationships.

Step 12. Use the **show ip ospf interface fa0/0** command. Gather the following facts: IP address/mask, area, process ID, router ID, cost, State (DR/BDR/DROther), Designated Router ID, Hello Interval, Dead Interval.

_____

_____

_____

Step 13. Move to router R1 from the simulator user interface and move into user mode.

Step 14. Display detailed OSPF information about R1's Fa0/0 interface, and make a list of the same information gathered in Step 12 on router R3.

_____

_____

Step 15. Compare the information gathered in Steps 12 and 14. Which items differ? Of the listed items, which ones prevent OSPF routers from becoming neighbors?

_____

_____

_____

_____

If you looked further, you would find that R2 and R4 both use a mask of /23 on the LAN in the center of Figure 1. R3 has errantly used a /24 mask, which in turn prevents R3 from becoming an OSPF neighbor with the other routers. The final steps of Part 2 work through fixing that problem and testing to ensure that the problem is fixed.

Step 16. Move back to R3 from the simulator user interface and move into enable mode.

Step 17. Configure R3's Fa0/0 interface with IP address 10.123.123.3, mask /23 (255.255.254.0). Record your commands on the lines below. Move back to enable mode when finished.

_____

_____

Step 18. Display all known IP routes on R3. What routes are listed? Which routes are OSPF-learned routes?

_____

_____

_____

_____

Step 19. Use a **show** command to list R3's OSPF neighbors. What is the OSPF router ID of each neighbor? Which routers do you think use those IP addresses?

_____

_____

Step 20. Move to PC3 from the simulator user interface and ping the other three PCs again. Which pings work? Which ones fail?

_____

_____

_____

Step 21. At your option, record the problem you discovered and its solution in Table 4 in the "Reference Tables" section.

Part 3: Examine R4

At this point, PC1, PC2, and PC3 can all ping each other. However, PC4 cannot ping any other PCs, but PC4 can ping its default gateway IP address. As a result, R4's current state is suspicious. Part 3 examines router R4 to uncover any possible problems.

Step 22. Connect to router R4 from the simulator user interface and move into enable mode.

Step 23. Display all known IP routes on R4. What routes are listed? Which routes are OSPF-learned routes?

_____

_____

_____

Step 24. Use a **show** command to list R4's OSPF neighbors. What is the OSPF router ID of each neighbor? Which routers do you think use those IP addresses?

_____

_____

Step 25. Use the **show ip ospf interfaces brief** command to find out whether R4 has enabled OSPF on its two interfaces. On which interfaces is it enabled? For each interface, what is the OSPF process ID, OSPF area, and neighbor count?

_____

_____

_____

Step 26. Ping the IP addresses of the other three routers' Fa0/0 interfaces per the figure at the beginning of the lab. Do the pings work? Which ones do not?

_____

_____

As was the case on router R3, it is clear that R4's Fa0/0 interface is enabled for OSPF. R4 can ping the IP addresses of the other routers with which it could form a neighbor relationship. However, none of those relationships have formed. The rest of Part 3 examines why R4 has failed to form those neighbor relationships.

Step 27. Compare the information gathered in Step 14 on router R1 with the information found in Step 25. Which items do not match? Which of these items are a potential reason why OSPF routers would not form a neighbor relationship?

_____

_____

_____

_____

Step 28. Use the **show ip protocols** command, and look for the output heading "Routing for Networks." This section lists the same information that is configured in OSPF **network** commands. Record the information in the two lines of output in that section.

_____

_____

Step 29. Display R4's current configuration, and look for the "OSPF" section. Do the OSPF **network** commands match the information you found in the previous step?

_____

_____

Step 30. Configure R4 to replace the **network** command that puts Fa0/0 in area 1 with a **network** command that places the interface in area 0. Do not change any other details in this command. What commands did you use during this process? When completed, move back to enable mode.

_____

_____

_____

_____

Step 31. Display all known IP routes on R4. What routes are listed? Which routes are OSPF-learned routes?

_____

_____

_____

_____

Step 32. Use a **show** command to list R4's OSPF neighbors. What is the OSPF router ID of each neighbor? Which routers do you think use those IP addresses?

_____

_____

Step 33. Move to PC4 from the simulator user interface and ping the other three PCs again. Which pings work? Which ones fail?

_____

At your option, record the problem you discovered and its solution in Table 4 in the "Reference Tables" section.

Hints and Answers

Table 5 is a completed version of Table 3, listing the subnets from the perspective of the four PCs in this internetwork.

Table 5   IP Subnet Reference, According to the PC's View of the Subnet

Device	Subnet Number	First IP Address	Last IP Address
PC1	10.1.1.0	10.1.1.1	10.1.1.126
PC2	10.2.2.0	10.2.2.1	10.2.2.62
PC3	10.3.3.0	10.3.3.1	10.3.3.30
PC4	10.4.4.0	10.4.4.1	10.4.4.14

Table 6 is a completed version of Table 4, listing the two problems found in this lab and their solutions. Table 7 provides hints and tips for any lab steps that do not supply complete details and provides answers for any lab steps that ask questions.

Table 6   **Problems Found in This Lab**

Problem	Description and Suggested Configuration Changes
1	R3 uses mask 255.255.255.0 on its Fa0/0 interface, whereas R1, R2, and R4 all use a 255.255.254.0 mask. As a result, OSPF on R3 cannot form any neighbor relationships with the other routers.
	To solve the problem, use the correct mask on R3:
	interface fastethernet0/0
	ip address 10.123.123.3 255.255.254.0
2	R4's OSPF configuration places Fa0/0 into area 1, whereas the other three routers on the same subnet are assigned to area 0. As a result, OSPF on R4 cannot form any neighbor relationships with the other routers.
	To solve the problem, assign R4's Fa0/0 interface to area 0 as follows:
	router ospf 10
	no network 10.123.123.0 0.0.0.255 area 1
	network 10.123.123.0 0.0.0.255 area 0

Table 7   **Hints and Answers**

Step	Hint or Answer
1	The information is correct.
2	The ping to PC2 works, and the pings to PC3 and PC4 fail.
3	The subnet is 10.1.1.0/25 with a range from 10.1.1.1 through 10.1.1.126. PC1's default gateway IP address setting is 10.1.1.1, which is in this range.
4	PC1's **ping 10.1.1.1** command works.
5	Table 5 is a completed version of Table 3.
6	All four hosts' IP addresses appear to be in the same subnet as their respective default gateways, and the pings to those default gateways work. However, PC3 and PC4 cannot ping any other PC. The most likely next devices to have problems are R3 and R4.
8	The **show ip route** command lists two connected routes but no OSPF-learned routes. The routes are:
	10.123.123.0/24
	10.3.3.0/27
9	The **show ip ospf neighbor** command lists no neighbors at all.
10	OSPF is enabled on both Fa0/0 and Fa0/1, both in area 0 (as they should be), OSPF process ID 11. Both interfaces list a count of 0 for the number of neighbors.
11	All the pings fail.

Step	Hint or Answer
12	10.123.123.3/24
	Area 0
	PID 11
	RID 3.3.3.3
	Cost 1
	State: DR
	Designated RID: 3.3.3.3
	Hello: 10
	Dead: 40
14	10.123.122.1/23
	Area 0
	PID 10
	RID 10.123.122.1
	Cost 1
	State: DR
	Designated RID: 10.123.122.1
	Hello: 10
	Dead: 40
15	The masks differ, the OSPF PIDs differ, and the RIDs differ. The RIDs must be different, so that is not a problem. The OSPF PIDs do not have to match. The masks, however, must be the same, but they are not the same.
17	**configure terminal** **interface fa0/0** **ip address 10.123.123.3 255.255.254.0** **end** (or press **Ctrl-Z**)
18	The **show ip route** command lists four routes, the last two of which are OSPF routes: 10.123.122.0/23 10.3.3.0/27 10.1.1.0/25 (OSPF) 10.2.2.0/26 (OSPF)
19	The **show ip ospf neighbors** command lists two neighbors with RIDs: 10.123.122.1 (R1) 10.123.122.2 (R2)
20	Pings to PC1 and PC2 work, but pings to PC4 fail.
21	Table 5 details the first problem and solution.

continues

Table 7   **Hints and Answers**   *(continued)*

Step	Hint or Answer
23	The **show ip route** command lists two connected routes but no OSPF-learned routes. The routes are 10.123.122.0/23 10.4.4.0/28
24	R4 does not currently have any neighbors.
25	OSPF is enabled on both Fa0/0 and Fa0/1, with Fa0/0 in area 1, and Fa0/1 in area 0, OSPF process ID 10. Both interfaces list a count of 0 for the number of neighbors.
26	All the pings work.
27	R4's Fa0/0 interface is in area 1, and the Fa0/0 interfaces of R1, R2, and R3 are in area 0. OSPF routers on a common subnet must be in the same OSPF area in order to become neighbors.
28	The output lists two lines: 10.123.122.0 0.0.0.255 area 1 10.4.4.0 0.0.0.255 area 0
29	The configuration contains the same information as the previous step, but with the network command in front: **network 10.123.122.0 0.0.0.255 area 1** **network 10.4.4.0 0.0.0.255 area 0**
30	The commands are: **configure terminal** **router ospf 10** **no network 10.123.122.0 0.0.0.255 area 1** **network 10.123.122.0 0.0.0.255 area 0**
31	The **show ip route** command lists five routes, the last three of which are OSPF routes: 10.123.122.0/23 10.4.4.0/28 10.1.1.0/25 (OSPF) 10.2.2.0/26 (OSPF) 10.3.3.0/27 (OSPF)
32	The **show ip ospf neighbors** command lists three neighbors with RIDs: 10.123.122.1 (R1) 10.123.122.2 (R2) 3.3.3.3 (R3)
33	Pings to PC1, PC2, and PC3 all work.
34	Table 5 details the second problem and solution.

Configuration

Example 1 shows the configuration commands added to R3 and R4 during this lab.

Example 1   Configuration on R3 and R4 During This Lab

```
R3's config:


interface FastEthernet0/0
 ip address 10.123.123.3 255.255.254.0


R4's config


router ospf 10
 no network 10.123.122.0 0.0.0.255 area 1
 network 10.123.122.0 0.0.0.255 area 0
```

ICND2 Troubleshooting Scenarios

Lab 7: Path Troubleshooting IV

Overview

In this lab, all the routers have been configured with IP addresses and with EIGRP enabled on all interfaces. The three PCs each have an IP address, mask, and default gateway that points to the local router's IP address. However, some pings do not appear to work. Your job is to find and document the root causes of the ping problems, and then solve the problems by changing the configuration.

Note: Use the password **ciscopress** for all routers in this lab.

Note: All switches in this lab use all default configuration with all interfaces in VLAN 1. The switches have no problems that affect the behavior of this lab.

Topology

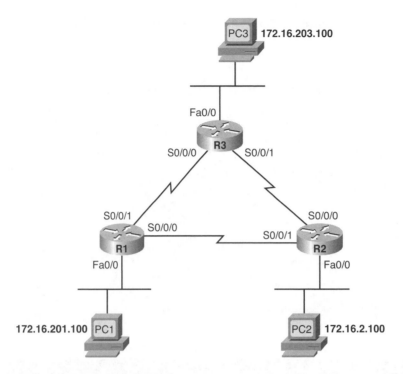

Figure 1   Network Topology for This Lab

General Lab Instructions

For this lab, you have two choices for how to proceed. One option is to follow the detailed steps in this lab. These steps guide you through the troubleshooting process as described in both the *CCENT/CCNA ICND1* and *ICND2 Official Exam Certification Guides*, 2nd Edition, from Cisco Press. (You do not need a copy of those books to do the lab, though.)

Alternately, you may follow any troubleshooting steps you like until you find the three root causes of IP routing problems in this lab. If you choose this option, you should start by pinging each PC from each other PC. When you find pairs of PCs that cannot ping each other, troubleshoot to find why the ping fails. Additionally, for this lab, you will find that PC2 can successfully ping PC3, but you should look for other problems that affect the path between these two PCs.

Regardless of whether you follow the specific steps in this lab, check your answers against the reference tables at the end of the lab, particularly Tables 7 and 8, which list the three root causes and the expected solution for this lab. For the lab to grade as correct, you must solve the three problems in the same way as suggested by this lab.

Note: As with many of the troubleshooting labs, the problems in this lab are introduced by configuration errors. However, the lab is more meaningful if you resist the urge to simply browse the configuration.

Reference Tables

Tables 1 through 5 provide handy places to record information as you work through the lab. Note that the detailed lab steps may not ask you to complete all parts of the tables.

Table 1   **Host IP Address, Mask, and Gateway**

Device	IP Address	Mask	Default Gateway
PC1			
PC2			
PC3			

Table 2   **IP Subnet Reference – From Perspective of PC's**

Device	Subnet Number	First IP Address	Last IP Address
PC1			
PC2			
PC3			

Table 3   **Ping Results at the Beginning of the Lab**

	PC1	PC2	PC3
PC1			
PC2			
PC3			

Table 4   **Problems Found in This Lab**

Problem Router	Description

Table 5   **Configuration Commands Used to Solve Each Problem**

Router	Configuration

Detailed Lab Steps

Part 1: Discover IP Addresses and Find Which PCs Cannot Ping Each Other

This part of the lab suggests steps for discovering IP addresses and for determining which PCs cannot ping each other.

Step 1.   Connect to each PC's user interface in succession. On each PC, use the **ipconfig /all** command to find its own IP address, mask, and default gateway, and record that information in Table 1. Confirm that the IP addresses match those shown in Figure 1.

Step 2.   Calculate the subnet number and range of addresses for each subnet. Record the information in Table 2.

Step 3.   From each PC, ping each other PC, and record which pings work and which don't work. (You can use Table 3 to record the results, or just make notes here. The important part is to note which pings fail.)

Step 4.   The first step in troubleshooting host connectivity problems is to ping the host's default gateway from that host. For each PC, ping its configured default gateway and list which pings did not work.

Part 2: Test the Forward Route from PC2 to PC1

The pings in Part 1 should reveal that PC3 cannot ping either PC1 or PC2, but that PC1 and PC2 can ping each other. Based on these results, one of the most likely root causes of the ping problems is something related to PC3. Part 2 examines PC3's ability to forward packets.

Step 5. Connect to PC3 from the simulator user interface and verify its IP address, mask, and default gateway settings once again. Record those values on the lines below.

_____

_____

_____

Step 6. Ping PC3's default gateway. Does the ping work?

_____

Step 7. Move to router R3 from the simulator user interface and move into enable mode.

Step 8. From R3, ping PC3's IP address. Does the ping work?

_____

Step 9. Display R3's IP routing table. List the details regarding the route connected to Fa0/0's interface. What is the range of addresses implied by the subnet number/mask for that connected subnet?

_____

_____

The problem is that R3's IP address/mask combination places that interface in a different subnet compared to PC3's subnet. To solve the problem, either PC3's or R3's Fa0/0 IP address must be changed. For this lab, you will change R3's Fa0/0 IP address.

Step 10. Enter configuration mode on R3 and configure interface Fa0/0 with IP address 172.16.203.33, mask 255.255.255.128.

Step 11. Move to PC3 from the Simulator user interface and use the **gateway 172.16.203.33** command to reconfigure PC3's default gateway to refer to R3's new IP address.

Step 12. Move back to R3's enable mode and ping PC3's IP address again. Does the ping work?

_____

_____

Step 13. At your option, record information about this problem and its solution in Tables 4 and 5 in the "Reference Tables" section.

Step 14. Connect to PC3 from the simulator user interface and repeat the ping tests of pinging both PC1 and PC2. Which pings work?

_____

_____

Part 3: PC1-PC3 Ping Problem

At this point, of the three combinations of pairs of PCs, only PC1 and PC3 cannot ping each other. All PCs can ping at least one other PC, which seems to imply that all PCs should not have any problems, at least, pinging their default gateways. So, Part 3 assumes that the problem is related in some way to IP routing and thus examines the IP routing tables of the various routers to attempt to find the root cause of the PC1-PC3 pinging problem.

Step 15. Connect to router R3 from the simulator user interface and move into user mode.

Step 16. Use one **show** command to display the specific route on R3 that matches packets sent to PC1's IP address. What command did you use? What route (subnet/mask) is listed? What is the outgoing interface and next-hop IP address?

_____

_____

_____

Step 17. Use CDP to confirm the topology details shown in Figure 1. What device is on the other end of the serial link listed as the outgoing interface in the previous step?

_____

_____

_____

Step 18. Move to router R1 from the simulator user interface and move into enable mode.

Step 19. Use one **show** command to display the specific route on R1 that matches packets sent to PC1's IP address. What command did you use? What route (subnet/mask) is listed? What is the outgoing interface and next-hop IP address?

_____

_____

_____

Step 20. Use one **show** command to display the specific route on R1 that matches packets sent to PC3's IP address. What route (subnet/mask) is listed? What is the outgoing interface and next-hop IP address?

_____

_____

_____

It appears that both routers have working routes for packets going to both PC1's and PC3's subnets. Next, the lab steps examine routing from the host perspective, starting with PC1.

Step 21. Move to PC1 from the simulator user interface and issue the **tracert 172.16.203.100** command to trace the route to PC3. List the IP addresses listed in the output.

_____

_____

Step 22. Again from PC1, confirm PC1's default gateway setting and ping that IP address. Does the ping work?

_____

_____

Step 23. Calculate the subnet number and range of IP addresses in PC1's subnet based on PC1's IP address and mask. What is the range of addresses? Do you see any surprises?

_____

_____

_____

Step 24. Describe the root cause of why PC1 cannot ping PC3 and record your answer in Table 4.

Several solutions exist. In this case, the lab asks that you change the mask used by both PC1 and R1's Fa0/0 interface to a /23 mask, which removes the problem of the overlapping subnets.

Step 25. From PC1's user interface, change the mask from 255.255.252.0 to 255.255.254.0 using the **ip address 172.16.201.100 255.255.254.0** command.

Step 26. Move to R1 from the simulator user interface and move to enable mode.

Step 27. Configure R1's Fa0/0 interface with the same IP address that it currently has, but a mask of 255.255.254.0. What commands did you use? Record your answers on the lines below or in Table 5.

_____

_____

_____

Step 28. Move back to PC1 from the simulator user interface and ping PC3. Does the ping work now?

_____

Part 4: PC2-PC3 Long Route Problem

The final problem may be difficult to see at first because, at this point, all PCs should be able to ping each other.

Step 29. Connect to PC2 from the simulator user interface and ping to confirm that PC2 can indeed send packets to and receive packets from PC1 and PC3.

Step 30. Use the **tracert 172.16.203.100** command to trace the route from PC2 to PC3. List the IP addresses displayed by this command. How many addresses are listed?

_____

_____

_____

Step 31. Clearly, the first IP address in the list should be router R2, which is the only possible default gateway that PC2 could use. So, connect to R2 from the simulator user interface and move into enable mode.

Step 32. Use one **show** command to display the specific route on R2 that matches packets sent to PC3's IP address. What route (subnet/mask) is listed? What is the outgoing interface and next-hop IP address? What is the next-hop router (R1, R2, or R3) based on this information and Figure 1?

_____

_____

_____

Step 33. Use CDP to confirm whether R1 is truly the next-hop router. According to CDP, what device is on the other end of the serial link listed as the outgoing interface in the previous step?

_____

_____

_____

The route from R2 to PC3's subnet clearly takes the longer path through the network, a path that could actually be the best path based on metric. Next, examine R2's Routing Protocol status to discover if this longer route is indeed best or if the route directly through R3 has some problem.

Step 34. Display the interface status of R2's interface that connects to R3. What is the interface type/number? What is the status? What is the configured IP address/mask?

_____

_____

_____

Step 35. Display all CDP neighbors. Does R2 see R3 as a neighbor on the S0/0/0 interface? What is the listed IP address for the neighbor listed on the other end of S0/0/0?

Step 36. Display all of R2's EIGRP neighbors. How many neighbors are listed? Which IP addresses are listed as neighboring routers?

At this point, it appears that R3 is not an EIGRP neighbor of R2, although the link between R2 and R3 appears to be up. The final steps in this last part complete the process of discovering the root cause and fixing the problem.

Step 37. Move to R3 from the simulator user interface and move into enable mode.

Step 38. Display R3's S0/0/1 interface, which, according to Figure 1, connects to R2. What is the interface status? What is the configured IP address/mask?

Step 39. From the information about IP addresses and masks gathered in Steps 33 and 37, calculate the subnet number and range of addresses for the subnet on the R2-R3 serial link. Do the routers have the same opinion about the subnet number on the link? Are the addresses in the same subnet?

Step 40. Although the serial link can be in an "up/up" state if the IP addresses on the ends of the link are not in the same subnet, EIGRP will not form a neighbor relationship with the router on the other end of the link. Record this root cause in Table 4.

Step 41. Fix this problem by assigning R3's S0/0/1 interface the IP address 172.16.101.123, mask 255.255.255.240. What commands did you use?

Step 42. Exit configuration mode and display R3's EIGRP neighbors. Does R3 list R2's 172.16.101.122 IP address as a neighbor?

_____

_____

_____

Step 43. Move back to PC2 from the simulator user interface and trace the route to PC3. Do the packets take the seemingly shorter path through R2 and then R3, instead of going through R1?

_____

Hints and Answers

Table 6 provides a completed version of Table 2, listing the subnet numbers and ranges of IP addresses as calculated based on the IP address/mask for each of the PCs in this lab. Table 7 provides a completed version of Table 4, listing the three problems found in this lab with Table 8 summarizing the suggested solutions. Table 9 provides hints and tips for any lab steps that do not supply complete details and provides answers for any lab steps that ask questions.

Table 6   IP Subnet Reference – According to the PC's View of the Subnet

Device	Subnet Number	First IP Address	Last IP Address
PC1	172.16.200.0	172.16.200.1	172.16.203.254
PC2	172.16.2.0	172.16.2.1	172.16.2.254
PC3	172.16.203.0	172.16.203.1	172.16.203.126

Table 7   Problems Found in This Lab

Problem	Description and Suggested Configuration Changes
1	R3's Fa0/0 interface has IP address 172.16.203.203 with mask 255.255.255.128, making the range of IP addresses in that subnet 172.16.203.129 through 172.16.203.254. PC3's IP address is 172.16.203.100, a number that is not in that range of addresses for the subnet connected to R3's Fa0/0 interface, so R3's connected route for its Fa0/0 interface does not help R3 forward packets to PC3.
2	Based on both R1's Fa0/0 IP address and PC1's IP address, the subnet on R1's LAN is 172.16.200.0/22 with a range of addresses from 172.16.200.1 through 172.16.203.254. This range overlaps with R3's LAN subnet. One result of this problem is that PC1, when it wants to send a packet to PC3, thinks that PC3's IP address of 172.16.203.100 is on the same subnet as PC1.

Problem	Description and Suggested Configuration Changes
3	On the serial link between R2 and R3, R2's 172.16.101.122/28 address/mask and R3's 172.16.101.133/28 address/mask mean that the two addresses are in different subnets. As a result, the link can be in an "up/up" state, but EIGRP will not form a neighbor relationship.

Table 8   Suggested Solutions to the Three Problems in this lab

Problem	Description and Suggested Configuration Changes
1	One solution is to change R3's Fa0/0 IP address to 172.16.203.33/25, as follows: **interface fa0/0** **ip address 172.16.203.33 255.255.255.128**
2	The solution shown in this lab is to change the mask on both R1 and PC1 to be 255.255.254.0, which makes the range of addresses 172.16.200.1 through 172.16.201.254, removing the overlapping IP addresses. On R1: **interface fa0/0** **ip address 172.16.201.1 255.255.254.0** On PC1: **ip address 172.16.201.100 255.255.254.0**
3	The solution is to correctly configure the IP addresses into the same subnet. For example, on R3: **interface serial0/0/1** **ip address 172.16.101.123 255.255.255.240**

Table 9   Hints and Answers

Step	Hint or Answer
1	The IP addresses match those shown in Figure 1.
3	All pings to/from PC3 fail. The other pings work.
4	PC1 and PC2 can ping their respective default gateway IP addresses. PC3's ping fails.
5	PC3 has IP address 172.16.203.100, mask 255.255.255.128, and default gateway 172.16.203.203.
6	The **ping 172.16.203.203** command fails.
8	The **ping 172.16.203.100** command fails.
9	The **show ip route** command lists a connected route of 172.16.203.128/25 as the connected route off R3's Fa0/0 interface. The range of addresses is 172.16.203.129—172.16.203.254. PC3's 172.16.203.100 IP address is not in that range of addresses.

continues

Table 9　Hints and Answers　*continued*

Step	Hint or Answer
10	Use the following commands: **configure terminal** **interface fastethernet0/0** **ip address 172.16.203.33 255.255.255.128**
12	The ping should now work.
14	PC3 should now be able to ping PC2, but the ping to PC1 still fails.
16	The **show ip route 172.16.201.100** command should list a route for subnet 172.16.200.0/22, outgoing interface S0/0/0, next-hop address 172.16.101.1.
17	The **show cdp neighbors** detail command should list that router R1 is indeed on the other end of R3's S0/0/0 interface.
19	The **show ip route 172.16.201.100** command should list a route for subnet 172.16.200.0/22, outgoing interface Fa0/0 with no next-hop IP address because the route is a connected route.
20	Assuming you made the changes suggested in Part 2 to solve one of the problems in this lab, the **show ip route 172.16.203.100** command lists a route for subnet 172.16.203.0/25 with S0/0/1 as the outgoing interface and IP address 172.16.101.3 as the next-hop address.
21	The command does not list any IP addresses.
22	The **ping 172.16.201.1** command works.
23	The range is 172.16.200.1 through 172.16.203.254, which includes PC3's IP address.
24	PC1's host forwarding logic means that PC1 will try to forward packets to PC3 as if PC3 were on the same LAN, because PC3's IP address appears to be in the same subnet.
25	Use command **ip address 172.16.201.100 255.255.254.0**. Note that this command is not used on any specific PC Operating System; it is just a command created for the Simulator's PCs.
27	Use the following commands: **configure terminal** **interface fastethernet0/0** **ip address 172.16.201.1 255.255.254.0**
28	The ping should work.
29	Use the **ping 172.16.201.100** and **ping 172.16.203.100** commands.
30	The command lists the following four addresses: 172.16.2.2 (R2 F0/0) 172.16.101.71 (R1 S0/0/0) 172.16.101.3 (R3 S0/0/0) 172.16.203.100 (PC3)

Step	Hint or Answer
32	Assuming you made the changes suggested in Part 2 to solve one of the problems in this lab, the **show ip route 172.16.203.100** command lists a route for subnet 172.16.203.0/25 with S0/0/1 as the outgoing interface and IP address 172.16.101.71 as the next-hop router IP address.
33	The **show cdp neighbors detail** command lists router R1 as being on the other end of S0/0/1.
34	The **show interfaces S0/0/0** command lists the details, including a status of "up/up" and an IP address/mask of 172.16.101.122/28.
35	The **show cdp neighbors detail** command lists router R3 as being on the other end of S0/0/0 with IP address 172.16.101.133.
36	The **show ip eigrp neighbors** command lists only one neighbor, 172.16.101.71, which is R1.
38	The **show interfaces s0/0/1** command lists the details, including a status of "up/up" and an IP address/mask of 172.16.101.133/28.
39	R3's IP address implies subnet 172.16.101.128/28, range 172.16.101.129—172.16.101.142. R2's IP address implies subnet 172.16.101.112, range 172.16.101.113—172.16.101.126.
41	Use the following commands: **configure terminal** **interface serial0/0/1** **ip address 172.16.101.123 255.255.255.240**
42	The **show ip eigrp neighbors** command does list R2's 172.16.101.122 IP address as a neighbor.
43	The **tracert 172.16.203.100** command shows a one-hop-shorter route with next-hop 172.16.101.123 (R3's new S0/0/0 IP address) as one of the hops.

Configuration

Example 1 shows the configuration commands added to R1, R2, R3, and PC1 during this lab.

Example 1 Configuration Added During This Lab

```
R1's config:


interface Fastethernet0/0
  ip address 172.16.201.1 255.255.254.0



! PC1's config:
  ip address 172.16.203.100 255.255.254.0
```

continues

Example 1   Configuration Added During This Lab   *continued*

```
! On Router R3:


interface Fastethernet0/0
  ip address 172.16.203.33 255.255.255.128


interface serial0/0/1
  ip address 172.16.101.123 255.255.255.240
```

ICND2 Skill Builders

Part 5: Scaling IP

Lab 8: IPv6 Address Configuration I

Overview

This lab begins with a fully configured IPv4 network, including RIP-2 routing. On top of that topology, you'll configure IPv6 addresses and review the configuration. In this lab, instead of using the EUI-64-style IPv6 address configuration, you will specify the entire IPv6 address.

Topology

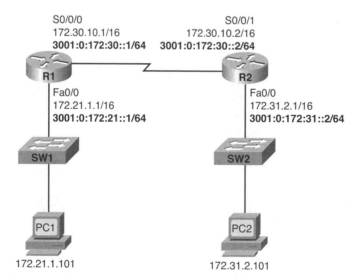

Figure 1   Network Topology for This Lab

Detailed Lab Steps

Step 1. Connect to R1 from the simulator user interface; use password **ciscopress**.

Step 2. Issue the **enable** command and log in with the password **ciscopress**.

Step 3. Enter global configuration mode using the **configure terminal** command.

Step 4. To configure the IPv6 address on interface Fa0/0, enter interface configuration mode using the command **interface fa0/0**.

Step 5. Configure the IPv6 address shown for R1's Fa0/0 interface in Figure 1. To do so, add the command **ipv6 address 3001:0:172:21::1/64**. In this command, what does **/64** represent? What does **::** represent in this case? What would the full IPv6 address look like with no abbreviations?

_____

_____

_____

Step 6. Configure the IPv6 address on the serial interface by entering address configuration mode using the command **interface serial0/0/0**.

Step 7. Configure the IPv6 address for the serial interface using the command **ipv6 address 3001:0:172:30::1/64**. How would you write down the subnet number in which this IPv6 address resides?

_____

_____

Step 8. Enter the **end** command to return to privileged exec mode.

Step 9. Use the command **show ipv6 interface brief** to see information about the addresses you just configured. On each interface, do you see the addresses you configured? What other IPv6 addresses do you see? What are these addresses, and what is their first quartet's value?

_____

_____

_____

Step 10. Use the command **show ipv6 route** to see information about the IPv6 routes on R1. (Note that R1 does not have any IPv6 routing protocols enabled.) What connected routes do you see? What local routes? What differs about the prefix length listed for these two types of routes?

_____

_____

_____

Hints and Answers

Table 1 provides hints and tips for any lab steps that do not supply complete details and provides answers for any lab steps that ask questions.

Table 1   Hints and Answers

Step	Hint or Answer
5	**/64** is the prefix length, meaning that the first 64 bits of the address represents the prefix; all IPv6 addresses that begin with the same 64 bits are in the same subnet. :: generally means some number of consecutive quartets with four hex 0s; in this case, it represents three such quartets. The full, unabbreviated address would be 3001:0000:0172:0021:0000:0000:0000:0001.
7	By convention, the subnet number is listed with the prefix, but with all 0s in the host part of the number. In this case, the subnet number is 3001:0:172:30::/64. Note that the difference is that the non-zero parts of the host address (1 in the last quartet) are not included.
9	The output lists the two configured IPv6 addresses, as well as the link local address on each interface. The link local addresses begin with FE80.
10	The IPv6 routing table lists a connected route for the subnet connected to both S0/0/0 (3001:0:172:30::/64) and Fa0/0 (3001:0:172:21::/64). It also includes a local route for the specific IPv6 address assigned to each interface; these routes are noted with a /128 prefix, meaning that the route is a host route.

Configuration Steps

Example 1 shows a sample of the lab exercise being completed from R1.

Example 1   Example of Performing This Lab

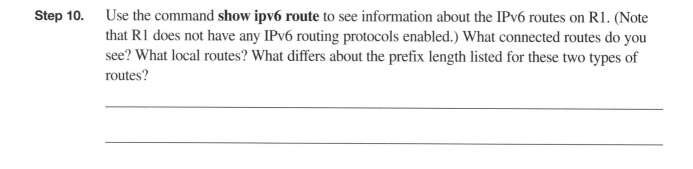

```
R1#configure terminal
R1(config)#interface Fastethernet0/0
R1(config-if)#ipv6 address 3001:0:172:21::1/64
R1(config-if)#interface Serial0/0/0
R1(config-if)#ipv6 address 3001:0:172:30::1/64
R1(config-if)#end
R1#
```

ICND2 Skill Builders

Part 5: Scaling IP

Lab 9: IPv6 Address Configuration II

Overview

This lab begins with a fully configured IPv4 network, including RIP-2 routing. On top of that topology, you'll configure IPv6 addresses and review the configuration. In this lab, you will use the EUI-64-style IPv6 address configuration.

Topology

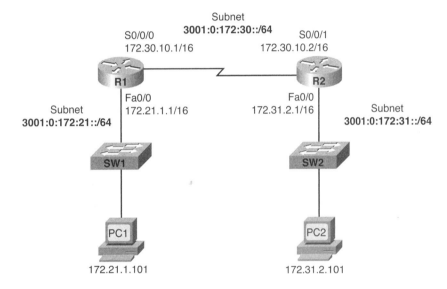

Figure 1   **Network Topology for This Lab**

Detailed Lab Steps

Step 1.   Connect to R1 from the simulator user interface; use password **ciscopress**.

Step 2.   Issue the **enable** command and log in with the password **ciscopress**.

Step 3.   Examine Figure 1. Note that it does not supply the specific IPv6 addresses but does supply the prefix and prefix length. What 64-bit prefix is listed for R1's Fa0/0 interface in Figure 1?

Step 4. Examine R1's Fa0/0 MAC address using the **show interfaces fa0/0** command. Record both the burned-in MAC address and the currently used MAC address on the lines below. After you configure the EUI-64-style IPv6 address on Fa0/0, what IPv6 address do you expect Fa0/0 to use?

_____

_____

_____

Step 5. Enter global configuration mode using the **configure terminal** command.

Step 6. To configure the IPv6 address on interface Fa0/0, enter interface configuration mode using the command **interface fa0/0**.

Step 7. Configure the IPv6 subnet using the command **ipv6 address 3001:0:172:21::/64 eui-64**. This command does not explicitly configure the IPv6 address on the interface; rather, it defines the subnet, and the router autoconfigures the IP address using the modified EUI-64 format. This is based on the MAC address.

Step 8. Configure the IPv6 address on the serial interface by entering address configuration mode using the command **interface serial0/0/0**.

Step 9. Configure the IPv6 subnet for the serial interface using the command **ipv6 address 3001:0:172:30::/64 eui-64**.

Step 10. Enter the **end** command to return to privileged exec mode.

Step 11. Use the command **show ipv6 interface brief** to see information about the addresses you just configured. List the full IPv6 address on each interface. Does Fa0/0's IPv6 address match your prediction from Step 3?

_____

_____

_____

Step 12. Continue looking at the output of the **show ipv6 interface brief** command. Does the second half of the IPv6 address on S0/0/0 match Fa0/0's IPv6 address? Why or why not?

_____

_____

_____

Hints and Answers

Table 1 provides hints and tips for any lab steps that do not supply complete details and provides answers for any lab steps that ask questions.

Table 1   Hints and Answers

Step	Hint or Answer
3	The prefix is 3001:0:172:21::/64, meaning that the first 64 bits (or the first four quartets of four hex digits each) comprise the prefix.
4	R1's Fa0/0 MAC address is 0000.1234.5678 and its burned-in address is 0013.197B.1101. R1 will use the first 64 bits of the number that will be configured, as gathered in Step 3. R1 will then add the first six digits of the MAC address, insert FFFE as the next four digits, and then use the last six digits of the MAC address. R1 will also change the seventh bit in the first byte to a binary 1 as needed. The address will be 3001:0:172:21:0200:12FF:FE34:5678.
11	The output should list these global unicast IPv6 addresses: Fa0/0: 3001:0:172:21:0200:12FF:FE34:5678 S0/0/0: 3001:0:172:30:0213:19FF:FE7b:1101
12	Serial interfaces do not have built-in MAC addresses. In cases where IOS needs to use an interface MAC address, IOS uses the burned-in MAC address of the lowest-numbered interface that does have a MAC address: Fa0/0 in this case. So, the second half of S0/0/0's IPv6 address is generated using the burned-in MAC address of Fa0/0.

Configuration Steps

Example 1 shows a sample of the lab exercise being completed from R1.

Example 1   Example of Performing This Lab

```
R1#configure terminal
R1(config)#interface Fastethernet0/0
R1(config-if)#ipv6 address 3001:0:172:21::/64 eui-64
R1(config-if)#interface Serial0/0/0
R1(config-if)#ipv6 address 3001:0:172:30::/64 eui-64
R1(config-if)#end
R1#
```

ICND2 Skill Builders

Part 5: Scaling IP

Lab 10: IPv6 Address Configuration III

Overview

This lab begins with a fully configured IPv4 network, including RIP-2 routing. On top of that topology, you'll configure IPv6 addresses on the serial link between the routers and then ping from one router to the other to test reachability.

Topology

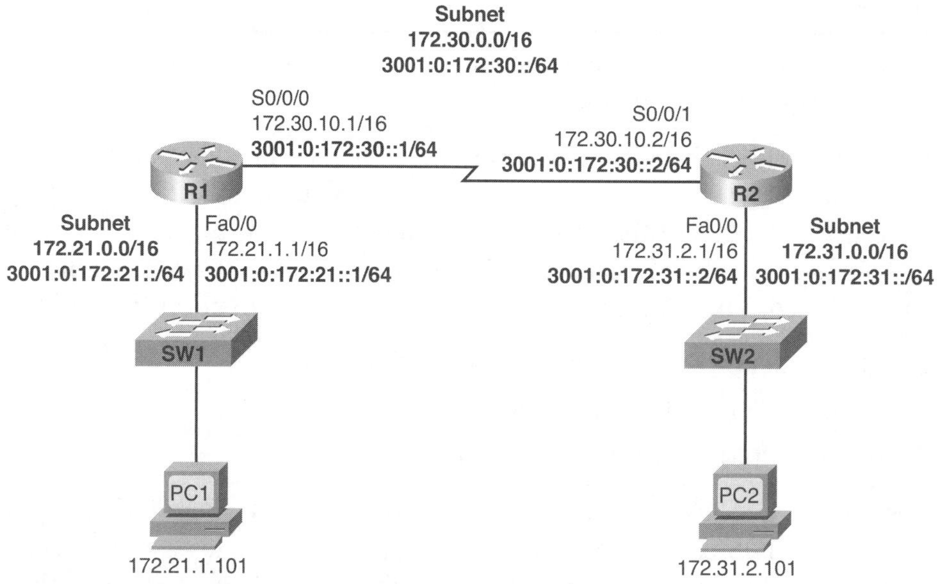

Figure 1   **Network Topology for This Lab**

Detailed Lab Steps

Step 1. Connect to R1 from the simulator user interface; use password **ciscopress**.

Step 2. Issue the **enable** command and log in with the password **ciscopress**.

Step 3. Examine Figure 1 and note both the IPv4 and the IPv6 subnets. Knowing that the routers have been fully configured for IPv4, including full configuration for RIP 2, what IP routes would you expect to see in R1's routing table?

_____

_____

_____

Step 4. Display R1's IPv4 routing table using the **show ip route** command. How many routes are listed? How many connected routes, and how many RIP routes?

_____

Next, you will configure IPv6 addresses on both ends of the serial link and confirm that the two routers can ping each other.

Step 5. Enter global configuration mode using the **configure terminal** command.

Step 6. Configure the IPv6 address on the serial interface by entering address configuration mode using the command **interface serial0/0/0**.

Step 7. Configure the IPv6 address for the serial interface using the command **ipv6 address 3001:0:172:30::1/64**.

Step 8. Switch to R2 by connecting to it from the simulator user interface and use the **enable** command to move privilege mode. All passwords are **ciscopress**.

Step 9. Configure the IPv6 address on the serial interface by entering interface configuration mode using the commands **configure terminal** and **interface serial0/0/1**.

Step 10. Assign the IPv6 address using the command **ipv6 address 3001:0:172:30::2/64**.

Step 11. Issue the **end** command to return to the privileged exec prompt.

Step 12. Ping from R2 to R1 using **ping 3001:0:172:30::1**. Does the ping work?

_____

Step 13. Move back to R1 and move into user mode.

Step 14. Examine R1's IPv6 routing table using the **show ipv6 route** command. How many connected routes do you see? Do you see any routes learned by a routing protocol? What are the connected routes?

_____

_____

Hints and Answers

Table 1 provides hints and tips for any lab steps that do not supply complete details and provides answers for any lab steps that ask questions.

Table 1   Hints and Answers

Step	Hint or Answer
3	R1 should know about all three IPv4 networks: 172.21.0.0 /16 172.30.0.0 /16 172.31.0.0 /16
4	There will be two connected routes: 172.21.0.0 /16 172.30.0.0 /16 plus one RIP-learned route: 172.31.0.0 /16
12	The ping should work.
14	Because R1 has configured IPv6 on only one interface and has not enabled any IPv6 routing protocols, R1 has a single connected route: the route for subnet 3001:0:172:30::/64 off interface S0/0/0.

Configuration Steps

Example 1 shows a sample of the lab exercise being completed from R1 and R2.

Example 1   Example of Performing This Lab

```
! Configuration on router R1:
R1#configure terminal
R1(config)#interface Serial0/0/0
R1(config-if)#ipv6 address 3001:0:172:30::1/64
R1(config-if)#end
R1#
! Configuration on router R2:
R2#configure terminal
R2(config)#interface Serial0/0/1
R2(config-if)#ipv6 address 3001:0:172:30::2/64
R2(config-if)#end
R2#
```

Troubleshooting Labs
Troubleshooting I

Lab 1: Router Configuration

Overview

This lab uses a scenario in which you just took a job with a new company and are placed on a project that was recently planned and implemented. However, the internetwork is having some problems, and it is your job to solve the problems. The trouble ticket for this is shown as follows. Investigate the network problems, make corrections to the network as necessary, and report your findings.

You can find the problems in this lab by examining the network configuration and looking for errors. The topology for this network is provided in Figure 1. Note: The switches in this network pass data but do not require configuration.

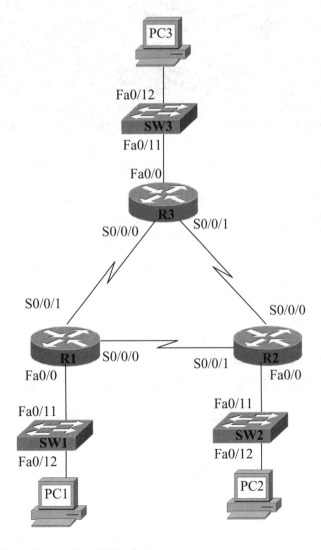

Figure 1   Network Topology for This Lab

Table 1 is provided to record the problems discovered in the network configuration. As you find each problem, add the discovered problem to Table 1, along with the actions to be taken to resolve the problem.

Table 1   Record Root Causes and Solutions

1

2

3

4

5

6

7

Troubleshooting Labs
Troubleshooting II

Lab 2: Routing Protocols

Overview

In this scenario, the internetwork is having some problems. Your job is to locate and identify the problems and make corrections to the network configurations as needed. The trouble ticket for this is shown as follows. Investigate the network problems, make corrections to network as necessary, and report your findings.

Trouble Ticket – L24   Date: 4/12/11

Problem: There appears to be problems with routing between the networks. The routing problems appear to be limited to R2, R3, and R4, although configuration problems with R1 could be contributing to the problem.

Assigned to: Networking Admin

Findings: _____

_____

_____

_____

Date Completed

You can find the problems in this lab by examining the network configuration and looking for errors. The topology for this network is provided in Figure 1. Note: The switches in this network pass data but do not require configuration.

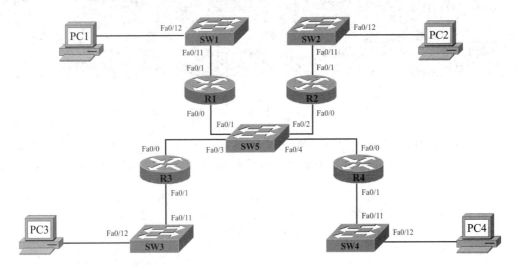

Figure 1   Network Topology for This Lab

Table 1 is provided to record the problems discovered in the network configuration. As you find each problem, add the discovered problem to Table 1, along with the actions to be taken to resolve the problem.

Table 1   Record Root Causes and Solutions

1	
2	
3	
4	
5	
6	
7	

Troubleshooting Labs
Troubleshooting IX

Lab: IPv6 Configuration Problems

Overview

There are errors in the Internet Protocol version 6 (IPv6) setup on both routers. The PCs and switches do not require configuration. Make corrections to the network setup as needed to fix the problems.

Note: Use the password **ciscopress** for all routers in this lab.

Topology

The internetwork is having some problems, and it is your job to solve the problems. The trouble ticket for this is shown as follows. Investigate the network problems, make corrections to the network as necessary, and report your findings.

Trouble Ticket – L31   **Date:** 4/12/11

Problem: There appears to be problems on Router R1 and R2 in the network provided. Correct the problems as soon as possible and restore IPv6 network connectivity.

Assigned to: Network Administrator

Findings: _____

_____

_____

_____

Date Completed

You can find the problems in this lab by examining the network configuration and looking for errors. The topology for this network is provided in Figure 1. Note: The switches in this network pass data but do not require configuration.

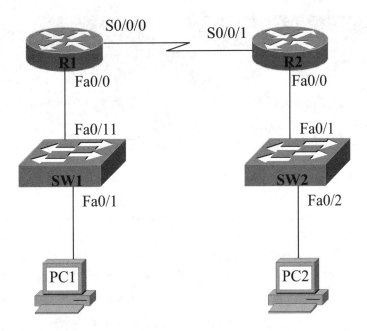

Figure 1   Network Topology for This Lab

The IP addresses for all the applicable interfaces used in this exercise are listed in Table 1.

Table 1   IP Addresses

LAN 1	IPv6 Address
PC1	—
SW1	—
R1-S0/0/0	2002:a10b:0:1:0:0:0:1/64
R1-Fa0/0	2002:a10b:0:2:213:19ff:fe7b:1101/64

LAN 2	IPv6 Address
PC2	—
SW2	—
R2-S0/0/1	2002:a10b:0:1:0:0:0:2/64
R2-Fa0/0	2002:a10b:0:3:213:19ff:fe7b:2201/64

Configuration Labs

Part 3: IPv6 Configuration and IP Address Management

Lab 2: IPv6 Router Configuration

Objective

The overall objective of this laboratory exercise is to gain experience configuring Internet Protocol version 6 (IPv6) on Cisco routers. Your objective is to configure the two routers with IPv6 so that they can communicate. The routers are missing all the configuration necessary to support IPv6. You must configure the routers for IPv6 forwarding. Next, you should configure the interfaces with the specified IPv6 addresses. In this lab, you will gain an introductory understanding of the following:

- The steps to statically configure an IPv6 address on the WAN interfaces.

- The steps to statically configure an IPv6 address on the LAN interfaces.

- Configuring the computer's network interface.

Topology

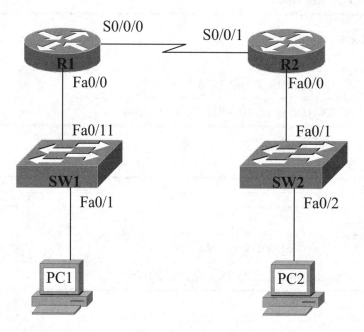

Figure 1   Network Topology for This Lab

Reference

The following simulator exercises provided with the CCNA 640-802 Network Simulator should be reviewed prior to starting this virtual laboratory exercise:

- IPv6 Configuration I

- IPv6 Configuration II
- IPv6 Address Configuration I–IX
- IPv6 Routing Configuration I, II, III

Key Concepts

The following concepts, terms, commands, and steps should have been mastered in this exercise:

- List the steps required to enable IPv6 routing.

- For the steps needed to enable the forwarding of IPv6 unicast datagrams, use the **ipv6 unicast-routing** command in global configuration mode.

- List the command used to enable IPv6 routing.

- The steps to add IPv6 addressing to a WAN interface.

- List the command used to observe the IPv6 address added to the interface.

- How IPv6 addresses can be abbreviated by dropping leading zeros and substituting :: for successive fields of zeros.

- Examine IPv6 routes on a router using the **show ipv6 route** command.

- Verify IPv6 connectivity between the two routers using the **ping ipv6** command to ping from one interface to the IPv6 address of another interface.

- The purpose of the **eui-64** option when configuring an IPv6 interface.

- The steps for assigning host names to IPv6 addresses.

Reference Table

Table 1 provides the IP addresses and masks for all necessary interfaces used to complete this lab.

Table 1   IP Addresses, Subnet Masks, and VLAN Assignments for Lab 2

Computer/Interface – R1	IPv6 Address
FA0/0	2001:C16C:0000:0002:0000:0000:0000:0000/64
S0/0/0	2001:C16C:0000:0001:0000:0000:0000:0001/64

Computer/Interface – R2	IPv6 Address
FA0/0	2001:C16C:0000:0003:0000:0000:0000:0000/64
S0/0/1	2001:C16C:0000:0001:0000:0000:0000:0002/64

Detailed Lab Steps

Task 1

In this lab, you will configure the two routers, R1 and R2, with IPv6 so that they can communicate. The routers are missing all the configuration necessary to support IPv6. To establish IPv6 on Cisco routers, there are two basic steps. First, you must configure the routers for IPv6 forwarding. Next, you should configure the interfaces with specified IPv6 addresses. This lab tests your ability to configure support for IPv6 and verify the configuration. The IPv6 addresses are provided in Table 1. You will not use the PCs in this lab.

Step 1. Enter the privileged mode on Router R1 and enter the command to enable IPv6 routing. List the steps required to enable IPv6 routing.

_____

_____

_____

Step 2. Enter privileged mode on Router R2 and enter the command to enable IPv6 routing. List the steps required to enable IPv6 routing.

_____

_____

_____

Step 3. In the next step, you now need to add IPv6 addresses to the WAN interfaces. Add the IPv6 address 2001:C16C:0000:0001:0000:0000:0000:0001/64 to the serial 0/0/0 interface of R1. What command is required to add this address? Add the address and enable the interface.

_____

_____

_____

Step 4. Next add the IPv6 address to the serial interface of R2. You are to use the abbreviated version of IPv6 address 2001:C16C:0000:0001:0000:0000:0000:0002/64, add the address to the serial 0/0/1 interface of R2, and enable the interface. List the command sequence used.

_____

_____

_____

Step 5. Use the command on R1 to observe the address added to the serial 0/0/0 interface. What command is used? What addresses are shown?

_____

_____

_____

Step 6. Issue the **show running-config** command on R1 and examine the command you added to add the IPv6 address to the serial 0/0/0 interface. What address is shown in the command? What has changed from the original entry?

_____

_____

_____

Step 7. Next, use the **show ipv6 interface brief** command to verify that the serial interface is operational. What indicates that the serial 0/0/0 interface is operational?

_____

_____

_____

Step 8. Examine the IPv6 routes on R2 with the **show ipv6 route** command. What networks are added?

_____

_____

_____

Step 9. Verify IPv6 connectivity between the two routers. To do this, use the **ping ipv6** command to ping from R2 to the IPv6 address of R1's serial interface. Was the ping successful? List the command used to verify IPv6 connectivity.

_____

_____

_____

Step 10. In the next step, you are to assign the host name R1-WAN to R1's s0/0/0 IP address using the **ipv6 host R1-LAN 2001:C16C:0:1::1/64** command.

Assign the host name R2-WAN to R2's s0/0/0 IP address using the **ipv6 host R2-LAN 2001:C16C:0:1::2/64** command.

Now test the **ping** command using the newly assigned host names for R1 and R2. List the commands used and the result.

_____

_____

_____

Step 11. Next, you are to configure the IPv6 addresses on the LAN interfaces. For this configuration, you will use the EUI-64 format. For R1's FastEthernet 0/0 interface, use the IPv6 subnetwork address 2001:C16C:0000:0002:0000:0000:0000:0000/64. What is the abbreviated format for this network?

_____

_____

_____

Step 12. List the command that is used to configure the IPv6 address on the FastEthernet 0/0 interface of R1. You are to use the abbreviated address format and the **eui-64** option to specify the ID of the interface. Add the IPv6 addresses to R1's Fa0/0 interface using the **eui-64** option and enable the interface. List the commands required to do this.

_____

_____

_____

Step 13. Next, add the IPv6 address to the R2 Fa0/0 interface. You are to use a subnet address of 2001:C16C:0:3::/64 and the **eui-64** option. Also, enable the interface. List the command sequence required to do this.

_____

_____

_____

Step 14. Use the **show ipv6 interface brief** command to verify that R2's Fa0/0 interface is properly configured. What indicates that the interface is properly configured?

_____

_____

_____

Step 15. On Router R2, enter the **show ipv6 interface brief** command to confirm that the correct address has been added. Verify that you have proper routes for your network.

_____

_____

_____

Task 2: Configuration List

The following is a partial list of the items displayed when you issue the **show running-configuration [sh run]** command on a switch. Your task is to define each item and its purpose. You might need to go to the Cisco website (http://www.cisco.com) and look up what each of these commands means.

1. **ipv6 unicast-routing**

_____

_____

_____

2. **no ipv6 unicast-routing**

_____

_____

_____

3. **ipv6 address 2001:C16C:0:2:213:19FF:FE7B:1101/64 eui-64**

_____

_____

_____

4. **no ip domain lookup**

5. **ipv6 address 2001:C16C:0:1::1/64**

6. **ipv6 host R1-LAN 30ef:1:2:aaaa::1**

7. **ipv6 rip ciscopress enable**

8. **ipv6 router rip ciscopress**

9. **ipv6 summary-address eigrp 1 2001:0DB8:0:1::/64**

10. Router(config-if)# **ipv6 traffic-filter cisco in**

LANs

Table 9-1 lists the labs for this unit. Check with your instructor or class syllabus to confirm what labs you should perform for class.

Table 9-1   Unit 9 Labs

Date	ICND1/ ICND2	Type	Part	Number	Name	Page
	ICND1	SB	2	1	Interface Settings I	497
	ICND1	SB	2	4	Switch Forwarding I	500
	ICND1	SB	2	5	Switch IP Connectivity I	502
	ICND1	SB	2	6	VLANs I	504
	ICND2	SB	1	2	VLAN Configuration II	507
	ICND2	SB	1	3	VLAN Configuration III	510
	ICND2	SB	1	11	Trunking Configuration I	512
	ICND1	CS	2	1	Switch Interfaces and Forwarding	515
	ICND2	CS	1	3	VLAN Trunking I	522
	ICND2	TS	1	1	Path Analysis	529
	Ungraded	CL	1	4	Configuring Switch Port Security	539
	Ungraded	CL	2	1	Basic Switch Configuration and the CLI	547
	Ungraded	CL	2	2	Static VLAN Configuration	552
	Ungraded	TL	1	3	Troubleshooting Lab III	559
	Ungraded	TL	1	5	Troubleshooting Lab V	561
	Ungraded	TL	1	8	Troubleshooting Lab VIII	563

ICND1 Skill Builders

Part 2: LAN Switching

Lab 1: Interface Settings I

Overview

In this lab, you're starting with a switch with two connected hosts and one router. The switch has been minimally configured. You now need to configure speed and duplex settings on each port connected to a host so that the settings match those of the hosts. This is sometimes called "nailing up" the port settings—that is, configuring them manually to avoid any speed or duplex conflict that may result from automatic configuration.

Topology

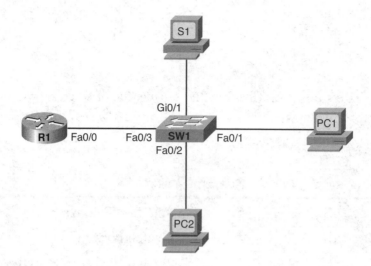

Figure 1   Network Topology for This Lab

Detailed Lab Steps

Step 1.   Connect to SW1 from the simulator user interface, and enter user mode by using the console password **ciscopress**.

Step 2.   Enter global configuration mode by entering the **enable** command and the password **ciscopress**.

Step 3.   Enter configuration mode by entering the **configure terminal** command. Note that the command prompt changes to include (config) near the end of the prompt.

Step 4.   Enter port configuration mode for interface FastEthernet 0/1 by using the **interface f0/1** global configuration command. Note that the command prompt again changes to show (config-if) near the end of the prompt.

Step 5.   Configure the switch port for 100 Mbps, full duplex using the **speed 100** and **duplex full** commands. Return to the global configuration prompt using the **end** command or by pressing **Ctrl-Z**.

Step 6.   Check to see the effect of the configuration commands you have issued by using the **show interfaces fa0/1** command. What is the duplex setting? The speed setting? Record your answers on the lines below.

_____

_____

Step 7.   Configure the switch ports connected to PC2 and R1 to 10 Mbps, full duplex. Enter global configuration mode using the **configure terminal** command.

Step 8.   Enter the configuration mode for a range of contiguous interfaces using the **interface range fa0/2 - 3** command. Notice how the prompt now indicates that you are configuring a range of interfaces with the (config-if-range) portion of the prompt.

Step 9. Configure the range of switch ports to 10 Mbps and full duplex using the **speed 10** and **duplex full** commands. Exit from configuration mode using the **end** command or by pressing **Ctrl-Z**.

Step 10. Confirm that both ports are configured correctly using the **show run** command. What other command could you have used to verify this configuration?

_____

_____

Hints and Answers

Table 1 provides hints and tips for any lab steps that do not supply complete details and provides answers for any lab steps that ask questions.

Table 1   Hints and Answers

Step	Hint or Answer
6	The line that contains the most valuable output is: Full-duplex, 100Mb/s, media type is 100BaseTX
10	You could also use **show interfaces status**.

Configuration Steps

Example 1 shows a sample of the lab exercise being completed from SW1's CLI.

Example 1   Example of Performing This Lab

```
(Press enter)
Password: ciscopress
SW1>enable
Password: ciscopress
SW1#configure terminal
SW1(config)#interface fa0/1
SW1(config-if)#speed 100
SW1(config-if)#duplex full
SW1(config-if)#end
!
! The next section begins at step 8.
!
SW1#configure terminal
SW1(config)#interface range fa0/2 - 3
SW1(config-if-range)#speed 10
SW1(config-if-range)#duplex full
SW1(config-if-range)#end
```

ICND1 Skill Builders

Part 2: LAN Switching

Lab 4: Switch Forwarding I

Overview

In this lab, you learn how switches build forwarding tables. Starting with each PC configured and a switch that has been minimally configured, you'll explore how the switches learn and store MAC addresses.

Topology

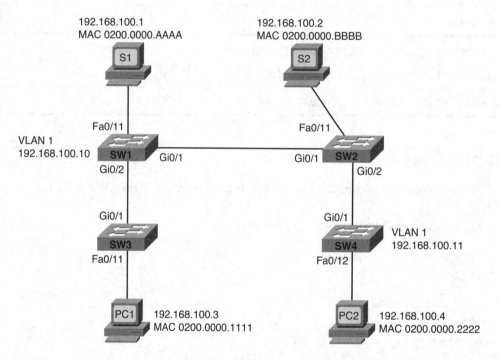

Figure 1   Network Topology for This Lab

Author's Note: The figure shown here omits some disabled links; the Simulator user interface shows the working and nonworking links.

Detailed Lab Steps

Step 1.   Connect to S1 from the simulator user interface.

Step 2.   To populate the MAC address tables of the switches, ping each of the other PCs from S1 as follows: **ping 192.168.100.2**, **ping 192.168.100.3**, and **ping 192.168.100.4**.

Step 3. Connect to the SW1 switch from the simulator user interface; use password **ciscopress**.

Step 4. Enter privileged exec mode by entering the **enable** command and the password **ciscopress**.

Step 5. Before viewing the MAC address table, write the port on the SW1 switch on which you expect to see each host connect.

_____

_____

_____

_____

_____

Step 6. View the MAC address table on switch SW1 by issuing the **show mac address-table** command. Notice that each connected host MAC address is mapped to a particular port, even if that host is not directly connected to the SW1 switch. Note the correlation between the MAC address table and the location of each host. Compare it to your answers for the preceding step.

Step 7. Connect to the SW4 switch from the simulator user interface. Use password **ciscopress**.

Step 8. Enter privileged exec mode by entering the **enable** command and the password **ciscopress**.

Step 9. View the MAC address table on switch SW4 by issuing the **show mac address-table** command. Notice the different MAC address mappings compared to the SW1 switch. Based on this, can you see how you can use MAC address tables to track down the location of a particular host in a multiple-switch environment?

_____

_____

Hints and Answers

Table 1 provides hints and tips for any lab steps that do not supply complete details and provides answers for any lab steps that ask questions.

Table 1   Hints and Answers

Step	Hint or Answer
2	Use the ping 192.168.100.2, ping 192.168.100.3, and ping 192.168.100.4 commands.

5	Your answer should resemble the following:

MAC Address	Port
0200.0000.AAAA	Fa0/11
0200.0000.BBBB	Gi0/1
0200.0000.1111	Gi0/2
0200.0000.2222	Gi0/1

9	Your answer should resemble the following:

MAC Address	Port
0200.0000.2222	Fa0/12
0200.0000.1111	Gi0/1
0200.0000.AAAA	Gi0/1
0200.0000.BBBB	Gi0/1

Note that you should be able to discover the location of each host's MAC address, relative to each switch, by looking at the port in the MAC address table.

Configuration Steps

This lab does not require any configuration.

ICND1 Skill Builders

Part 2: LAN Switching

Lab 5: Switch IP Connectivity I

Overview

In this lab, you'll configure a switch so that it can communicate using the Internet Protocol (IP) with other hosts, for management and administration purposes.

Topology

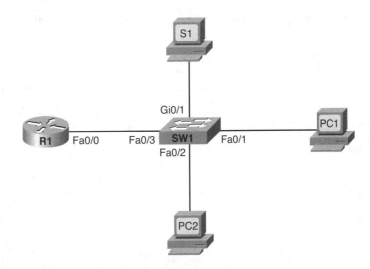

Figure 1 **Network Topology for This Lab**

Detailed Lab Steps

Step 1. Connect to SW1 from the simulator user interface; use password **ciscopress**.

Step 2. Enter privileged exec mode by entering the **enable** command and the password **ciscopress**.

Step 3. Enter global configuration mode using the **configure terminal** command.

Step 4. Enter interface configuration mode for the VLAN 1 interface using the **interface vlan 1** command.

Step 5. Configure the switch's VLAN 1 interface IP address and subnet mask using the **ip address 192.168.100.2 255.255.255.0** command.

Step 6. Enable the VLAN 1 interface by issuing the **no shutdown** command.

Step 7. Return to global configuration mode using the **exit** command.

Step 8. In global configuration mode, set the switch's default gateway using the **ip default-gateway 192.168.100.1** command.

Step 9. Use the **end** command to exit configuration mode.

Step 10. From SW1's enable mode prompt, ping R1's Fa0/0 IP address, 192.168.100.1, using the command **ping 192.168.100.1.**

Step 11. Verify that R1 answers. The output should look like this:

```
SW1#ping 192.168.100.1

Type escape sequence to abort.
Sending 5, 100-byte ICMP Echos to 192.168.100.1, timeout is 2 seconds:
!!!!!
Success rate is 100 percent (5/5), round-trip min/avg/max = 1/5/16 ms
```

Configuration Steps

Example 1 shows a sample of the lab exercise being completed from SW1's CLI.

Example 1   Example of Performing This Lab

```
SW1#configure terminal
SW1(config)#int vlan 1
SW1(config-int)#ip address 192.168.100.2 255.255.255.0
SW1(config-int)#no shutdown
SW1(config-int)#exit
SW1(config)#ip default-gateway 192.168.100.1
SW1(config)#end
SW1#ping 192.168.100.1


Type escape sequence to abort.
Sending 5, 100-byte ICMP Echos to 192.168.100.1, timeout is 2 seconds:
!!!!!
Success rate is 100 percent (5/5), round-trip min/avg/max = 1/5/16 ms
```

ICND1 Skill Builders

Part 2: LAN Switching

Lab 6: VLANs I

Overview

In this lab, you'll start with a switch with its default virtual LAN (VLAN) configuration. Then you'll create another VLAN, put one of the connected PCs into that VLAN, and test the effect of having two VLANs.

Topology

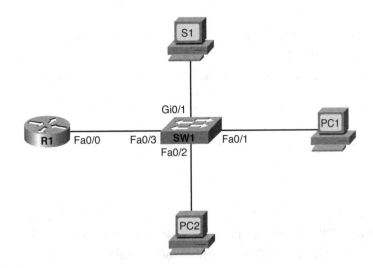

Figure 1   **Network Topology for This Lab**

Detailed Lab Steps

Step 1.   Connect to PC1 from the simulator user interface. Ping PC2 by entering **ping 172.20.20.2** at the command prompt. Does the output imply that the ping worked or the ping failed?

_____

Step 2.   Connect to SW1 from the simulator user interface; use password **ciscopress**.

Step 3.   Enter privileged exec mode by entering the **enable** command and the password **ciscopress**.

Step 4.   Enter global configuration mode using the **configure terminal** command.

Step 5.   By default, all switch ports are in the same VLAN, VLAN 1. Configure a new VLAN, VLAN 2, by issuing the **vlan 2** command. Did any messages occur confirming the addition of the VLAN? Record the message below. Also, note the contents of the command prompt listed on the next line.

_____

_____

Step 6.   From VLAN configuration mode, name the VLAN by issuing the command **name VLAN_Two.** Note the underscore, which is necessary because the switch will not accept VLAN names with spaces in them.

Step 7.   Configure the port to which PC2 is connected, Fa0/2, to be in VLAN 2 by issuing these two commands: **interface fa0/2** and then **switchport access vlan 2**.

Step 8. Return to the privileged exec prompt by issuing the **end** command or by pressing **Ctrl-Z**.

Step 9. Use the **show vlan brief** command to view the VLAN configuration. Look in the list that runs down the left side of this command's output. What is the name of the VLAN numbered 2? What interfaces are listed to the right on that same line?

_____

_____

_____

Step 10. Connect to PC1 from the simulator user interface. As before, ping PC2 by entering **ping 172.20.20.2** at the command prompt. Does the command list five periods (not successful) or five exclamation points (successful)?

_____

_____

_____

Hints and Answers

Table 1 provides hints and tips for any lab steps that do not supply complete details and provides answers for any lab steps that ask questions.

Table 1   Hints and Answers

Step	Hint or Answer
1	The **ping** command should work, as shown with the repeated messages that state "reply from 172.20.20.2…."
5	The **vlan** command moves the user interface into VLAN configuration mode, as noted by config-vlan in the command prompt. However, the creation of a VLAN with the **vlan** command does not cause a confirmation message to appear.
9	Note the presence of the new VLAN 2 and its name, VLAN_Two, along with the fact that the Fa0/2 port is assigned to VLAN 2. All other ports are assigned to VLAN 1.
10	The **ping** command no longer works, because PC1 and PC2 are in different VLANs. Switch SW1 will not forward frames directly between interfaces in different VLANs.

Configuration Steps

Example 1 shows a sample of the lab exercise being completed from SW1's CLI.

Example 1　Example of Performing This Lab

```
(Press enter)
Password: ciscopress
SW1>enable
Password: ciscopress
SW1#configure terminal
SW1(config)#vlan 2
SW1(config-vlan)#name VLAN_Two
SW1(config-vlan)#interface fa0/2
SW1(config-if)#switchport access vlan 2
SW1(config-if)#end
SW1#
```

ICND2 Skill Builders
Part 1: VLANs and Trunking

Lab 2: VLAN Configuration II

Overview

This lab begins with a working internetwork with hosts S1, PC1, and PC2 assigned to VLAN 1. During this lab, you will create a new VLAN, migrate PC1 and PC2 to the new VLAN, and confirm that they can ping each other at the end of the migration.

Topology

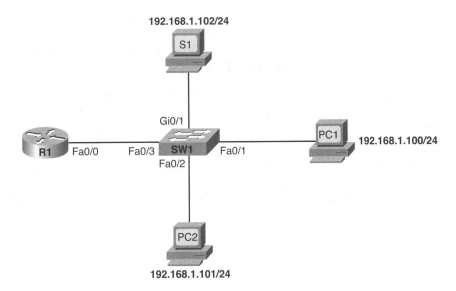

Figure 1　Network Topology for This Lab

Detailed Lab Steps

Step 1. Connect to PC1 from the simulator user interface.

Step 2. Ping PC2 by issuing the **ping 192.168.1.101** command. Did the ping work? Ping S1 using the **ping 192.168.1.102** command. Did the ping work?

_____

_____

Step 3. Connect to switch SW1 from the simulator user interface; use password **ciscopress**.

Step 4. Enter privileged exec mode using the password **ciscopress**.

Step 5. Show the current VLAN setup by issuing the **show vlan brief** command. To what VLAN are interfaces Gi0/1, Fa0/1, and Fa0/2 assigned? Do S1's, PC1's, and PC2's IP addresses (shown in Figure 1) appear to be in the same subnet? Is that important? Does VLAN 3 exist at this point?

_____

_____

Step 6. Move to global configuration mode using the **configure terminal** command.

Step 7. Enter the interface configuration mode for the range of interfaces Fa0/1 through Fa0/2 using the **interface range fa0/1 - 2** command.

Step 8. Assign both interfaces to VLAN 3 by issuing the **switchport access vlan 3** command. What action does it appear the switch took at this point besides assigning these interfaces to VLAN 3?

_____

_____

_____

Step 9. Exit configuration mode using the **end** command, and repeat the **show vlan brief** command. To what VLAN are interfaces Fa0/1 and Fa0/2 assigned? How about server S1?

_____

_____

Step 10. Connect to PC1 from the simulator user interface.

Step 11. Ping PC2 by issuing the **ping 192.168.1.101** command. Did the ping succeed?

_____

_____

Step 12. Ping S1, which has remained in VLAN 1, by issuing the **ping 192.168.1.102** command. Did the ping work? Why?

_____

_____

Hints and Answers

Table 1 provides hints and tips for any lab steps that do not supply complete details and provides answers for any lab steps that ask questions.

Table 1   Hints and Answers

Step	Hint or Answer
2	Both pings succeeded.
5	All three interfaces are currently in VLAN 1, and all three hosts' IP addresses appear to be in the same subnet. That is important, because on a LAN, the addresses in a single IP subnet should be assigned to the same VLAN.
8	The message that appears states that while VLAN 3 does not yet exist, the switch is now creating the VLAN.
9	Fa0/1 and Fa0/2 are now assigned to VLAN 3, but Gi0/1 is still assigned to VLAN 1.
11	The ping worked.
12	The ping fails. Although S1 is in a different VLAN and different broadcast domain from PC1, their IP addresses are in the same subnet. Because they are in the same subnet, PC1 would attempt to ARP to discover S1's MAC address, a process that uses a broadcast. The switch will not forward broadcasts between different VLANs, so that ARP request would fail, preventing the ping from working.

Configuration Steps

Example 1 shows a sample of the lab exercise being completed from SW1's CLI.

Example 1   Example of Performing This Lab

```
SW1#configure terminal
SW1(config)#interface range fa0/1 - 2
SW1(config-if-range)#switchport access vlan 3
SW1(config-if-range)#end
```

ICND2 Skill Builders

Part 1: VLANs and Trunking

Lab 3: VLAN Configuration III

Overview

This lab begins with a switch configuration that uses all defaults for the commands related to VLANs. The three hosts (PC1, PC2, and server S1) and router R1 all have IP addresses in the same Class C network (192.168.1.0/24), and they can all ping each other at the beginning of the lab.

During this lab, you will create a new VLAN (VLAN 4), assign S1's port to that VLAN, and confirm that S1 can no longer ping the other hosts because S1 is now in a different VLAN.

Topology

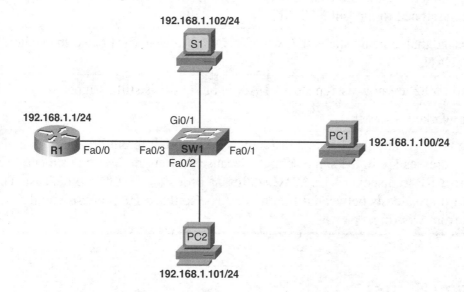

Figure 1   Network Topology for This Lab

Detailed Lab Steps

Step 1.   Connect to S1 from the simulator user interface.

Step 2.   Ping the IP addresses of PC1, PC2, and R1, whose IP addresses are listed in Figure 1. Which pings work? Which ones fail?

_____

_____

Step 3. Connect to SW1 from the simulator user interface by using the password **ciscopress**.

Step 4. Enter privileged exec mode using the password **ciscopress**.

Step 5. Show the current VLAN setup by issuing the **show vlan brief** command. To what VLAN are interfaces Gi0/1, Fa0/1, Fa0/2, and Fa0/3 assigned?

_____

_____

Step 6. Display all SW1 trunks using the **show interface trunk** command. Is SW1's Fa0/3 interface, which connects to R1, trunking?

_____

_____

Step 7. Next, create VLAN 4 and assign S1's port to the new VLAN. To begin, move to global configuration mode using the **configure terminal** command.

Step 8. Enter the interface configuration mode for interface Gi0/1 by issuing the **interface gi0/1** command.

Step 9. Insert the interface into VLAN 4 by issuing the **switchport access vlan 4** command. What action does it appear the switch took at this point besides assigning this interface to VLAN 4?

_____

_____

_____

Step 10. Exit configuration mode using the **end** command, and repeat the **show vlan brief** command. To what VLAN is Gi0/1 assigned?

_____

_____

Step 11. Connect to S1 from the simulator user interface and ping PC1, PC2, and R1. Which of the **ping** commands work? Why or why not?

_____

_____

Hints and Answers

Table 1 provides hints and tips for any lab steps that do not supply complete details and provides answers for any lab steps that ask questions.

Table 1   Hints and Answers

Step	Hint or Answer
2	All the pings worked.
5	All four interfaces have (by default) been assigned to VLAN 1.
6	The output just lists a single blank line, which means that SW1 has no trunks.
9	SW1's message states that because VLAN 4 does not yet exist, SW1 will now create the VLAN, in addition to assigning the port to VLAN 4.
10	Gi0/1 is now assigned to VLAN 4.
11	All pings fail. Although S1 sees the other hosts as being in the same subnet (Layer 3), because the switch has assigned Gi0/1 (S1's port) to VLAN 4, SW1 won't forward the frame sent by S1 to ports assigned to other VLANs.

Configuration Steps

Example 1 shows a sample of the lab exercise being completed from SW1's CLI.

Example 1   Example of Performing This Lab

```
SW1#configure terminal
SW1(config)#interface gi0/1
SW1(config-if)#switchport access vlan 4
SW1(config-if)#end
```

ICND2 Skill Builders

Part 1: VLANS and Trunking

Lab 11: Trunking Configuration I

Overview

This lab begins with a working internetwork that includes SW1, SW3, PC1, and S1. The other two switches and other two hosts are ignored for this lab. For the purposes of this lab, only switches SW1 and SW3 will be used.

During this lab, you will enable trunking on the link between SW1 and SW3 by configuring SW1 to statically trunk.

Topology

Figure 1   Network Topology for This Lab

Detailed Lab Steps

Step 1.   Connect to SW3 from the simulator user interface, using the password **ciscopress**.

Step 2.   View SW3's trunking configuration by issuing the **show interface trunk** command. Which ports show up as current trunks?

_____

_____

Step 3.   View details about SW3's Gi0/1 interface, particularly details about its trunk settings, using the **show interface gi0/1 switchport** command. What setting is listed on the line reading "Administrative Mode"? "Operational Mode"? Based on this command's output, what do you believe the configuration setting for the **switchport mode** interface subcommand to be for SW3's Gi0/1 interface?

_____

_____

Step 4. Connect to SW1 from the simulator user interface and then use the **enable** command to move to privileged mode. (All passwords are **ciscopress**.)

Step 5. View details about SW1's Gi0/2 interface, which is on the other end of the cable connected to SW3's Gi0/1, using the **show interface gi0/2 switchport** command. What setting is listed on the "Administrative Mode" line? On the "Operational Mode" line? Based on this command's output, what do you believe the configuration setting for the **switchport mode** interface subcommand to be for SW1's Gi0/2 interface?

_____

_____

Now that you have confirmed that both SW3 and SW1 have the (default) setting for the **switchport mode** command, you will enable trunking by telling SW1 to always trunk on interface Gi0/2. As it turns out, the default of **switchport mode dynamic auto** tells the switch to negotiate trunking, but only if the other switch initiates the process.

Step 6. To begin the configuration process, move to global configuration mode using the **configure terminal** command.

Step 7. Enter interface configuration mode for the Gi0/2 interface by issuing the **interface gi0/2** command.

Step 8. Manually configure the interface to be a trunk by issuing the **switchport mode trunk** command.

Step 9. Exit back into enable mode by issuing the **end** command.

Step 10. View SW1's trunking configuration by issuing the **show interface trunk** command. Which ports show up as current trunks?

_____

_____

Step 11. Repeat the **show interface gi0/2 switchport** command. What setting is listed on the "Administrative Mode" line? On the "Operational Mode" line? Does it appear that the link is now trunking?

_____

_____

Hints and Answers

Table 1 provides hints and tips for any lab steps that do not supply complete details and provides answers for any lab steps that ask questions.

Table 1   Hints and Answers

Step	Hint or Answer
2	This command lists no trunks.
3	The output lists the following: Administrative Mode: dynamic auto Operational Mode: static access It appears that the (default) setting of **switchport mode dynamic auto** is used.
5	The output matches the output found on SW3 in Step 3.
10	SW1 now has a single trunk, its Gi0/2 interface.
11	Unlike the results in Step 5, the output from this command now lists the following: Administrative Mode: trunk Operational Mode: trunk

Configuration Steps

Example 1 shows a sample of the lab exercise being completed from SW1's CLI.

Example 1   Example of Performing This Lab

```
SW1#configure terminal
SW1(config)#interface gi0/2
SW1(config-if)#switchport mode trunk
SW1(config-if)#end
```

ICND1 Configuration Scenarios
Part 2: LAN Switching

Lab 1: Switch Interfaces and Forwarding

Overview

This lab guides you through the process of enabling interfaces, identifying whether auto-negotiation affected the operation of the interface, and understanding how switches forward traffic.

Note: Any password necessary for this lab, unless otherwise specified, is **ciscopress**.

Topology

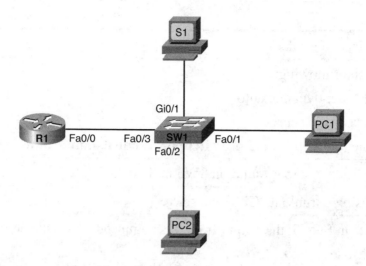

Figure 1   Network Topology for This Lab

Detailed Lab Steps

Part 1: Examine Initial Interface Status

Step 1.   Connect to SW1 from the simulator user interface and move into user mode.

Step 2.   Use the **show interfaces status** command to discover the current status, duplex setting, and speed for each of the four SW1 interfaces shown in Figure 1. Record those settings in Table 1.

Table 1   Initial Switch Interface Settings

Interface	Status	Duplex	Speed
Fa0/1			
Fa0/2			
Fa0/3			
Gi0/1			

Step 3.   Use commands like **show interfaces fa0/1** to find the two-part interface status for each of the four switch interfaces shown in Figure 1. List those status values on the lines below.

_____

_____

_____

Step 4. Try to predict any interface subcommands that you expect are currently configured for the SW1 interfaces listed in Table 1 and in Figure 1. Record those commands on the lines below.

_____

_____

_____

_____

Step 5. The "disabled interface" status (from the **show interface status** command) and the "administratively down" status (from the **show interfaces** command) state that the interface is configured with a **shutdown** command. To confirm this, display the switch's current configuration and find the **shutdown** commands configured on each interface.

_____

_____

Part 2: Experiment with SW1's Fa0/1 and Fa0/2 Interfaces

Part 2 of this lab enables SW1's Fa0/1 interface and examines the resulting interface's status values.

Step 6. Move into configuration mode on SW1 and then move into interface configuration mode for the Fa0/1 interface.

Step 7. Enable the interface using the **no shutdown** interface subcommand and then exit configuration mode.

Step 8. Use the **show interfaces status** command to discover the current status, duplex setting, and speed for interface Fa0/1, recording the information on the lines below. What do you suppose the "a-" in "a-full" and "a-100" represents?

_____

_____

Step 9. Use the **show interfaces fa0/1** command and find the two-part interface status as well as the speed and duplex settings. Does the speed and duplex information imply anything about whether auto-negotiation is used?

_____

_____

_____

Step 10. Move back to configuration mode and then move into interface configuration mode for Fa0/2.

Step 11. Set the duplex to "full," enable the interface using the **no shutdown** interface subcommand, and then exit configuration mode.

Step 12. Use the **show interfaces status** command to discover the current status, duplex setting, and speed for interface Fa0/2, recording the information on the lines below. Which settings did SW1's Fa0/2 interface auto-negotiate? Which ones were not auto-negotiated?

_____

_____

Part 3: Experiment with SW1's Fa0/3 Interface

Part 3 examines the output of **show** commands on switch SW1 depending on settings on router R1.

Step 13. Use the **show interfaces status** command to discover the current status, duplex setting, and speed for interface Fa0/3, which is connected to router R1.

_____

_____

Step 14. Display the switch's current configuration and confirm that the only interface subcommand is the **shutdown** command.

Step 15. Move into configuration mode on SW1 and then move into interface configuration mode for the Fa0/3 interface.

Step 16. Enable the interface using the **no shutdown** interface subcommand and then exit configuration mode.

Step 17. Use the **show interfaces status** command to discover the current status, duplex setting, and speed for interface Fa0/3. Which values are different from those in Step 13?

_____

_____

Step 18. From the simulator user interface, connect to router R1 and move into enable mode.

Step 19. From enable mode, use the **show interfaces Fa0/0** command. What two-part interface status is listed?

_____

_____

Step 20. Move to configuration mode and then move into interface configuration mode for Fa0/0.

Step 21. Manually set R1's Fa0/0 interface to use full duplex, but do not configure a speed setting.

Step 22. Administratively enable R1's Fa0/0 interface and then exit configuration mode.

Step 23. From the simulator user interface, connect to switch SW1 again and move to enable mode.

Step 24. Use the **show interfaces status** command to discover the current status, duplex setting, and speed for interface Fa0/3, which is connected to router R1. Which settings were found due to auto-negotiation? Which were not?

_____

_____

_____

Part 4: Switch Forwarding

This final part of the lab examines SW1's MAC address table and interprets how SW1 will forward frames.

Step 25. From the simulator user interface, connect to PC1.

Step 26. From PC1, ping S1 (192.168.4.11), PC2 (192.168.4.2), and R1's Fa0/0 interface (192.168.4.62). Which pings worked?

_____

_____

Step 27. Display PC1's ARP cache. Record the IP address/MAC address pair associated with S1, PC2, and R1. Also display PC1's MAC address from its user interface and record its value as well.

_____

_____

_____

Step 28. Now that you know each device's MAC address, you can better interpret SW1's MAC address table. From the simulator user interface, connect to SW1 again and move to user mode.

Step 29. Display only the dynamic entries in the switch's MAC address table. What command did you use?

_____

_____

_____

Step 30. Predict the path taken by a packet sent by PC1 to PC2. Which entries in SW1's MAC address table would be matched when forwarding the frame? Out which port would SW1 forward such a frame?

_____

_____

_____

Step 31. Predict the path taken by a packet sent by R1 to PC1. Which entries in SW1's MAC address table would be matched when forwarding the frame? Out which port would SW1 forward such a frame?

_____

_____

_____

Hints and Answers

Table 2 provides hints and tips for any lab steps that do not supply complete details and provides answers for any lab steps that ask questions.

Table 2   Hints and Answers

Step	Hint or Answer
1	Click the SW1 icon, press **Enter**, and supply the password **ciscopress**.
3	All four interfaces have the same status: "administratively down" and "down."
4	The interfaces all have a **shutdown** command configured, but no other configuration commands.
5	Use the **show running-config** command to see the currently used configuration.
6	Use the **configure terminal** command and then the **interface fa0/1** command.
7	Press **Ctrl-Z** or use the **end** command to exit configuration mode completely.
8	The prefix "a-" means that the switch used IEEE auto-negotiation to discover the setting.
9	The **show interfaces fa0/1** command does list the duplex and speed, but it does not state anything about whether auto-negotiation was used or not.
10	Use the **configure terminal** command and then the **interface fa0/2** command.
11	Use the **duplex full** command and **no shutdown** command. Then press **Ctrl-Z** or use the **end** command to exit configuration mode completely.
12	The output for interface Fa0/2 lists "full" instead of "a-full," meaning that the switch did not auto-negotiate that setting. However, the speed listed as "a-100" means that SW1 auto-negotiated the speed.

Step	Hint or Answer
13	The status will be "disabled" with the duplex and speed listed as "auto."
14	Use the **show running-config** command to see the currently used configuration.
15	Use the **configure terminal** command and then the **interface fa0/3** command.
16	Press **Ctrl-Z** or use the **end** command to exit configuration mode completely.
17	The status will be "notconnect," as opposed to "disabled" at Step 13. This status means that the other end of the link (R1's Fa0/0) is not working. The duplex and speed are listed as "auto" just as in Step 13.
19	The status will be "administratively down" and "down."
20	Use the **configure terminal** command and then the **interface fa0/0** command.
21	Use the **duplex full** command.
22	Use the **no shutdown** command and then press **Ctrl-Z** or use the **end** command to exit configuration mode completely.
24	SW1's **show** command output lists "a-full" and "a-100" because SW1 had to learn both settings through auto-negotiation. You may recall that in Step 12, after you configured SW1's Fa0/2 with a setting of "full," the **show interface status** command listed a duplex of "full," implying that SW1 did not need to use auto-negotiation. However, in this case, the manual setting to "full" was made at the device on the other end of the cable (R1), so SW1 had to learn the setting through auto-negotiation.
26	The ping to PC2 and R1 should work. However, the ping of S1 should fail, because SW1's Gi0/1 interface is still administratively disabled.
27	You can use the **arp –a** command to display the following information:
	PC2: 192.168.4.2, MAC address 0200.2222.2222
	R1: 192.168.4.62, MAC address 0200.BBBB.BBBB
	Note that because SW1's Gi0/1 interface is shut down, PC1 cannot learn an ARP table entry for S1.
29	Use the **show mac address-table dynamic** command.
30	Because PC2's IP address is 192.168.4.2, you know from Step 27 that PC2's MAC address is 0200.2222.2222. SW1's MAC address table lists 0200.2222.2222 off port Fa0/2, so SW1 would forward this frame out its Fa0/2 port.
31	Because PC1's IP address is 192.168.4.1, you know from Step 27 that PC1's MAC address is 0200.1111.1111. SW1's MAC address table lists 0200.1111.1111 off port Fa0/1, so SW1 would forward this frame out its Fa0/1 port.

Configuration Steps

Example 1 shows the configuration commands added to both R1 and SW1 during this lab.

Example 1 Configuration on R1 and SW1 Added During This Lab

```
On R1:


interface Fa0/0
 duplex full
 no shutdown



On SW1:


interface Fa0/1
 no shutdown


interface Fa0/2
 duplex full
 no shutdown


interface Fa0/3
 no shutdown
```

ICND2 Configuration Scenarios

Part 1: VLANs and Trunking

Lab 3: VLAN Trunking I

Overview

During this lab, you will configure three 2960 switches for trunking. The lab begins with all potential trunks shut down. During the lab, you will enable the possible trunks between switches SW1, SW2, and SW4, while ignoring SW3. The lab asks you to perform various configuration commands and see the results of whether the switches then trunk or not.

Note: Any password necessary for this lab, unless otherwise specified, is **ciscopress**.

Topology

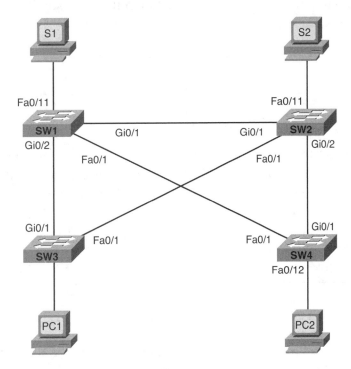

Figure 1   **Network Topology for This Lab**

Detailed Lab Steps

Part 1: Enable the Port on SW1 That Is Connected to SW2

Step 1.   Connect to SW1 from the simulator user interface and enter into enable mode.

Step 2.   Identify in Figure 1 the port on SW1 that connects to SW2, and record the information on the line below.

_____

Step 3.   Identify the current administrative and operational state of the port. What command did you use? What is the current administrative mode? What is the current operational mode?

_____

_____

_____

Step 4. View the saved configuration in NVRAM. View the configuration section for the port you identified in Step 2. What command or commands are displayed in the configuration for the port?

_____

_____

Step 5. Move into global configuration mode.

Step 6. Move into interface configuration mode for the port identified in Step 2. Enable the port. What command did you use to enter interface configuration mode? What command did you use to enable the port? What informational message displayed after you enabled the port?

_____

_____

_____

Step 7. Move into enable mode and view the operational status of the port. Has the administrative or operational mode changed? What are the administrative and operational modes?

_____

_____

_____

Part 2: Enable SW1-SW2 Trunking Dynamically

Cisco 2960 switch ports by default operate as dynamic ports, meaning that they will attempt to negotiate trunking. If the negotiation process fails, the port acts as an access port. If the negotiation works, the interface acts as a trunk.

2960 switches default to a trunking mode of "dynamic auto," meaning that the switch will not initiate the negotiation of trunking, but it will respond to negotiation messages sent by the neighboring switch. Part 2 of this lab configures a port connecting two switches so that one of the switches begins the negotiation process, resulting in an operational trunk.

Step 8. Re-enter global configuration mode on SW1 and then enter interface configuration mode for the port identified in Step 2.

Step 9. Set the trunking negotiation of the port from auto to desirable. What command did you use?

_____

Step 10. Return to enable mode and again view the administrative and operational states of the port. Is there a difference in output from Step 7? What is the administrative mode? What is the operational mode?

_____

_____

_____

Step 11. Move to SW2's simulator interface and enter enable mode.

Step 12. Use Figure 1 to identify the port on SW2 that is directly connected to SW1. Record that port number on the line below.

_____

Step 13. What are the administrative and operational modes of this port? What command did you use to discover this information?

_____

_____

Step 14. Enter global configuration mode and then enter interface configuration mode for the port identified in Step 12.

Step 15. Enable the port.

Step 16. Move back to enable mode. View the administrative and operational modes of the port. What is the administrative mode? What is the operational mode?

_____

_____

Step 17. View all the ports on SW2 that are currently operating as trunks. What command did you use? Which ports are listed as currently trunking?

_____

_____

Part 3: Enable SW2-SW4 Trunking Statically

The final part of this lab shows how to configure a 2960 switch so that a port always trunks. In this case, SW2 will be configured so that it always trunks on its Gi0/2 interface, which connects to SW4.

Step 18. Use Figure 1 to identify the port on SW2 that connects to SW4. Still on SW2, display that port's administrative and operational trunking modes. What are the administrative and operational states?

_____

_____

Step 19. Enter global configuration mode and then enter the interface configuration mode for the port identified in Step 18.

Step 20. Configure the port with the **switchport mode trunk** command, administratively enable the port, and then move back to enable mode.

Step 21. Move to SW4's simulator user interface and enter enable mode.

Step 22. Again using Figure 1, identify the port on SW4 that is connected to SW2, and record that port number.

_____

Step 23. View the administrative and operational modes of this port. What are the current administrative and operational modes for this port?

_____

_____

Step 24. Enter global configuration mode and then move into interface configuration mode for the port identified in Step 22.

Step 25. Administratively enable the port and move back into enable mode.

Step 26. View the administrative and operational modes of the port again. What are the administrative and operational modes? Is the port trunking?

_____

_____

Hints and Answers

Table 1 provides hints and tips for any lab steps that do not supply complete details and provides answers for any lab steps that ask questions.

Table 1   Hints and Answers

Step	Hint or Answer
1	Use the **enable** command to enter privileged exec mode. When prompted for a password, use **ciscopress**.
2	According to the topology, SW1 and SW2 are connected via their Gi0/1 ports.

Step	Hint or Answer
3	Use the **show interface gigabitethernet 0/1 switchport** command. (You could also use **show interface gigabitethernet 0/1 trunk**.) The administrative mode of the port should be "dynamic auto." The operational mode should be "down."
4	Use the **show startup-config** command. Under the configuration section for Gi0/1, there should only be a **shutdown** command.
5	Use the **configure terminal** command.
6	Use the **interface gig 0/1** global configuration command. From interface configuration mode, issue the **no shutdown** command. After enabling the port, a message should scroll up the CLI stating "%LINK-3-UPDOWN: Interface GigabitEthernet0/1, changed state to down."
7	Use the **end** command to move directly into enable mode. Use the **show interface gig 0/1 switchport** command. No changes should have appeared in the output since Step 2.
8	Use the **configure terminal** command, followed by **interface gi0/1**.
9	Use the **switchport mode dynamic desirable** interface configuration mode command.
10	There is a difference in the outputs. Gigabitethernet port 0/1 should now have an administrative mode of "dynamic desirable." The operational mode should still be "down."
12	As identified earlier, the port used by SW2 to connect to SW1 is Gi0/1.
13	The administrative mode of port Gi0/1 should be "dynamic auto" and the operational mode should be "down." This can be seen with either the **show interface gigabitethernet 0/1 switchport** command or the **show interface gigabitethernet 0/1 trunk** command.
14	Use the **configure terminal** command, followed by **interface gi0/1**.
15	Use the **no shutdown** command to enable the port.
16	Use the **end** command to move back to enable mode. The administrative mode should still be "dynamic auto." The operational mode should now be "trunk." This can be seen with either the **show interface gigabitethernet 0/1 switchport** command or the **show interface gigabitethernet 0/1 trunk** command.
17	Use the **show interface trunk** enable mode command. Gigabitethernet port 0/1 should now be listed in the output.
18	The port on SW2 being used to connect to SW4 is Gi0/2. The administrative mode should be "dynamic auto" and the operational mode should be "down."
19	Use the **configure terminal** command, followed by **interface gigabitethernet0/2**.
20	Use the **switchport mode trunk** command, the **no shutdown** command, and the **end** command.
22	The port connected to SW2 from SW4 is Gi0/1. This can be seen with either the **show interface gigabitethernet 0/1 switchport** command or the **show interface gigabitethernet 0/1 trunk** command.
23	The administrative mode of port Gi0/1 should be "dynamic auto" and the operational mode should be "down."

continued

Table 1   **Hints and Answers** *continued*

Step	Hint or Answer
24	Use the **configure terminal** command, followed by the **interface gigabitethernet 0/1** command.
25	Use the **no shutdown** command and the **end** command.
26	The administrative mode for Gi0/1 should still be "dynamic auto." The operational mode should now be "trunk."

Configuration

Example 1 shows the configuration commands added to SW1, SW2, and SW4 during this lab.

Example 1   Configuration Added During This Lab

```
! Commands added to SW1 to enable the port and change the administrative state
interface gig 0/1
 switchport mode dynamic desirable
 no shutdown


! Commands added to SW2 to bring up the trunk to SW1
interface gigabitethernet 0/1
 no shutdown


! Commands added to SW2 to bring up the trunk to SW4
interface gigabitethernet 0/2
 switchport mode trunk
 no shutdown


! Commands added to SW4 to bring up trunk to SW2
interface gigabitethernet 0/1
 no shutdown
```

ICND2 Troubleshooting Scenarios

Lab 1: Path Analysis

Overview

This lab begins with a working internetwork. The lab then guides you through some analyses, first of the forwarding path of frames/packets through the network, and then of the control plane activities that determined the path.

In this particular lab, you will analyze the flow of packets sent by PC1 to PC2, determine the path the packets take, and examine the choices made by Spanning Tree Protocol (STP).

The goal of this lab is to predict the flow of frames between PC1 and PC2. You may use the lab steps detailed in this lab. However, you can also simply find the forwarding paths used when a packet is sent from PC1 to PC2, and then discover the impact and details of how STP, EIGRP, and router R1 determined the path.

Topology

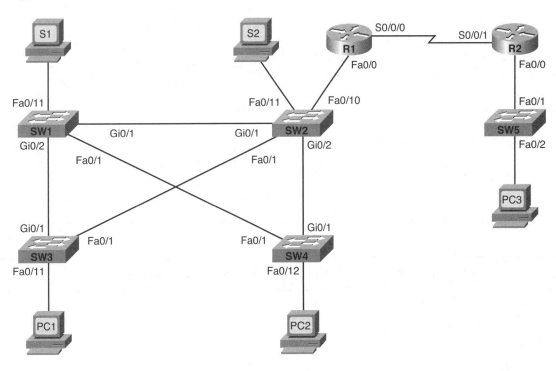

Figure 1   Network Topology for This Lab

Reference Tables

Table 1 provides a convenient place to record some important facts about the two hosts used when testing in this lab.

Table 1   Facts About Hosts in This Lab

	PC1	PC2
IP address		
Mask		
Default gateway		
MAC address		
Assigned VLAN		

Table 2 provides a convenient place to record the path taken for packets going from PC1 to PC2.

Table 2   Path Between PC1 and PC2

Sending Device	Outgoing Port	Receiving Device	Receiving Port	How Info Was Determined
PC1	N/A			

Note: The password for all devices that are intended to be accessible is **ciscopress**.

Note: You may assume that Figure 1 is accurate.

Detailed Lab Steps

Part 1: Discovery and Layer 3 Analysis

Part 1 of this lab discovers the IP addresses used on some of the devices in this lab and analyzes how the hosts use IP when PC1 sends an IP packet to PC2.

Step 1. From the simulator user interface, connect to PC2.

Step 2. Use the **ipconfig /all** command to complete as much of Table 1 as you can for PC2. What information couldn't be found in the output of this command?

_____

_____

Step 3. From the simulator user interface, move to PC1 and use commands to finish PC1's column in Table 1.

Step 4. Ping PC2's IP address from PC1. Does the ping succeed?

_____

_____

Step 5. Based on the information you have gathered so far, consider whether PC1 should send a packet to a router (in this case, probably R1) when it sends a packet to PC2. Explain why you think it should/shouldn't send the packet to a router.

_____

_____

_____

_____

Step 6. Examine PC1's ARP table. Does it list an entry for PC2's IP address? Does the corresponding MAC address match the MAC address you recorded for PC2 in Table 1?

_____

_____

Part 2: Layer 2 Analysis

At this point, this lab has shown how to confirm that PC1 should send the packet "directly" to PC2, not using a default gateway—at least from a Layer 3 perspective. You know that PC1 will send a packet directly to PC2, meaning that PC1 will put the packet in an Ethernet frame with PC2's MAC address as the destination, and send the frame. Part 2 of this lab examines how the Ethernet frame is forwarded from PC1 to PC2.

Step 7. Based on Figure 1, what switch interface first receives the frame after it has been sent by PC1? Record the answer below. Additionally, if you want to list the entire path in one place, add the switch's name and incoming interface into Table 2 in the partially completed row that lists PC1 as the sending device.

_____

_____

Step 8. Determine the VLAN in which the frame coming from PC1 should be forwarded. Start by determining the VLAN associated with the interface on SW3 in which the frame arrived (as noted in the previous step). To do so, first move to SW3's CLI using the simulator user interface.

Step 9. Use the **show interfaces status** command to list all interfaces, their status, and the assigned VLAN for access ports. To what VLAN is SW3's Fa0/11 interface assigned?

_____

_____

Step 10. Look for the frame's destination MAC address (0200.2222.2222) in switch SW3's MAC address table, but only pay attention to entries for the VLAN identified in the previous step. Was that MAC address in the MAC address table? Record the outgoing port as listed in the MAC address table, or note that it is not listed.

_____

_____

_____

Step 11. At this point, it appears that SW3 will process the frame as part of VLAN 12, and that SW3 will forward the frame out its Gi0/1 interface, meaning the next device will be SW1. Based on those discoveries, and Figure 1, complete the next row of Table 2 (if you are filling out that table), or at least note on the lines below that SW3 forwards the frame out its Gi0/1 interface.

_____

_____

Step 12. Examine the next forwarding step by connecting to SW1 from the simulator user interface and moving to user mode.

Step 13. Look for the frame's destination MAC address (0200.2222.2222) in switch SW1's MAC address table, dynamic entries only, and only pay attention to the VLAN identified in the previous step. What command did you use? Record the outgoing interface on the lines below or, if you are using Table 2, start a new row that lists SW1 in the first column and SW1's outgoing port in the next column.

_____

_____

_____

Step 14. Based on the information about where SW1 will forward the frame, which switch will get the frame next, and on which of that switch's interfaces will the frame arrive? Record that information below, or complete the latest row of Table 2.

_____

_____

Step 15. Examine the next forwarding step by connecting to SW2 from the simulator user interface and moving to user mode.

Step 16. Look for the frame's destination MAC address (0200.2222.2222) in switch SW2's MAC address table and only pay attention to the VLAN identified in Step 9. Record the outgoing interface on the lines below or, if you are using Table 2, start a new row that lists SW2 in the first column and SW2's outgoing port in the next column.

_____

_____

_____

Step 17. Based on the information about where SW2 will forward the frame, which switch will get the frame next, and on which of that switch's interfaces will the frame arrive? Record that information below, or complete the latest row of Table 2.

_____

_____

Step 18. Examine the last forwarding step, this time on switch SW4, by connecting to SW4 from the simulator user interface and moving to user mode.

Step 19. As usual, look for the frame's destination MAC address (0200.2222.2222) in switch SW4's MAC address table and only pay attention to the VLAN identified in Step 9. Record the outgoing interface on the lines below or, if you are using Table 2, start a new row that lists SW4 in the first column and SW4's outgoing port in the next column.

_____

_____

_____

Step 20. Complete the latest row of Table 2 by noting that the frame next arrives at PC2.

Part 3: STP Analysis—First Half

So far in this lab, you have confirmed that PC1 should send IP packets directly to PC2, at least from a Layer 3 perspective. You have also determined that the frames sent by PC1 to PC2 take a rather long Layer 2 path through the LAN switches. This part examines why STP chose a long path.

Step 21. Connect to SW3's console, using **ciscopress** as the password.

Step 22. Use the **show spanning-tree vlan 12** command to find some basic information about STP in VLAN 12. List which interfaces are in a forwarding state and which are in a blocking state. Also note which ports have a role of root, designated, or some other role.

_____

_____

Step 23. Consider for a moment that SW3's Fa0/1 interface is in a forwarding state. Consider reasons why SW3 did not forward the frame destined to PC2's 0200.2222.2222 MAC address out Fa0/1 toward SW2, which is clearly a shorter path.

_____

_____

Step 24. Still looking at STP status, record this switch's bridge ID (priority and MAC address). Also note the root switch's bridge ID. Did the root switch's bridge ID win the election based on a lower priority than this switch or based on a lower MAC address value?

_____

_____

_____

Step 25. Move to the next switch in the forwarding path, SW1, from the simulator user interface.

Step 26. Display information about the root switch for all VLANs by using the **show spanning-tree root** command. What root ID and root cost does this switch list for the root switch in VLAN 12?

Step 27. Display the STP status information for VLAN 12 again, this time from SW1. List which interfaces are in a forwarding state and which are in a blocking state. Also note which ports have a role of root, designated, or some other role.

_____

_____

_____

Step 28. Based on the information in the last two steps, which switch is root?

_____

Step 29. Consider for a moment that SW1's Fa0/1 interface is in a forwarding state. Consider reasons why SW1 did not forward the frame destined to PC2's 0200.2222.2222 MAC address out Fa0/1 toward SW4, which is clearly a shorter path.

_____

_____

Part 4: STP Analysis—Second Half

The STP analysis so far has only shown interfaces in a forwarding state in VLAN 12. As it turns out, switches SW2 and SW4 have enough interfaces blocking in VLAN 12 to prevent loops with a side effect of causing the long path between PC1 and PC2. This final part of the lab looks at those two switches, finding the interfaces that are in a blocking state. As you move through this final part, keep in mind that SW1 is the root in this case.

Step 30. From the simulator user interface, move on to SW2.

Step 31. Display the STP status information for VLAN 12 again, this time from SW2. List which interfaces are in a forwarding state and which are in a blocking state. Also note which ports have a role of root, designated, or some other role.

_____

_____

Step 32. Still looking at STP status, note the cost listed for the one blocking port. What is the cost? Is that a default setting or a configured setting?

_____

Step 33. Find the root cost that SW2 will use when sending BPDUs out its nonroot ports by looking again at the output of the **show spanning-tree vlan 12** command. To do so, note the cost listed in the "root" section of the output. What is the root cost?

_____

_____

At this point, SW2 would be sending BPDUs on the blocking interface Fa0/1, which would be received by SW3. However, SW2 believes it should not be the designated port on the SW2-SW3 segment. The next few steps show why.

Step 34. Move back to switch SW3 from the simulator user interface.

Step 35. Using the **show spanning-tree vlan 12** command again, note SW3's root cost and the cost associated with SW3's Fa0/1 interface—the interface connected to SW2. What are those costs?

_____

_____

Step 36. From your memory of how STP works, consider why SW3 wins the battle to have its Fa0/1 interface become the designated port, in turn causing SW2 to block on its Fa0/1 port. Describe your thinking on the lines below.

_____

_____

_____

_____

Step 37. Move on to switch SW4 from the simulator user interface.

Step 38. Display the STP status information for VLAN 12 again, this time from SW4. List which interfaces are in a forwarding state and which are in a blocking state. Also note which ports have a role of root, designated, or some other role.

_____

_____

Step 39. Still looking at STP status, note the cost listed for the one blocking port. What is the cost? Without looking further, can you theorize why SW4's Fa0/1 interface is blocking?

_____

_____

_____

Hints and Answers

Table 3 is a completed version of Table 1. Table 4 is a completed version of Table 2, listing the path that frames travel when going from PC1 to PC2. Table 5 provides hints and tips for any lab steps that do not supply complete details and provides answers for any lab steps that ask questions.

Table 3   Facts About Hosts in This Lab

	PC1	PC2
IP address	192.168.1.1	192.168.1.17
Mask	255.255.255.224	255.255.255.224
Default gateway	192.168.1.2	192.168.1.2
MAC address	0200.1111.1111	0200.2222.2222
Assigned VLAN	12	12

Table 4   Path Between PC1 and PC2

Sending Device	Outgoing Port	Receiving Device	Receiving Port	How Info Was Determined
PC1	N/A	SW3	Fa0/11	Figure 1
SW3	Gi0/1	SW1	Gi0/2	**show mac address-table**, Figure 1
SW1	Gi0/1	SW2	Gi0/1	**show mac address-table**, Figure 1
SW2	Gi0/2	SW4	Gi0/1	**show mac address-table**, Figure 1
SW4	Fa0/12	PC2	N/A	**show mac address-table**

Table 5   Hints and Answers

Step	Hint or Answer
2	The only thing not listed is the VLAN in which PC1 has been assigned.
3	Use the **ipconfig /all** command.
4	The ping works.
5	192.168.1.1/27 and 192.168.1.17/27 are in the same subnet, 192.168.1.0/27, with a range of addresses from 192.168.1.1 through 192.168.1.30. As a result, PC1 can try to send packets directly to PC2, not bothering with a default gateway.
6	The ARP table should list 192.168.1.17 with MAC address 0200.2222.2222, which is indeed PC2's MAC address.
7	Per Figure 1, the frame will first arrive in SW3's Fa0/11 interface.
9	It is in VLAN 12.

continues

Table 5 **Hints and Answers** *continued*

Step	Hint or Answer
10	Use the **show mac address-table** command, which lists outgoing interface Gi0/1.
13	Use the **show mac address-table dynamic** command, which lists outgoing interface Gi0/1.
14	The frame will next arrive in SW2's Gi0/1 interface.
16	The MAC address table lists outgoing interface Gi0/2.
17	The frame will arrive on SW4's Gi0/1 interface.
19	The MAC address table lists outgoing interface Fa0/12.
20	The frame next arrives at PC2.
22	SW3's ports should list the following: Fa0/1: Forwarding, Designated Fa0/11: Forwarding, Designated Gi0/1: Forwarding, Root
23	As will be seen in some upcoming steps, SW2 is actually blocking on its interface on the other end of the link.
24	The root has a lower priority than SW3.
26	The output lists root ID 24588 0019.e86a.1180 with a root cost of 0.
27	Use the **show spanning-tree vlan 12** command again. SW1's ports should list the following: Fa0/1: Forwarding, Designated Gi0/1: Forwarding, Designated Gi0/2: Forwarding, Designated
28	The output of the **show spanning-tree vlan 12** command lists the same bridge ID as root as it does for the local bridge ID, confirming that this switch is the root. The output also notes this fact about four lines into the command output with the phrase "This bridge is the root."
29	As will be seen in some upcoming steps, SW4 is actually blocking on its interface on the other end of the link.
31	The output of the **show spanning-tree vlan 12** command lists SW2's ports as follows: Fa0/1: Blocking, Alternate Fa0/10: Forwarding, Designated Gi0/1: Forwarding, Root Gi0/2: Forwarding, Designated
32	The default IEEE cost for Fast Ethernet interfaces is 19, which is the listed cost.
33	The root cost is listed as 4.
35	SW3's root cost is 3, but its Fa0/1 cost is listed as 18.
36	SW3 advertises the lower root cost (3) compared with SW2's Hello (root cost 4), so SW3's Fa0/1 becomes the Designated Port on the link from SW3 to SW4.

Step	Hint or Answer
38	The output of the **show spanning-tree vlan 12** command lists SW4's ports as follows:
	Fa0/1: Blocking, Alternate
	Fa0/12: Forwarding, Designated
	Gi0/1: Forwarding, Root
39	The port cost is listed as 300, a very high number compared to the default costs of 19 on Fast Ethernet interfaces and 4 on Gigabit interfaces. So, of SW4's two possible paths to the root switch (SW1), the path directly out Fa0/1 is likely the higher cost. Note that SW4 did choose its Gi0/1 interface as its root port.

Configuration

This lab does not require any configuration.

Configuration Labs

Part 1: Router Configuration

Lab 4: Configuring OSPF Routing

Objective

The overall objective of this laboratory exercise is to gain experience with configuring Open Shortest Path First (OSPF) routing between two routers using the Cisco 640-802 Network Simulator. In this lab, you will gain an introductory understanding of the following:

- Configuring the computer's IP address
- Configuring the gateway address
- Configuring the IP addresses for the router interfaces
- Configuring OSPF routing
- Troubleshooting configuration problems

Topology

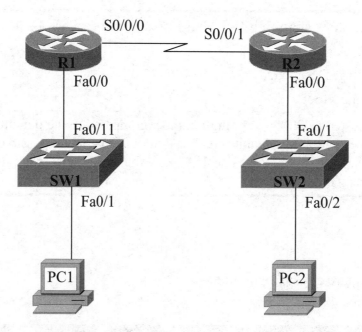

Figure 1   Network Topology for This Lab

Reference

The following simulator exercises provided with the CCNA 640-802 Network Simulator should be reviewed prior to starting this virtual laboratory exercise:

- OSPF Configuration I, II, and III
- OSPF Serial Configuration I–VI
- OSPF Router ID I, II
- OSPF Neighbors I–V

Key Concepts

The following concepts, terms, commands, and steps should have been mastered in this laboratory exercise:

- How to configure the IP address, subnet mask, and default gateway for the computers in your LAN.
- How the gateway address for your LAN router is configured.
- The steps for configuring the host name for your router.
- The steps for configuring the router interface's IP addresses and subnet masks.
- The commands for configuring OSPF routing from LAN-A to LAN-B.
- The two commands that can be used to verify that the routes are configured on the router.

- Using computers in your LAN to ping the computers in the adjacent LAN.

- Use the proper command to trace the route from a PC in LAN-A to the host in the connected LAN-B.

- Use the command to establish a Telnet connection to your router, and find out how to enable a Telnet connection to the router.

- The router command that displays the network routes stored in your router's routing table.

- The command used to save your router configuration to NVRAM.

- The command used to verify the routing protocol being used.

- The command that displays only the OSPF routes.

- The purpose of wildcard bits or inverse mask bits.

Reference Tables

Table 1 provides the IP addresses and masks of all necessary interfaces used to complete the lab.

Table 1   Computer IP Addresses, Subnet Masks, and Gateway Addresses for Lab 4

Computer/Interface - R1	IP Address	Subnet Mask	Gateway Address
PC1	172.20.15.8	255.255.255.224	172.20.15.1
R1-Fa0/0	172.20.15.1	255.255.255.224	—
R1-S0/0/0	10.10.1.1	255.255.255.252	—

Computer/Interface – R2	IP Address	Subnet Mask	Gateway Address
PC2	192.168.25.21	255.255.255.224	192.168.25.16
R2-Fa0/0	192.168.25.16	255.255.255.224	—
R2-S0/0/1	10.10.1.2	255.255.255.252	—

Detailed Lab Steps

Task 1

In this lab, you are configuring OSPF to the adjacent LAN for the network shown in Figure 1. You will be required to verify that computers in your LAN can ping the neighbor LAN. Note that a serial interface is being used to interconnect the LANs. You are configuring routing for both 172.20.15.0 and 192.168.25.0 networks. A subnet mask of 255.255.255.224 is being used. Use 56000 for the clock rate on the serial link (DCE interface). Use a subnet mask of 255.255.255.252 on the serial link connecting the two routers.

Step 1. Configure the gateway address for FastEthernet 0/0 and the serial s0/0/0 interfaces on Router R1. You also need to configure the IP address and the gateway address for PC-1. Use the IP address and subnet mask specified in Table 1. You will need to enable each interface and set the clock rate on the serial interface to 56000. List the router prompts and commands used to configure the interfaces.

_____

_____

_____

Step 2. Configure the gateway address for FastEthernet 0/0 and the serial s0/0/1 interfaces on Router R2. Use the IP addresses and subnet masks specified in Table 1. Enable each interface and list the router prompts and commands used to configure the interfaces.

_____

_____

_____

Step 3. Configure the host name for your routers. R1 should be renamed LAN-A, and R2 should be renamed LAN-B. List the router prompts and commands used to configure the router's host name.

_____

_____

_____

Step 4. List the proper commands to verify that the interfaces on the LAN-A and LAN-B routers have been properly configured. List the router prompts and commands used to configure the router's host name.

_____

_____

_____

Step 5. Configure OSPF routing between the LAN-A and LAN-B routers using a process ID of 100 and an area of 0. Use two commands to verify that the routes are configured. List the router prompts and commands used to configure the LAN-A and LAN-B routers.

_____

_____

_____

Step 6. Use the proper commands to display the routing table for both the LAN-A and LAN-B routers. Are all the possible network routes displayed? List the router prompts and commands used to display the routes.

_____

_____

_____

Step 7. Use the computers in each LAN to ping the computers in the adjacent LAN. List the commands used to ping the computer in the adjacent LAN.

_____

_____

_____

Step 8. Use the proper command to trace the route from the PC in LAN-A to the PC in LAN-B. Your trace should pass through two routers. List the command used and record the trace information. How may hops did you record?

_____

_____

_____

Step 9. Use the command to make a Telnet connection from the LAN-A router to the LAN-B router. Set the VTY password to **ciscopress** and enable remote login. Were you able to enter the privileged EXEC mode on the LAN-B router? Correct this problem if you can't enter the privileged EXEC mode on the LAN-B router. What did you have to do to correct the problem? List the commands used to establish the Telnet connection. What IP address did you use?

_____

_____

_____

Step 10. Use the command to save your router configuration to the startup configuration. What command did you use? Use the proper command to verify that the configuration has been saved to NVRAM. List the command prompts and the commands used.

_____

_____

_____

Step 11. What command is used to verify the routing protocol that is being used? List the command prompts and the commands used. Note that two commands can be used.

_____

_____

_____

Task 2

Answer the following questions regarding the Cisco IOS:

1. The command prompt changes on a Cisco router to reflect the current state the router is in. Define what each command prompt listed below represents:

   a. Router>

   _____

   b. Router#

   _____

   c. Router(config)#

   _____

   d. Router(config-if)#

   _____

   e. Router(config-router)#

   _____

   f. Router(config-line)#

   _____

2. Cisco IOS provides support for many editing functions in terms of "hot keys." A few of the functions are listed below. Briefly describe these functions.

   a. Delete

   _____

   b. Backspace

   _____

   c. Tab

   _____

d. Ctrl-Z

Task 3: Configuration List

The following is a partial list of the items you might see when you issue the **show running-configuration [sh run]** command. Your task is to define each item and its purpose. You might need to go to the Cisco website (http://www.cisco.com) and look up what each of these commands means.

1. ip cef

_____

_____

_____

2. no ip domain lookup

_____

_____

_____

3. log-adjacency-changes

_____

_____

_____

4. control-plane

_____

_____

_____

5. scheduler allocate 20000 1000

_____

_____

_____

6. description <—->

_____

_____

_____

Answer the following router questions:

1. What command is used to determine the version of the Cisco IOS?

_____

_____

_____

2. What version of IOS is running on the LAN-A router?

_____

_____

_____

3. What command is used to display the routing protocols configured on your router?

_____

_____

_____

4. What information is displayed when the **show start** command is entered?

_____

_____

_____

5. What router command is used to determine whether your serial interface is DTE or DCE?

_____

_____

_____

6. What is the command for setting the clock rate on a router's DCE serial interface to 56000?

_____

_____

_____

7. How long has it been since your router was last rebooted? Indicate how the system was restarted. Note: There is a Cisco command that provides this information. Cisco calls this the router uptime. The same command also specifies how the system was restarted.

_____

_____

_____

Configuration Labs

Part 2: Switch Configuration

Lab 1: Basic Switch Configuration and the Command-Line Interface

Objective

The overall objective of this laboratory exercise is to gain experience with basic Cisco switch configuration commands using the CCNA 640-802 Network Simulator and gain an introductory understanding of the following:

- Operating in the Cisco privileged mode
- Configuring the switch ports
- Configuring the computer's network interface
- Troubleshooting the switch interface

Topology

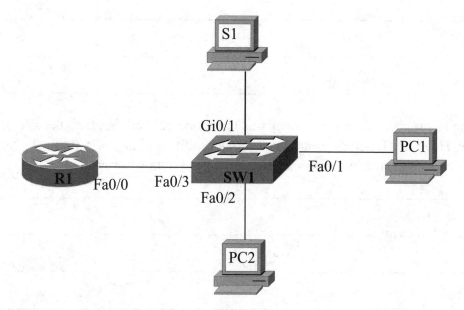

Figure 1   Network Topology for This Lab

Reference

The following simulator exercises provided with the CCNA 640-802 Network Simulator should be reviewed prior to starting this virtual laboratory exercise:

- Setting Switch Passwords

- Switch CLI EXEC Mode

- Switch CLI Configuration Process I, II

- Router CLI Configuration Process

- Interface Settings I, II, III

Key Concepts

The following concepts, terms, commands, and steps should have been mastered in this exercise:

- Steps to enter the switch's privileged EXEC mode (switch#).

- Use of the following commands to verify their operation in Cisco IOS:

  ?, show flash, show version [sh ver], show history [sh hist], show interfaces [sh int], configure terminal [conf t], interface FastEthernet [*interface number*] **[int fa 0/0], interface GigabitEthernet** [*interface number*] **[int gi 0/1], interface** [*vlan number*] **[int vlan 1]**

- What happens when you press the up-arrow key?

- How to change the host name of the switch.

- The steps for configuring the IP address for FastEthernet interface 0/0 [Fa0/0] on your switch.
- The use of the **no shut** command to enable the VLAN interface.
- The steps for configuring the default gateway for the switch.

Reference Tables

Table 1 provides the IP addresses and masks of all the necessary interfaces to complete the lab. All passwords are set to ciscopress.

Table 1   **Computer IP Addresses, Subnet Masks, and Gateway Addresses for Lab 1**

Computer	IP Address	Subnet Mask	Gateway Address
PC1	192.168.21.8	255.255.255.240	192.168.21.1
PC2	192.168.21.6	255.255.255.240	192.168.21.1
S1	192.168.21.5	255.255.255.240	192.168.21.1
SwitchA	192.168.21.10	255.255.255.240	192.168.21.1
R1-Fa0/0	192.168.21.1	255.255.255.240	—

Detailed Lab Steps

Task 1

Step 1. Configure the IP address settings for the router (R1), the computers (PC1 and PC2), and the switch (S1) for the network provided in Figure 1. Use the IP addresses provided in Table 1.

Step 2. Configure switch 1 (SW1) to operate in the network using the IP address, subnet mask, and gateway address specified in Table 1.

Step 3.   What command is used to enter the switch's privileged mode? List the prompt and the command.

_____

_____

_____

Step 4.   Use the following commands to verify their operation in Cisco IOS:

   a. What happens when you enter a ? at the switch# prompt?

_____

_____

_____

   b. What information is displayed when you enter **show flash** at the switch$ prompt?

_____

_____

_____

   c. What command can you use to view the switch's uptime?

_____

_____

_____

   d. How long has the switch been up?

_____

_____

_____

   e. What version of the Cisco IOS software is running on this simulator?

_____

_____

_____

f. What command can you use to view the past entries on this switch?

_____

_____

_____

g. What happens when you press the up/down keys on your keyboard?

_____

_____

_____

h. What is the command for listing the switch's current configuration?

_____

_____

_____

i. How many FastEthernet interfaces does the switch have?

_____

_____

_____

j. How many Gigabit interfaces does the switch have?

_____

_____

_____

Step 5. Enter the privileged mode and change the host name of the switch to SwitchA. List the command sequence required to accomplish this task. Indicate both the prompts and the commands.

_____

_____

_____

Configuration Labs

Part 2: Switch Configuration

Lab 2: Static VLAN Configuration and Trunking

Objective

The overall objective of this laboratory exercise is to gain experience with the basic steps for configuring a static VLAN on a Cisco switch using the CCNA 640-802 Network Simulator. In this exercise, you will create two VLANs, Finance and Office, and assign switchports to each VLAN. You are to configure the switch (SW1) so that server S1 and computer PC2 are assigned to VLAN 2, the Finance VLAN. You will also configure the switch so that computer PC1 is assigned to VLAN 3, the Office VLAN. The IP addresses used in this exercise will all be configured as part of a 192.168.X.X network. Configure switches and the computers to operate in the network using the IP addresses, subnet masks, and gateway addresses specified in Tables 1 and 2. You will gain an understanding of the following:

- Operating in the Cisco privileged mode
- Configuring and assigning names to the VLANs
- Assigning ports to the VLANs
- Steps for verifying port assignments
- Troubleshooting the switch interface and VLAN assignments

Topology

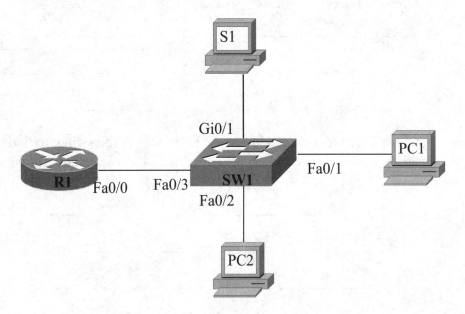

Figure 1   Network Topology for This Lab

Reference

The following simulator exercises provided with the CCNA 640-802 Network Simulator should be reviewed prior to starting this virtual laboratory exercise:

- VLAN Configuration I–V
- VLANs I–III
- Configuring VLANs

Key Concepts

The following concepts, terms, commands, and steps should have been mastered in this exercise:

- The steps to enter the switch's privileged EXEC mode (switch#).
- The steps for configuring the IP address for the VLAN 1 interface on your switch.
- The use of the **no shut** command to enable the VLAN interface.
- The use of the **sh vlan brief** command to verify that the interfaces have been configured.
- Use the **ping** command to verify network connectivity.
- The steps for verifying the entries in the switch's MAC address table.
- The steps for configuring the switch port settings.
- The steps for configuring the default gateway for the switch.
- The steps for configuring the VLAN interfaces.
- Using the **show vlan** command to verify that the VLANs have been created.
- The steps for assigning ports to the VLANs.

Reference Tables

Table 1 provides the IP addresses and masks for all the necessary interfaces to complete this lab.

Table 1   IP Addresses, Subnet Masks, and VLAN Assignments for Lab 2

Computer/Server – SW1	IP Address	Subnet Mask	Gateway Address
S1	192.168.1.1	255.255.255.192	192.168.1.62
PC2	192.168.2.1	255.255.255.192	192.168.2.62
PC1	192.168.3.1	255.255.255.192	192.168.3.62
VLAN1	192.168.1.61	255.255.255.192	192.168.1.62

Table 2   Router R1 Subinterface Settings for Lab 2

	IP Address	Subnet Mask
R1 Fa 0/0.1	192.168.1.62	255.255.255.192
R1 Fa 0/0.2	192.168.2.62	255.255.255.192
R1 Fa 0/0.3	192.168.3.62	255.255.255.192

The passwords for switch S1 and Router R1 are as follows:

- Console password: ciscopress

- Privileged EXEC mode password: ciscopress

- Enable secret: ciscopress

Detailed Lab Steps

Task 1

Step 1.   Your first task is to configure the IP address for VLAN1. The IP address is provided in Table 1. Enable the VLAN1 interface. List the command sequence required to accomplish this task. Indicate both the prompts and the commands.

_____

_____

_____

Step 2.   Next, configure the IP addresses for computers PC1 and PC2, server S1, and Router R1. After you have completed this task, verify that you have network connectivity from the switch SW1 to the computers and server. List the command sequence required to accomplish this task.

_____

_____

_____

Step 3.   Next, use the command that displays the current VLAN interface information.

_____

_____

_____

Step 4. Which ports currently belong to the default VLAN?

_____

_____

_____

Step 5. How many VLANs are set up by default on the switch? List the VLANs.

_____

_____

_____

Step 6. In the next step, you are to create two VLANs, VLAN2 (Finance) and VLAN3 (Office). List the command sequence required to create the VLANs and assign names to each VLAN.

_____

_____

_____

Step 7. Verify that the two new VLANs have been created. List the command sequence required to accomplish this task.

_____

_____

_____

Step 8. What ports are currently assigned to VLANs 2 and 3?

_____

_____

_____

Step 9. Issue the commands that assign the ports connecting S1, PC1, and PC2 to their respective VLANs.

_____

_____

_____

Step 10.   Use the proper command to verify that the switchports have been properly assigned. List the command sequence required to accomplish this task.

_____

_____

_____

Step 11.   Use the command to list the MAC addresses learned by SW1. Which interfaces are associated with the MAC addresses of S1, PC1, and PC2, and which VLAN number is listed for each entry?

_____

_____

_____

Step 12.   In the next step, you are to create the trunk connection from switch FastEthernet 0/3 interface to the router.

_____

_____

_____

Step 13.   Next, configure Router R1 to support trunking and inter-VLAN routing. This requires that the FastEthernet 0/0 and related subinterfaces be configured.

_____

_____

_____

Step 14.   Now that the VLANs and trunking have been configured, verify that PC1, PC2, and S1 can ping each other. List the commands used to verify this.

_____

_____

_____

Task 2: Configuration List

The following is a partial list of the items displayed when you issue the **show running-configuration [sh run]** command on a switch. Your task is to define each item and its purpose. You might need to go to the Cisco website (http://www.cisco.com) and look up what each of these commands means.

1. **switchport mode trunk**

2. **no aaa new-model**

3. **encapsulation dot1q 1 native**

4. **encapsulation dot1q 2**

5. **switchport mode access**

6. **switchport access vlan 2**

7. ip default-gateway 192.168.1.62

_____

_____

_____

8. line vty 0 4

_____

_____

_____

9. line vty 5 15

_____

_____

_____

Troubleshooting III

Lab 3: Switch and VLAN Problems

Overview

In this scenario, the internetwork is having some problems. Your job is to locate and identify the problems and make corrections to the configurations as needed. The trouble ticket for this is shown as follows. Investigate the network problems, make corrections to network as necessary, and report your findings.

Trouble Ticket – L25   **Date:** 4/12/11

Problem: There are reports that there are VLAN problems on SW1. Additionally, SW3 is not working correctly, and there are problems with network connectivity with PC2.

Assigned to: Network Operations Center

Findings: _____

_____

_____

_____

Date Completed

You can find the problems in this lab by examining the network configuration and looking for errors. The topology for this network is provided in Figure 1.

PC1

```
IP Address. . . . . . . . . . . . : 172.16.45.10
Subnet Mask . . . . . . . . . . . : 255.255.255.0
Default Gateway . . . . . . . . . : 172.16.45.1
```

PC2

```
IP Address. . . . . . . . . . . . : 172.16.45.31
Subnet Mask . . . . . . . . . . . : 255.255.255.0
Default Gateway . . . . . . . . . : 172.16.45.1
```

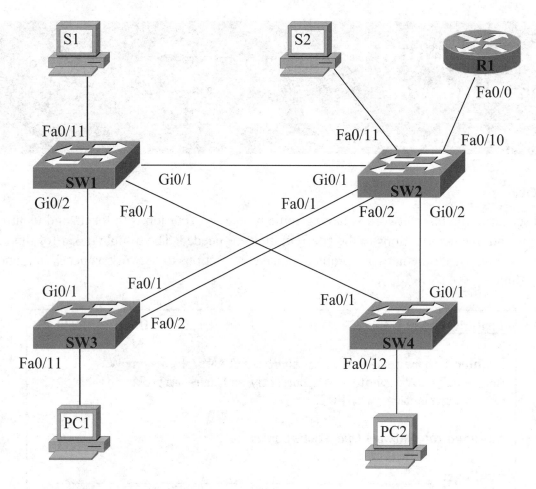

Figure 1   Network Topology for This Lab

You will need to verify that all machines can communicate with each other and also to loopback 0 on R1.

Table 1 is provided to record the problems discovered in the network configuration. As you find each problem, add the discovered problem to Table 1, along with the actions to be taken to resolve the problem.

Table 1   Record Root Causes and Solutions

1	
2	
3	
4	
5	
6	
7	

Troubleshooting Labs
Troubleshooting V

Lab 5: VLAN and Routing Problems

Overview

In this scenario, the internetwork is having some problems. Your job is to locate and identify the problems and make corrections to the configurations as needed. The trouble ticket for this is shown as follows. Investigate the network problems, make corrections to network as necessary, and report your findings.

Trouble Ticket – L27   **Date: 4/12/11**

Problem: There are reports of VLAN problems on switch SW5.
Additionally, there are reports of routing problems off Router2 (R2).

Assigned to: Network Operations Center

Findings: _____
_____
_____
_____

Date Completed

You can find the problems in this lab by examining the network configuration and looking for errors. The topology for this network is provided in Figure 1.

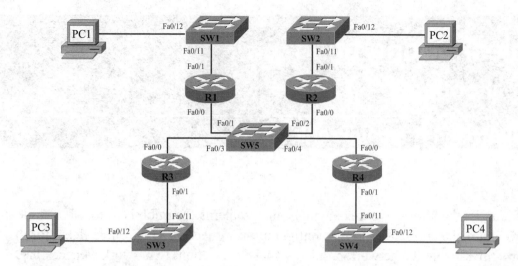

Figure 1   Network Topology for This Lab

Table 1 is provided to record the problems discovered in the network configuration. As you find each problem, add the discovered problem to Table 1, along with the actions to be taken to resolve the problem.

Table 1   Record Root Causes and Solutions

1	
2	
3	
4	
5	
6	
7	

Troubleshooting Labs
Troubleshooting VIII

Lab 8: Switch and VLAN Problems

Overview

In this scenario, the internetwork is having some problems. Your job is to locate and identify the problems and make corrections to the configurations as needed. The trouble ticket for this is shown as follows. Investigate the network problems, make corrections to the network as necessary, and report your findings.

Trouble Ticket – L30   **Date:** 4/12/11

Problem: There are reports of VLAN problems on SW1. Additionally, SW3 is not working correctly, and there are problems with network connectivity with PC2.

Assigned to: Network Operations Center

Findings: _____
_____
_____
_____

Date Completed

You can find the problems in this lab by examining the network configuration and looking for errors. The topology for this network is provided in Figure 1.

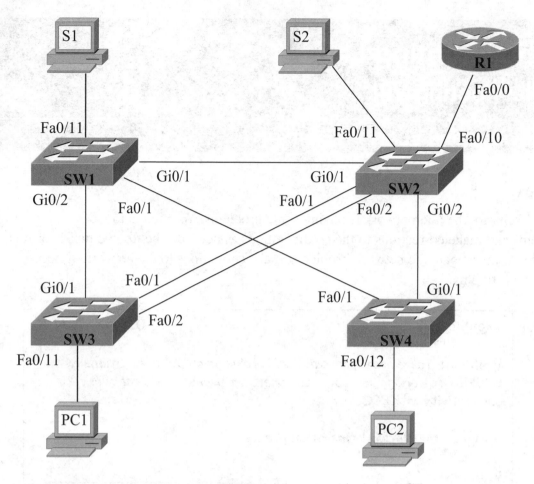

Figure 1   Network Topology for This Lab

This network contains three VLANs: the native VLAN, the LEFT_SIDE VLAN, and the RIGHT_SIDE VLAN. Just some basic things to fix to make it work.

Note: The network uses the password ciscopress for all devices in this lab.

Table 1 is provided to record the problems discovered in the network configuration. As you find each problem, add the discovered problem to Table 1, along with the actions to be taken to resolve the problem.

Table 1   Record Root Causes and Solutions

1
2
3
4
5
6
7

The IP addresses for the networking devices have been provided in Table 2.

Table 2   IP Addressing

LAN 1	IP Address	Def. Gateway
S1	10.20.2.10/24	10.20.2.1
SW1	10.20.1.11/24	10.20.1.1

LAN 2	IP Address	Def. Gateway
S2	10.20.3.10/24	10.20.3.1
SW2	10.20.1.12/24	10.20.1.1
R1-Fa0/0.1	10.20.1.1/24	—
R1-Fa0/0.2	10.20.2.1/24	—
R1-Fa0/0.3	10.20.3.1/24	—

LAN 3	IP Address	Def. Gateway
PC1	10.20.2.11/24	10.20.2.1
SW3	10.20.1.13/24	10.20.1.1

LAN 4	IP Address	Def. Gateway
PC2	10.20.3.11/24	10.20.3.1
SW4	10.20.1.14/24	10.20.1.1

WANs

Table 10-1 lists the labs for this unit. Check with your instructor or class syllabus to confirm what labs you should perform for class.

Table 10-1   Unit 10 Labs

Date	ICND1/ ICND2	Type	Part	Number	Name	Page
	ICND1	SB	3	27	Serial Link Configuration I	567
	ICND1	SB	3	28	Serial Link Configuration II	569
	ICND2	SB	4	3	Serial Authentication I	572
	ICND2	SB	4	5	Frame Relay Configuration I	574
	ICND2	SB	4	7	Frame Relay Configuration III	577
	ICND2	SB	4	10	Frame Relay Verification I	581
	ICND2	CS	4	1	Frame Relay Configuration I	584
	ICND2	CS	4	2	Frame Relay Inverse ARP	593
	Ungraded	TL	1	4	Troubleshooting Lab IV	600

ICND1 Skill Builders

Part 3: IP Addressing, Routing, and WANs

Lab 27: Serial Link Configuration I

Overview

In this lab, you will configure the serial interfaces on R1. You will need to enable the interfaces, assign IP addresses, and configure a clock rate. You will then verify your configuration by attempting to ping the neighboring router's IP address.

Topology

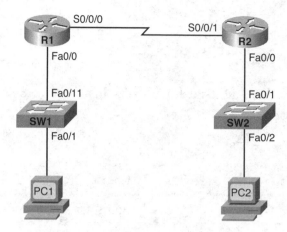

Figure 1   Network Topology for This Lab

Detailed Lab Steps

Step 1.   Connect to R1 from the graphical user interface. Use the password **ciscopress** to log into the router.

Step 2.   Enter privileged exec mode by entering the **enable** command and the password **ciscopress**.

Step 3.   Enter global configuration mode by entering the **configure terminal** command.

Step 4.   Enter interface subconfiguration mode by entering the **interface serial0/0/0** command.

Step 5.   Assign the appropriate IP address from Table 1.

Table 1   IP Addresses

Device	Interface	IP Address
R1	S0/0/0	192.168.10.45/30
R2	S0/0/1	192.168.10.46/30

Step 6.   Configure the clock rate with the **clock rate 64000** command.

Step 7.   Enable the interface with the **no shutdown** command.

Step 8.   Exit interface configuration mode by entering **end**.

Step 9.   Attempt to ping the serial interface on R2.

Step 10.   Verify that R1's Serial 0/0/0 interface is the DCE side by executing the **show controllers serial0/0/0** command. Where in the output does it show whether S0/0/0 is the DCE or DTE side?

_____

_____

Hints and Answers

Table 2 provides hints and tips for any lab steps that do not supply complete details and provides answers for any lab steps that ask questions.

Table 2   Hints and Answers

Step	Hint or Answer
10	The command lists the fact that R1's S0/0/0 interface has a V.35 DCE cable installed, which means R1 does indeed need the **clock rate** command configured.

Configuration Steps

Example 1 shows a sample of the lab exercise being completed from R1's CLI.

Example 1   Example of Performing This Lab

```
R1#configure terminal
R1(config)#interface serial0/0/0
R1(config-if)#ip address 192.168.10.45 255.255.255.252
R1(config-if)#clock rate 64000
R1(config-if)#no shutdown
R1(config-if)#end
```

ICND1 Skill Builders

Part 3: IP Addressing, Routing, and WANs

Lab 28: Serial Link Configuration II

Overview

In this lab, you will continue to configure your serial interface by changing the configuration from HDLC encapsulation to PPP encapsulation. Currently, you have two routers that are connected via their serial link. You will verify that HDLC encapsulation is currently being used, and then you will configure PPP on both interfaces.

Topology

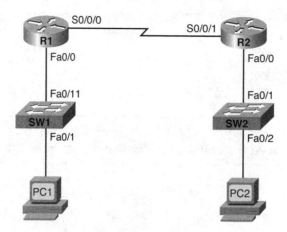

Figure 1   Network Topology for This Lab

Detailed Lab Steps

Step 1.   Connect to R1 from the simulator user interface. Use the password **ciscopress** to log into the router.

Step 2.   Enter privileged exec mode by entering the **enable** command and the password **ciscopress**.

Step 3.   Enter **show interface serial0/0/0** to view information about your serial interface. Verify the encapsulation type is HDLC. What is the current status of the interface?

_____

_____

Step 4.   Enter global configuration mode by entering **configure terminal**.

Step 5.   Enter interface mode by entering **interface serial0/0/0**.

Step 6.   Change the encapsulation type to PPP by entering **encapsulation ppp**.

Step 7.   Exit interface mode by entering **end**.

Step 8.   Enter **show interface serial0/0/0** again. What is the interface status?

_____

_____

Step 9.   Connect to R2 using the simulator user interface. Log into the router using the password **ciscopress**.

Step 10. Enter privileged exec mode using the **enable** command with password **ciscopress**.

Step 11. Navigate to interface subconfiguration mode by entering the **configure terminal** command followed by **interface serial0/0/1**.

Step 12. Change the encapsulation type to PPP by entering the **encapsulation PPP** command.

Step 13. Exit interface subconfiguration mode by entering **end**.

Step 14. Switch back to router R1 from the simulator user interface, and then check the interface status by entering the **show interface serial0/0/0** command. What is the interface status now?

_____

_____

Hints and Answers

Table 1 provides hints and tips for any lab steps that do not supply complete details and provides answers for any lab steps that ask questions.

Table 1   Hints and Answers

Step	Hint or Answer
3	The status is found in the first line of output and reflects both the Layer 1 and Layer 2 status. The current status should be "up" and "up," meaning that the serial link is working.
8	Because R1 is now using PPP and R2 is still using HDLC, the serial link has failed. It should be in an "up" and "down" status, which generally means that the Layer 1 details of the link are up and working, but the Layer 2 details have a problem.
14	Now that the two routers' serial data link protocols match again (PPP), the link has recovered and is now in an "up" and "up" state.

Configuration Steps

Example 1 shows a sample of the lab exercise being completed from R1 and R2.

Example 1   Example of Performing This Lab

```
R1#configure terminal
R1(config)#interface serial0/0/0
R1(config-if)#encapsulation ppp
R1(config-if)#end
R1#


R2#configure terminal
R2(config)#interface serial0/0/1
R2(config-if)#encapsulation ppp
R2(config-if)#end
```

ICND2 Skill Builders

Part 4: WAN

Lab 3: Serial Authentication I

Overview

This lab begins with a working internetwork with valid IP addresses on all routers and all PCs, and EIGRP configured on all routers. This lab shows the configuration of the PPP CHAP authentication on the serial interface.

Topology

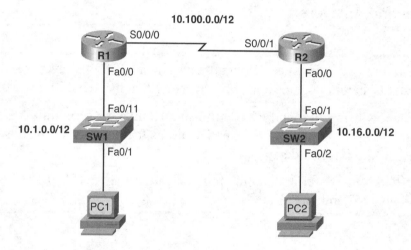

Figure 1   Network Topology for This Lab

Detailed Lab Steps

Step 1.   Connect to R1 from the simulator user interface using the password **ciscopress**.

Step 2.   Enter privileged exec mode using the **enable** command with password **ciscopress** and then move to global configuration mode using the **configure terminal** command.

Step 3.   Configure a username and password to use for PPP authentication by issuing the **username R2 password ciscopress** command.

Step 4.   Enter interface configuration mode for the S0/0/0 interface by issuing the **interface s0/0/0** command.

Step 5.   Change the encapsulation of the interface to PPP by issuing the **encapsulation ppp** command. Did R1 issue a message telling you that the serial interface went down?

Step 6.   Enable PPP CHAP authentication by issuing the **ppp authentication chap** command.

Step 7. Connect to R2 from the simulator user interface using the password **ciscopress**.

Step 8. Enter privileged exec mode using the **enable** command with password **ciscopress** and then move to global configuration mode using the **configure terminal** command.

Step 9. Configure a username and password to use for PPP authentication by issuing the **username R1 password ciscopress** command.

Step 10. Enter interface configuration mode for the S0/0/1 interface by issuing the **interface s0/0/1** command.

Step 11. Change the encapsulation of the interface to PPP by issuing the **encapsulation ppp** command. Did R2 issue a message telling you that S0/0/1 just came up? Why or why not?

_____

_____

Step 12. Enable PPP CHAP authentication by issuing the **ppp authentication chap** command. Did R2 issue a message telling you that S0/0/1 just came up? Why or why not?

_____

_____

Step 13. Exit back into enable mode by entering the **end** command.

Step 14. Show R2's S0/0/1 interface by issuing the **show interfaces S0/0/1** command. What is the interface status? Look about five lines into the output. What is the LCP status?

_____

_____

Hints and Answers

Table 1 provides hints and tips for any lab steps that do not supply complete details and provides answers for any lab steps that ask questions.

Table 1   Hints and Answers

Step	Hint or Answer
5	R1 should display a console message stating that the S0/0/0 interface went down. The reason is that now R1's encapsulation setting of PPP no longer matches R2's.
11	Although the encapsulation matches, R2 does not yet have PPP CHAP authentication enabled, so PPP LCP cannot come up yet.
12	Now R2 issues a message stating the its S0/0/1 interface is now up.
14	The interface should have a line status of "up" and a line protocol status of "up" as well. The LCP status should be "open."

Configuration Steps

Example 1 shows a sample of the lab exercise being completed from the CLI of both R1 and R2.

Example 1   Example of Performing This Lab

```
R1#configure terminal

R1(config)#username R2 password ciscopress

R1(config)#interface s0/0/0

R1(config-if)#encapsulation ppp

R1(config-if)#ppp authentication chap

R1(config-if)#end


! Next commands are on R2

R2#configure terminal

R2(config)#username R1 password ciscopress

R2(config)#interface s0/0/1

R2(config-if)#encapsulation ppp

R2(config-if)#ppp authentication chap
```

ICND2 Skill Builders

Part 4: WAN

Lab 5: Frame Relay Configuration I

Overview

This lab demonstrates basic Frame Relay configuration with the IP addresses configured on the physical interfaces of both R1 and R2. The lab begins with IP addresses assigned to the LAN interfaces on both R1 and R2, as well as the serial interfaces on R1 and R2 that connect to the Frame Relay network. EIGRP is already enabled on both routers in anticipation of the completion of the Frame Relay configuration. (R3 and R4, as seen in the Simulator topology window, are not used for this lab.) This lab shows the configuration of Frame Relay between R1 and R2 on their physical interfaces.

Topology

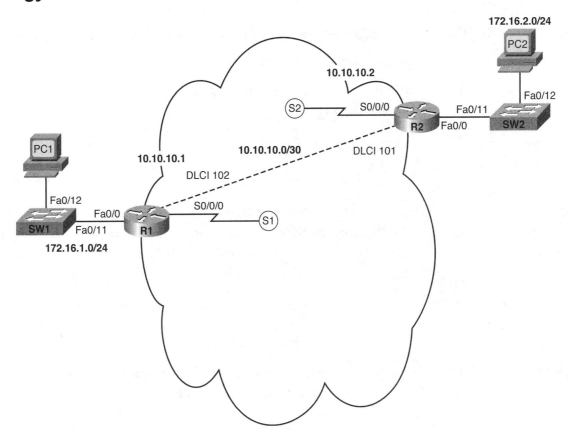

Figure 1   Network Topology for This Lab

Detailed Lab Steps

Step 1. Connect to R1 from the simulator user interface by using the password **ciscopress**.

Step 2. Display R1's S0/0/0 IP address using the **show ip interface brief** command. Record that IP address on the lines below.

_____

_____

Step 3. Enter privileged exec mode using the **enable** command with password **ciscopress** and then move to global configuration mode using the **configure terminal** command.

Step 4. Enter interface configuration mode for interface S0/0/0 by issuing the **interface s0/0/0** command.

Step 5. Enable Frame Relay encapsulation by issuing the **encapsulation frame-relay** command.

Step 6. Connect to R2 from the simulator user interface by using the password **ciscopress**.

Step 7. Enter privileged exec mode using the **enable** command with password **ciscopress** and then move to global configuration mode using the **configure terminal** command.

Step 8. Enter interface configuration mode for interface S0/0/0 by issuing the **interface s0/0/0** command.

Step 9. Enable Frame Relay encapsulation by issuing the **encapsulation frame-relay** command.

Step 10. Exit configuration mode using the **end** command.

Step 11. Use the **ping 10.10.10.1** command to test R2's ability to send packets to R1's S0/0/0 interface. Does the ping work?

_____

_____

Step 12. View the dynamic mapping between R1's IP address (10.10.10.1) and the Frame Relay DLCI used for the PVC between R1 and R2 by using the **show frame-relay map** command. What DLCI is listed as being used to reach 10.10.10.1? What does the "dynamic" keyword represent?

_____

_____

Step 13. View the Frame Relay PVC status by issuing the **show frame-relay pvc** command. What is the status of the PVC whose DLCI was found in the previous step?

_____

_____

Hints and Answers

Table 1 provides hints and tips for any lab steps that do not supply complete details and provides answers for any lab steps that ask questions.

Table 1   Hints and Answers

Step	Hint or Answer
2	R1's S0/0/0 IP address is 10.10.10.1. R2's is 10.10.10.2.
11	R2's **ping 10.10.10.1** command, which pings R1's S0/0/0 IP address, should now work.
12	The output lists DLCI 101 as being used to reach 10.10.10.1. The "dynamic" keyword means that this information was learned dynamically using Inverse ARP.
13	The PVC with DLCI 101 is listed as ACTIVE.

Configuration Steps

Example 1 shows a sample of the lab exercise being completed from the CLI of both R1 and R2.

Example 1   Example of Performing This Lab

```
! The next commands we used on R1:
R1#configure terminal
R1(config)#interface s0/0/0
R1(config-if)#encapsulation frame-relay
R1(config-if)#end


! The next commands we used on R2:
R2#configure terminal
R2(config)#interface s0/0/0
R2(config-if)#encapsulation frame-relay
R2(config-if)#end
```

ICND2 Skill Builders

Part 4: WAN

Lab 7: Frame Relay Configuration III

Overview

In this lab you will gain valuable experience configuring a multipoint subinterface for Frame Relay. The lab begins with a topology that is partially configured with IP addresses and EIGRP. Your job is to view R3's configuration as an example of how to configure a Frame Relay multipoint subinterface, and then configure a similar multipoint subinterface on R1. When successfully configured, you will then be able to ping IP addresses on the R3 and R4 routers from the R1 router.

Topology

The topology for this lab consists of four routers. R2 is not used in this lab. R3 and R4 are connected to R1 in a full mesh topology.

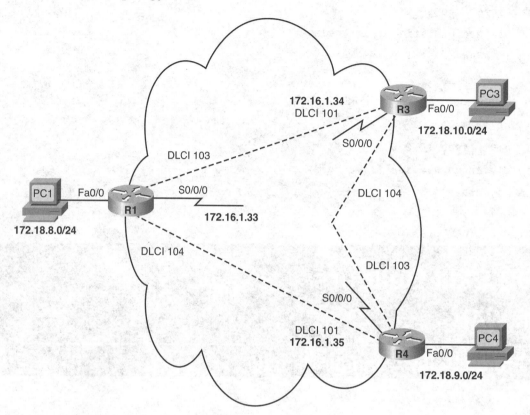

Figure 1   Network Topology for This Lab

Detailed Lab Steps

Step 1.   Connect to R3 from the simulator user interface using the password **ciscopress**.

Step 2.   Enter privileged exec mode using the **enable** command with password **ciscopress**.

Step 3.   View the Frame Relay configuration under R3's S0/0/0 interface using the **show running-config** command. Record the configuration commands listed for the serial interface S0/0/0 and multipoint subinterface S0/0/0.1.

_____

_____

_____

_____

Step 4. You will use the configuration on R3 as a guide to create the configuration for R1 by changing R1's IP address and by changing the details of the two **frame-relay map** commands—one for the PVC to R3 and one for the PVC to R4. To prepare to choose R1's configuration, examine Figure 1 and note R1's serial IP address, the DLCI used on the PVC connected to both R3 and R4, and the IP addresses listed for R3 and R4. Record that information on the lines below.

_____

_____

_____

_____

Step 5. Using R3's S0/0/0 and S0/0/0.1 interface configuration as a guide, write down the configuration you expect to add to R1.

_____

_____

_____

_____

Step 6. Connect to R1 using the simulator user interface. Use a password of **ciscopress** when prompted, and move into privileged exec mode by entering **enable** and using the password **ciscopress**.

Step 7. Enter global configuration mode by entering **configure terminal**, and then use the **interface s0/0/0** command to move into interface configuration mode for S0/0/0.

Step 8. Configure the **encapsulation frame-relay** command to enable Frame Relay on the physical interface.

Step 9. Create a multipoint subinterface by entering **interface serial0/0/0.1 multipoint**. Why do you think the interface is configured as multipoint?

_____

_____

_____

_____

Step 10. Configure an IP address on your subinterface by entering **ip address 172.16.1.33 255.255.255.240**.

Step 11. Map R3's IP address to the DLCI R1 should use when sending traffic to R3 by entering **frame-relay map ip 172.16.1.34 103 broadcast**. Does the DLCI (103) match your notes from Step 4? Does the 172.16.1.34 IP address? Notice the use of the keyword **broadcast** at the end of the map. What does this keyword do?

_____

_____

_____

Step 12. Configure the next mapping by entering **frame-relay map ip 172.16.1.35 104 broadcast**.

Step 13. Exit subinterface configuration mode by entering **end**.

Step 14. Verify that Frame Relay is working correctly by entering **ping 172.16.1.34**. This verifies connectivity to R3. Finish by verifying connectivity to R4 by entering **ping 172.16.1.35**.

Hints and Answers

Table 1 provides hints and tips for any lab steps that do not supply complete details and provides answers for any lab steps that ask questions.

Table 1   Hints and Answers

Step	Hint or Answer
3	The existing configuration on R3's S0/0/0.1 subinterface is **interface serial0/0/0** 　**encapsulation frame-relay** **interface serial0/0/0.1 multipoint** 　**ip address 172.16.1.34 255.255.255.240** 　**frame-relay map ip 172.16.1.33 101 broadcast** 　**frame-relay map ip 172.16.1.35 104 broadcast**
4	R1's IP address is 172.16.1.33. R1 uses DLCI 103 on its PVC for R3 (IP address 172.16.1.34) and DLCI 104 for its PVC for R4 (IP address 172.16.1.35).
5	**interface serial0/0/0** 　**encapsulation frame-relay** **interface serial0/0/0.1 multipoint** 　**ip address 172.16.1.33 255.255.255.240** 　**frame-relay map ip 172.16.1.34 103 broadcast** 　**frame-relay map ip 172.16.1.35 104 broadcast**
9	A subinterface on a serial link can be configured as a point-to-point or multipoint subinterface. Multipoint subinterfaces are useful when more than two routers are grouped into a single subnet; multipoint essentially means that there are more devices than on a point-to-point link.

Step	Hint or Answer
11	The command lists R1's local DLCI (103) for the PVC that connects to R3 and R3's serial IP address, as noted at Step 4.
	The **broadcast** keyword allows for broadcast and multicast traffic to propagate out of the serial interface. Because your routers are configured for EIGRP, you need this keyword at the end of your **map** statements to allow EIGRP traffic to traverse across your Frame Relay cloud.
13	You could also have used the shortcut **Ctrl-Z**.
14	Both pings should work.

Configuration Steps

Example 1 shows a sample of the lab exercise being completed from R1's CLI.

Example 1   Example of Performing This Lab

```
R1#configure terminal
R1(config)#interface serial0/0/0
R1(config-if)#encapsulation frame-relay
R1(config-if)#interface serial0/0/0.1 multipoint
R1(config-subif)#ip address 172.16.1.33 255.255.255.240
R1(config-subif)#frame-relay map ip 172.16.1.34 103 broadcast
R1(config-subif)#frame-relay map ip 172.16.1.35 104 broadcast
R1(config-subif)#end
```

ICND2 Skill Builders

Part 4: WAN

Lab 10: Frame Relay Verification I

Overview

In the last few labs you had the opportunity to configure Frame Relay. This configuration does you no good, however, unless you know how to verify that the configuration is properly working as intended. The most common method of verifying that your Frame Relay configuration is properly working is to check the status of your permanent virtual circuit (PVC). This lab gives you experience verifying the status of PVCs by using the **show frame-relay pvc** command.

In this lab you will enter this command on routers that have been preconfigured for Frame Relay. You will verify a working PVC and view the impact on a Frame Relay wide-area network when an interface goes down.

Topology

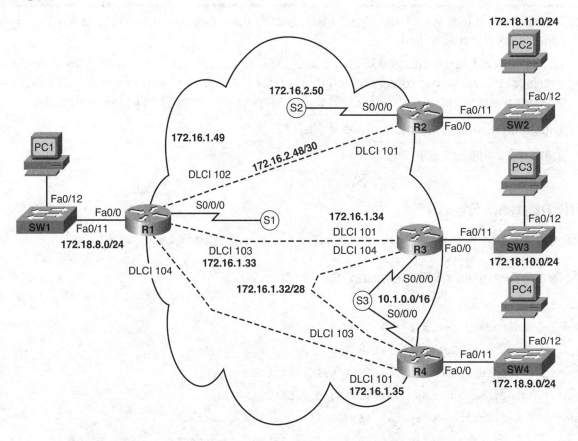

Figure 1   Network Topology for This Lab

Detailed Lab Steps

Step 1.   Connect to R1 from the simulator user interface by using the password **ciscopress**.

Step 2.   Enter the **show frame-relay pvc** command and examine the output. What DLCIs are in use on this router?

_____

_____

_____

Step 3.   Notice the status of each of the PVCs. The status can be "active," "inactive," or "deleted." What are the statuses of the PVCs?

_____

_____

_____

Step 4. Next you will discover the impact on a PVC when an interface goes down. You will be shutting down the serial interface on R2 and viewing the results on R1. Begin by connecting to R2 from the simulator user interface, using the password **ciscopress** when prompted.

Step 5. Enter privileged exec mode by entering **enable**. Enter the password **ciscopress**.

Step 6. Enter global configuration mode by entering **configure terminal**.

Step 7. Enter interface configuration mode by entering **interface serial0/0/0**.

Step 8. Shut down the serial interface by entering the **shutdown** command.

Step 9. Shutting down the interface will bring down the PVC between R1 and R2. You should verify this, so connect back to R1 from the simulator user interface.

Step 10. Verify the status of the PVC between R1 and R2 by entering the **show frame-relay pvc** command. What is the status of the PVC now?

Hints and Answers

Table 1 provides hints and tips for any lab steps that do not supply complete details and provides answers for any lab steps that ask questions.

Table 1   Hints and Answers

Step	Hint or Answer
2	DLCIs 102, 103, and 104 are in use.
3	All three PVCs should be in "active" state.
10	The PVC should be in "inactive" state.

Configuration Steps

Example 1 shows a sample of the lab exercise being completed from R2.

Example 1   Example of Performing This Lab

```
R2#configure terminal
R2(config)#interface serial0/0/0
R2(config-if)#shutdown
```

ICND2 Configuration Scenarios

Part 4: WAN

Lab 1: Frame Relay Configuration I

Overview

During this lab, you will configure a hub-and-spoke Frame Relay WAN between four routers. One router (R1) will be the hub router for the Frame Relay network, and R2, R3, and R4 will serve as the spokes. This lab focuses primarily on using Fame Relay point-to-point subinterfaces.

The lab begins with passwords and host names configured, IP addresses assigned to router LAN interfaces and hosts, but with none of the Frame Relay configuration. Also RIP version 2 is already configured in anticipation of the Frame Relay configuration. The lab guides you through the process of configuring Frame Relay between routers R1, R2, R3, and R4.

Note: Any password necessary for this lab, unless otherwise specified, is **ciscopress**.

Reference Tables

Tables 1, 2, 3, and 4 list the IP addresses planned for this lab. Refer to these tables as needed during the lab.

Table 1   IP Addressing Chart for R1

Interface	DLCI	IP Address
Serial 0/0/0.2	102	10.22.1.1/30
Serial 0/0/0.3	103	10.22.1.5/30
Serial 0/0/0.4	104	10.22.1.9/30
FastEthernet 0/0		10.21.1.1/24

Table 2   IP Addressing Chart for R2

Interface	DLCI	IP Address
Serial 0/0/0.1	101	10.22.1.2/30
FastEthernet 0/0		10.21.2.2/24

Table 3   IP Addressing Chart for R3

Interface	DLCI	IP Address
Serial 0/0/0.1	101	10.22.1.6/30
FastEthernet 0/0		10.21.3.3/24

Table 4   IP Addressing Chart for R4

Interface	DLCI	IP Address
Serial 0/0/0.1	101	10.22.1.10/30
FastEthernet 0/0		10.21.4.4/24

Topology

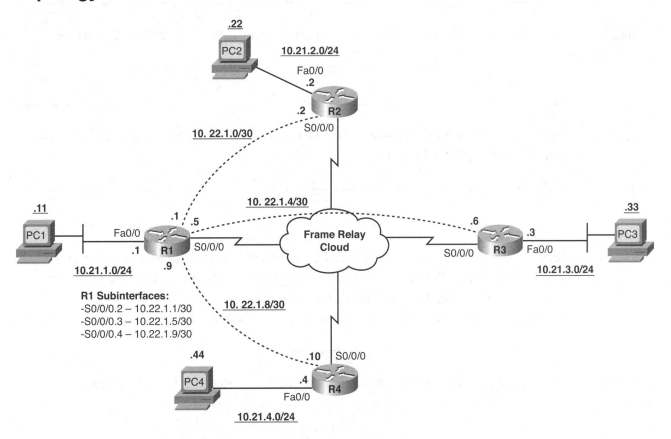

Figure 1   Network Topology for This Lab

Detailed Lab Steps

Part 1: Configure a Frame Relay Between R1 and R2, Using Point-to-Point Subinterfaces

The network design engineer that assigned you the task of configuring Frame Relay has dictated that you should use point-to-point subinterfaces when configuring the PVC between R1 and R2. This part guides you through the process of configuring Frame Relay to support the R1-R2 PVC.

Step 1. Connect to router R1 from the simulator user interface and move into enable mode.

Step 2. Display the current configuration and pay close attention to interface S0/0/0 with which R1 connects to the Frame Relay network. What is the encapsulation on the interface? What is the IP address? Do any subinterfaces exist?

_____

_____

Step 3. Configure Frame Relay encapsulation on S0/0/0 interface on R1's S0/0/0 interface.

_____

_____

Step 4. Configure a Frame Relay point-to-point subinterface S0/0/0.2 on R1, and assign it the appropriate IP address from Table 1.

_____

_____

Step 5. Because this is a point-to-point Frame Relay circuit, you need to associate the DLCI used on the R1-R2 PVC with this subinterface using the **frame-relay interface-dlci** command. Examining Figure 1 and Table 1, choose the correct syntax of the command and configure the local DLCI. Record the command on the line below.

_____

Step 6. Move to router R2 from the simulator user interface and move into enable mode.

Step 7. Plan the matching Frame Relay configuration on R2. In this case, use the details outlined in Table 2. Record the commands you intend to configure on the lines below, and then check your planned commands versus the configuration shown in Table 5 in the "Hints and Answers" section near the end of this lab.

_____

_____

_____

_____

Step 8. Configure the commands you planned in the previous step, and then exit configuration mode.

Step 9. Display the current status of R2's S0/0/0 physical interface. What is the status?

_____

_____

Step 10. Display the status of the Frame Relay LMI using the **show frame-relay lmi** command. What is the LMI type? How long ago was the last full status requested and received? Do these values make you think the LMI between the router and Frame Relay switch is working?

_____

_____

Step 11. Examine the status of R2's PVC that connects to R1. What command did you use? What is the PVC's status?

_____

Step 12. Examine the interface status of the subinterface you configured on R2. What is the line and line protocol status?

_____

Step 13. Test the IP traffic across the Frame Relay link by pinging R1's IP address on the other end of the PVC. What address did you ping? Did the ping work?

_____

_____

Part 2: Configure a Frame Relay Point-to-Point Circuit Between R1 and R3, Using Subinterfaces and Non-Subinterfaces

In Part 2 of this lab, you will continue the Frame Relay configuration by configuring Frame Relay between R1 and R3. You will again use a point-to-point subinterface on router R1, but configure R3 using only the physical interface and no subinterfaces.

Step 14.   Move back to router R1 from the simulator user interface and move into enable mode.

Step 15.   To configure R1 to send traffic over the PVC that connects to R3, per the design engineer's instructions, you will configure a new subinterface (.3), assign an IP address, and assign a DLCI to the subinterface. Use the information in Table 1 and Figure 1 to plan your configuration, and write those commands on the lines below.

_____

_____

_____

_____

Step 16.   Move into configuration mode on R1 and configure the commands you planned in the previous step. Exit configuration mode when finished.

Step 17.   Move to router R3 from the simulator user interface and move into enable mode.

Step 18.   Move into configuration mode and configure Frame Relay encapsulation on the S0/0/0 interface on R3. What commands did you use?

_____

_____

Step 19.   Configure the IP address on this same serial interface: 10.22.1.6/30. Do not configure the IP address under any subinterface. What command did you use?

_____

_____

Step 20.   Exit configuration mode and confirm that the PVC from R3 to R1 is up. According to Figure 1, what DLCI is used by R3 for this PVC? What is the status of the PVC with that DLCI according to the **show frame-relay pvc** command?

_____

_____

Step 21.   Ping R1's S0/0/0.3 IP address (10.22.1.5). Does the ping work?

_____

Step 22. Examine the IP-DLCI mapping information on R3 using the **show frame-relay map** command. Do you see R1's IP address (10.22.1.5)? What interface/subinterface is listed in that section of output? What is the significance of the **dynamic** keyword in the output?

___

Part 3: Configure a Frame Relay Between R1 and R4, Using Point-to-Point Subinterfaces

The final part of this lab completes the Frame Relay configuration by configuring the PVC between R1 and R4. As was the case between R1 and R2, both routers will use point-to-point subinterfaces.

Step 23. Connect to router R4 from the simulator user interface and move into enable mode.

Step 24. Plan the Frame Relay configuration on R4. In this case, use the details outlined in Table 4, including the subinterface number, the DLCI to use, and the IP address/mask. Record the commands you intend to configure on the lines below, and then check your planned commands versus the configuration shown in Table 5 in the "Hints and Answers" section.

___

___

___

___

___

Step 25. Configure the commands you planned in the previous step, and then exit configuration mode.

Step 26. Move to router R1 from the simulator user interface and move into enable mode.

Step 27. Plan the matching Frame Relay configuration on R1. In this case, use the details outlined in Table 1. Record the commands you intend to configure on the lines below, and then check your planned commands versus the configuration shown in Table 5. Note that R1's S0/0/0 encapsulation has already been configured for Frame Relay.

___

___

___

___

___

Step 28. Configure the commands you planned in the previous step, and then exit configuration mode.

Step 29. Display the current status of R1's S0/0/0 physical interface. What is the status?

_____

_____

Step 30. Examine the status of R1's PVC that connects to R4. What command did you use? What is the PVC's status?

_____

Step 31. Examine the interface status of the new subinterface you configured on R1. What is the line and line protocol status?

_____

Step 32. Test the IP traffic across the Frame Relay link by pinging R4's IP address (10.22.1.10) on the other end of the PVC. What address did you ping? Did the ping work?

_____

_____

Hints and Answers

Table 5 provides hints and tips for any lab steps that do not supply complete details and provides answers for any lab steps that ask questions.

Table 5   Hints and Answers

Step	Hint or Answer
1	Use the **enable** command to move to privileged exec mode.
2	The **show running-config** command reveals that S0/0/0 has no interface subcommands—no IP address, no **encapsulation** command, and no subinterfaces. The encapsulation defaults to HDLC as a result.
3	To enter global configuration mode, use the **configure terminal** command, and then move to interface configuration mode using the command **interface serial 0/0/0**. At the interface configuration prompt, change the encapsulation to Frame Relay with the **encapsulation frame-relay** interface command.
4	To configure a point-to-point subinterface and the IP addresses, use the following two commands: **interface serial 0/0/0.2 point-to-point** command. Then enter the IP address at the subinterface prompt. Use the command **ip address 10.22.1.1 255.255.255.252**.
5	While still at the subinterface configuration prompt, configure the DLCI to be 102, with the command **frame-relay interface-dlci 102**.

Step	Hint or Answer
6	Use the **enable** command to move to privileged exec mode.
7	The configuration commands will be **interface serial 0/0/0** **encapsulation frame-relay** **interface serial 0/0/0.1 point-to-point** **ip address 10.22.1.2 255.255.255.252** **frame-relay interface-dlci 101**
9	The **show interface s0/0/0** command shows the interface status as line up, line protocol up.
10	The LMI type is "cisco." The last status updates should have been within the last minute, signifying that the LMI messages continue to flow in both directions, meaning that the LMI is working and that the access link between R1 and the local Frame Relay switch is working.
11	The **show frame-relay pvc** command lists a PVC with DLCI 101, as configured earlier on R2. The status is "active."
12	Using the **show interface serial 0/0/0.1** command, R2 shows the status is "up/up."
13	The **ping 10.22.1.1** command should work.
14	Use the **enable** command to move to privileged mode.
15	**interface serial 0/0/0.3 point-to-point** **ip address 10.22.1.5 255.255.255.252** **frame-relay interface-dlci 103**
16	Use the **configure terminal** command to move into configuration mode, and either press **Ctrl-Z** or enter the **end** command to exit.
17	Use the **enable** command to move to privileged mode.
18	Use the **configure terminal** command to move into configuration mode. Then configure **interface serial 0/0/0** **encapsulation frame-relay**
19	**ip address 10.22.1.6 255.255.255.252**
20	The PVC with DLCI 101 is listed as "active."
21	The **ping 10.22.1.5** command should work. (Use the **end** command or press **Ctrl-Z** to exit configuration mode.)
22	R1's 10.22.1.5 IP address is listed with interface S0/0/0. The **dynamic** keyword means that the mapping between DLCI 101 and IP address 10.22.1.5 was dynamically learned (using InARP).
23	Use the **enable** command to move to privileged exec mode.

continues

Step	Hint or Answer
24	The configuration commands will be **interface serial 0/0/0** **encapsulation frame-relay** **interface serial 0/0/0.1 point-to-point** **ip address 10.22.1.10 255.255.255.252** **frame-relay interface-dlci 101**
26	Use the **enable** command to move to privileged exec mode.
27	The configuration commands will be **interface serial 0/0/0.4 point-to-point** **ip address 10.22.1.9 255.255.255.252** **frame-relay interface-dlci 104**
29	The **show interface s0/0/0** command shows the interface status as line up, line protocol up.
30	The **show frame-relay pvc** command lists a PVC with DLCI 104, as configured earlier on R1. The status is "active."
31	Using the **Show Interface Serial 0/0/0.4** command, R1 shows the status is "up/up."
32	The **ping 10.22.1.10** command should work.

Configuration Steps

Example 1 shows the configuration commands added to R1, R2, R3, and R4 during this lab.

Example 1   Configuration Added During This Lab

```
! Added on R1:
interface serial 0/0/0
 encapsulation frame-relay
interface serial 0/0/0.2 point-to-point
 ip address 10.22.1.1 255.255.255.252
 frame-relay interface-dlci 102
interface serial 0/0/0.3 point-to-point
 ip address 10.22.1.5 255.255.255.252
 frame-relay interface-dlci 103
interface serial 0/0/0.4 point-to-point
 ip address 10.22.1.9 255.255.255.252
 frame-relay interface-dlci 104
```

continues

Example 1 Configuration Added During This Lab *continued*

```
! Added on R2:


interface serial 0/0/0
 encapsulation frame-relay
interface serial 0/0/0.1 point-to-point
 ip address 10.22.1.2 255.255.255.252
 frame-relay interface-dlci 101



! Added on R3:


interface serial 0/0/0
 encapsulation frame-relay
 ip address 10.22.1.6 255.255.255.252


! Added on R4:


interface serial 0/0/0
 encapsulation frame-relay
interface serial 0/0/0.1 point-to-point
 ip address 10.22.1.10 255.255.255.252
 frame-relay interface-dlci 101
```

ICND2 Configuration Scenarios

Part 4: WAN

Lab 2: Frame Relay Inverse ARP

Overview

You have been given the task of configuring Frame Relay without the use of Inverse ARP. First, you will configure Frame Relay across three routers using multipoint subinterfaces and view the dynamically learned mappings with the **show frame-relay map** command. Then, you will manually configure the mappings and verify those mappings with the **show frame-relay map** command.

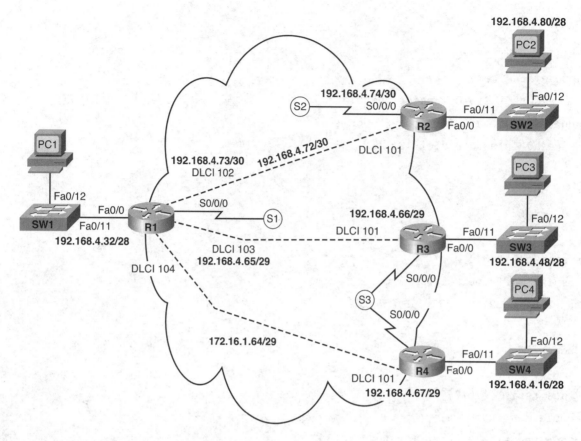

Figure 1   Network Topology for This Lab

Reference Table

Table 1 shows the IP addresses used in this exercise.

Table 1   IP Addresses

Device	Interface	IP Address	Subnet Mask
R1	Fa0/0	192.168.4.33	255.255.255.240
	S0/0/0.1	192.168.4.65	255.255.255.248
	S0/0/0.2	192.168.4.73	255.255.255.252
R2	Fa0/0	192.168.4.81	255.255.255.240
	S0/0/0	192.168.4.74	255.255.255.252
R3	Fa0/0	192.168.4.49	255.255.255.240
	S0/0/0.1	192.168.4.66	255.255.255.248
	S0/0/0.2	192.168.4.77	255.255.255.252
R4	Fa0/0	192.168.4.17	255.255.255.240
	S0/0/0.1	192.168.4.67	255.255.255.248
	S0/0/0.2	192.168.4.78	255.255.255.252

Note: All passwords are **ciscopress** unless otherwise noted.

Detailed Lab Steps

Part 1: Configure Frame Relay with Inverse ARP

Step 1.   Connect to R1 from the simulator user interface.

Step 2.   Navigate to serial interface configuration mode for interface S0/0/0.

Step 3.   Change the encapsulation type from the default to Frame Relay encapsulation.

Step 4.   Create a multipoint Serial 0/0/0.1 subinterface and assign it the IP address specified in Table 1.

Step 5.   Assign two DLCIs (103 and 104) to this subinterface—one for the PVC to R3 and one for the PVC to R4—using the **frame-relay interface-dlci** command. What commands did you configure?

_____

_____

Step 6.   Connect to R3 from the simulator user interface. Navigate to serial interface configuration mode for interface S0/0/0.

Step 7.   Change the encapsulation type to Cisco Frame Relay encapsulation.

Step 8.   Create a multipoint Serial 0/0/0.1 subinterface and configure its IP address according to Table 1.

Step 9.   Assign one DLCI (101) to this subinterface, for the PVC to R1, using the **frame-relay interface-dlci** command. What commands did you configure?

_____

_____

Step 10.   Connect to R4 and navigate to Serial 0/0/0 configuration mode.

Step 11.   Change the default encapsulation type to Cisco Frame Relay encapsulation.

Step 12.   Create a multipoint Serial 0/0/0.1 subinterface and assign it the IP address listed Table 1.

Step 13.   Assign one DLCI to this subinterface, for the PVC to R1, using the **frame-relay interface-dlci** command. What commands did you configure?

_____

_____

Verify Configuration

should test your configuration to verify the dynamic Frame Relay mappings.

14. Connect to R1.

Step 15. Enter **show frame-relay map** to view the dynamic Frame Relay mappings. Record the DLCIs used for the mappings to R3 (192.168.4.66) and R4 (192.168.4.67).

_____

_____

_____

_____

Step 16. Connect to R3.

Step 17. Enter the **show frame-relay map** command and record the DLCI used to connect to R1 (192.168.4.65).

_____

_____

Step 18. Connect to R4.

Step 19. Enter the **show frame-relay map** command and record the DLCI used to connect to R1 (192.168.4.65).

_____

_____

Part 3: Statically Map DLCI and IP Address

Next you will configure R1, R2, and R3 to use manually configured mapping information rather than rely on Inverse ARP.

Step 20. Connect to R1. Navigate to Serial 0/0/0.1 subinterface configuration mode.

Step 21. Remove the two **frame-relay interface-dlci** commands you configured in Step 5.

Step 22. Configure a Frame Relay map for R3 using the DLCI you discovered earlier. Be sure to allow for broadcast traffic to traverse the Frame Relay wide-area network.

Step 23. Configure a map for R4 using the DLCI you discovered earlier. Again, be sure to allow for broadcasts.

Step 24. Connect to R3. Navigate to subinterface configuration mode.

Step 25. Remove the **frame-relay interface-dlci** command you configured in Step 9.

Step 26. Configure a map to R1 using the DLCI you learned earlier. Be sure to allow for broadcasts.

Step 27. Connect to R4. Navigate to Serial 0/0/0.1 subinterface configuration mode.

Step 28. Remove the **frame-relay interface-dlci** command you configured in Step 13.

Step 29. Configure a map to R1 using the DLCI you learned earlier. Be sure to allow for broadcasts.

Part 4: Verify Frame Relay

Now you will verify your Frame Relay configuration.

Step 30. Connect to R1.

Step 31. Enter **show frame-relay map**. If you successfully configured Frame Relay, you should see a static mapping to R3 and R4. Does the mapping information (DLCI and IP address) match what you found at Steps 14 and 16 earlier in this lab? Do these entries have a **dynamic** keyword listed in the output, like the output at Steps 14 and 16? Why or why not?

_____

_____

_____

_____

Hints and Answers

Table 2 provides hints and tips for any lab steps that do not supply complete details and provides answers for any lab steps that ask questions.

Table 2   Hints and Answers

Step	Hint or Answer
2	Enter **enable** to enter privileged exec mode. Next, enter **configure terminal** to navigate to global configuration mode. Finally, enter **interface serial0/0/0** to enter serial interface configuration mode.
3	To change to Frame Relay encapsulation, enter **encapsulation frame-relay**.
4	Enter **interface serial0/0/0.1 multipoint** to create the subinterface. Once in subinterface configuration mode, enter **ip address 192.168.4.65 255.255.255.248** to configure the IP address.
5	Use these commands: **frame-relay interface-dlci 103** **frame-relay interface-dlci 104**
6	To navigate to serial interface configuration mode, first enter the **enable** command. Next, enter **configure terminal**. Finally, enter **interface serial0/0/0**.

continues

Table 2   **Hints and Answers**   *continued*

Step	Hint or Answer
7	Enter **encapsulation frame-relay**.
8	Enter **interface serial0/0/0.1 multipoint** to create the subinterface. Enter **ip address 192.168.4.66 255.255.255.248** to configure the IP address.
9	Use this command: **frame-relay interface-dlci 101**
10	Enter **enable** to enter privileged exec mode. Enter **configure terminal** to enter global configuration mode. Finally, enter **interface serial0/0/0** to enter serial interface configuration mode.
11	Enter **encapsulation frame-relay**.
12	Enter **interface serial0/0/0.1 multipoint** to create the subinterface. Then enter **ip address 192.168.4.67 255.255.255.248** to configure an IP address.
13	Use this command: **frame-relay interface-dlci 101**
15	R1 uses a DLCI of 103 to connect to R3 (192.168.4.66) and a DLCI of 104 to connect to R4 (192.168.4.67).
17	R3 uses a DLCI of 101 to connect to R1 (192.168.4.65).
19	R4 uses a DLCI of 101 to connect to R1 (192.168.4.65).
20	To navigate to the subinterface, enter **enable** (use a password of **ciscopress** when prompted), **configure terminal**, and **interface serial0/0/0.1 multipoint**.
21	Use these commands: **no frame-relay interface-dlci 103** **no frame-relay interface-dlci 104**
22	Enter **frame-relay map ip 192.168.4.66 103 broadcast**.
23	Enter **frame-relay map ip 192.168.4.67 104 broadcast**.
24	To enter subinterface configuration mode, enter **enable** (enter a password of **ciscopress**), **configure terminal**, and **interface serial0/0/0.1 multipoint**.
25	Use this command: **no frame-relay interface-dlci 101**
26	Enter **frame-relay map ip 192.168.4.65 101 broadcast**.
27	To navigate to the subinterface, enter **enable** (use a password of **ciscopress** when prompted), **configure terminal**, and **interface serial0/0/0.1 multipoint**.
28	Use this command: **no frame-relay interface-dlci 101**
29	Enter **frame-relay map ip 192.168.4.65 101 broadcast**.

Step	Hint or Answer

31   The output should match what was seen at Steps 14 and 16:

On R3:

DLCI 101 IP address 192.168.4.65

On R4:

DLCI 101 IP address 192.168.4.65

The output does not list the **dynamic** keyword; that keyword refers to table entries learned with Inverse ARP.

Configuration Steps

Example 1 shows a sample of the lab exercise being completed from routers R1, R3, and R4.

Example 1   Example of Performing This Lab

```
R1#configure terminal
R1(config)#interface serial0/0/0
R1(config-if)#encapsulation frame-relay
R1(config-if)#interface serial0/0/0.1 multipoint
R1(config-subif)#ip address 192.168.4.65 255.255.255.248
R1(config-subif)#frame-relay interface-dlci 103
R1(config-subif)#frame-relay interface-dlci 104


R3#configure terminal
R3(config)#interface serial0/0/0
R3(config-if)#encapsulation frame-relay
R3(config-if)#interface serial0/0/0.1 multipoint
R3(config-subif)#ip address 192.168.4.66 255.255.255.248
R3(config-subif)#frame-relay interface-dlci 101


R4#configure terminal
R4(config)#interface serial0/0/0
R4(config-if)#encapsulation frame-relay
R4(config-if)#interface serial0/0/0.1 multipoint
R4(config-subif)#ip address 192.168.4.67 255.255.255.248
R4(config-subif)#frame-relay interface-dlci 101
```

continues

Example 1 Example of Performing This Lab *continued*

```
R1#configure terminal

R1(config-if)#interface serial0/0/0.1 multipoint

R1(config-subif)#no frame-relay interface-dlci 103

R1(config-subif)#no frame-relay interface-dlci 104

R1(config-subif)#frame-relay map ip 192.168.4.66 103 broadcast

R1(config-subif)#frame-relay map ip 192.168.4.67 104 broadcast


R3#configure terminal

R3(config-if)#interface serial0/0/0.1 multipoint

R3(config-subif)#no frame-relay interface-dlci 101

R3(config-subif)#frame-relay map ip 192.168.4.65 101 broadcast


R4#configure terminal

R4(config)#interface serial0/0/0.1 multipoint

R4(config-subif)#no frame-relay interface-dlci 101

R4(config-subif)#frame-relay map ip 192.168.4.65 101 broadcast
```

Troubleshooting Labs

Troubleshooting IV

Lab 4: Frame Relay

Overview

In this scenario, the Frame Relay network is having some problems. This lab contains four fully configured LANs interconnected through Frame Relay using Routing Information Protocol (RIP) routing between sites. There is a configuration error that prevents communication on the serial interface from R1 to R3. Another error exists in the Frame Relay setup between R3 and R4. The last error is on R2, which prevents route advertising to R1. Your job is to locate and identify the network problems and make corrections to the router configurations as needed. The network topology is provided in Figure 1. Note: All passwords are set to ciscopress.

Topology

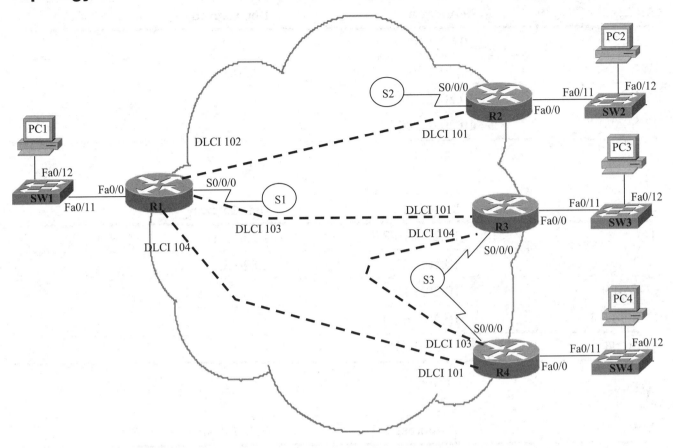

Figure 1   Network Topology for This Lab

The trouble ticket for this is shown as follows. Investigate the Frame Relay network problems, make corrections to the network as necessary, and report your findings.

The IP addresses for the network are provided in Tables 1(a)–1(d).

Table 1   Reference Tables

(a)

LAN 1	IP Address	Def. Gateway
PC1	10.20.1.10/24	10.20.1.1
SW1	10.20.1.2/24	10.20.1.1
R1-FA0/0	10.20.1.1/24	—
R1-S0/0/0.2	10.20.0.1/30	—
R1-S0/0/0.3	10.20.0.5/30	—
R1-S0/0/0.4	10.20.0.9/30	—

(b)

LAN 2	IP Address	Def. Gateway
PC2	10.20.2.10/24	10.20.2.1
SW2	10.20.2.2/24	10.20.2.1
R2-FA0/0	10.20.2.1/24	—
R2-S0/0/0	10.20.0.2/30	—

(c)

LAN 3	IP Address	Def. Gateway
PC3	10.20.3.10/24	10.20.3.1
SW3	10.20.3.2/24	10.20.3.1
R3-FA0/0	10.20.3.1/24	—
R3-S0/0/0.1	10.20.0.6/30	—
R3-S0/0/0.2	10.20.0.13/30	—

(d)

LAN 4	IP Address	Def. Gateway
PC4	10.20.4.10/24	10.20.4.1
SW4	10.20.4.2/24	10.20.4.1
R4-FA0/0	10.20.4.1/24	—
R4-S0/0/0.1	10.20.0.10/30	—
R4-s0/0/0.2	10.20.0.14/30	—

This network has multiple network problems. Your task is to identify and correct all the problems. Prepare a list of the network problems found and what was done to correct the problem. The information provided in this lab gives you enough information to enable you to start testing with **ping** commands and then work to discover why certain devices cannot ping each other. You should start by pinging each PC from another PC. When you find pairs of PCs that cannot ping each other, troubleshoot to find why the ping fails. By following that general process, you should discover the problems that exist in this lab.

Table 2 is provided to record the problems discovered in the network configuration. As you find each problem, add the discovered problem to Table 2, along with the actions to be taken to resolve the problem.

Table 2   **Record Root Causes and Solutions**

1	
2	
3	
4	
5	
6	
7	

LAB NOTES

Notes

Notes

Notes

Notes

Notes

Notes

Notes